PLASMIDS

PLASMIDS

Paul Broda
University of Edinburgh

48,916

W. H. FREEMAN AND COMPANY
OXFORD AND SAN FRANCISCO

Library of Congress Cataloging in Publication Data

Broda, Paul, 1939–
  Plasmids.
  Bibliography: p.
  Includes index.
  1. Plasmids.   I. Title.
QR76.6.B76   589.9   79–10665
ISBN 0–7167–1111–7

Phototypeset by Western Printing Services Ltd, Bristol
Printed in the United States of America

Contents

Preface   ix

Chapter 1. Introduction   1

  What are plasmids?   1
  Plasmids are studied for their own sake   3
  Plasmids are tools for molecular biology   3

Chapter 2. Isolation and Sizing of Plasmid DNA   5

Isolation of plasmid DNA   5
  Use of density gradient centrifugation   5
  Isolation of intact plasmid molecules   7
  Purification of covalently closed circular DNA   8
  Simplified methods for plasmid isolation   10
  Transformation and transduction   10

The sizes of plasmid molecules   12
  Cells may carry several plasmids   15
  Association and dissociation of plasmids   16
  'Transition' or amplification   17

Summary   22

Chapter 3. Structure and Evolution of Plasmids   23

Relationships between plasmids   23
  Molecular hybridization   25
  Electron microscopy of heteroduplexes   26
  F is partially homologous with ColV and R1   28
  Other groups of related plasmids   30

Physical mapping of plasmids   33
  The Campbell model and Hfr and F' formation   35
  Hotspots in Hfr and F' formation   36

Insertion sequences and transposons   36
  Inverted repeats   36

Insertion sequences   38
Transposition of ampicillin resistance   43
Other transposons   45

Endonucleases and plasmid structure   46
Restriction enzymes   46
Generation of chimaeras   47
Use of endonucleases in mapping plasmids   49

Summary   50

Chapter 4. Replication   53

Modes of replication   54
Replication is semi-conservative   54
Replicative intermediates   54
Origin and direction of plasmid replication   57
Relaxation complexes and replication   59
Plasmid copy-number   60
Copy-number mutants   61
Secondary plasmids   62

Segregation   63

Role of host functions in plasmid replication   65
Effect of *pol* mutations   66
Effect of 'sudden stop' mutations   66
Effect of initiation mutations: integrative suppression   68
Supercoiling   70

Other functions affecting plasmid replication   70
Replication mutants   72
Plasmid replication *in vitro*   74

Incompatibility   74

Control   76
Relaxed and stringent control   77
Replication and the cell cycle   78
The mechanism of control   80

Summary   82

Chapter 5. Conjugational Transfer   83

Contact formation   83
Pili   84
Surface exclusion   85
Role of the female in contact formation   87

DNA transfer   87
A unique strand is transferred   87
Is replication a necessary concomitant to transfer?   88

Genetic analysis of the F transfer system   89
Regulation of *tra* expression   90

Plasmid spread through populations   92
Plasmid mobilization by other plasmids   93

Chromosome transfer   95
F$^+$ strains   95
Hfr transfer   95

Other conjugation systems   96
F-like plasmids   96
Other transmissible plasmids in *E. coli*   96
Conjugation in some other groups of bacteria   97
Barriers to conjugation   98

Summary   99

Chapter 6. Plasmids in Human and Veterinary Medicine   101

Enterobacteria and the gut   103
The classification of enterobacteria and their plasmids   104
The rise and fall of *Salmonella typhimurium* type 29   105
Chloramphenicol-resistant typhoid bacilli   107

The ecology of E. coli *and its R factors*   109
R plasmid transfer between bacterial strains *in vivo*   111

Pseudomonas aeruginosa *and other opportunist pathogens*   113

R plasmids in Haemophilus *and gonococci*   114

R plasmids in Gram-positive bacteria   115

Mechanisms of drug-resistance   116
Resistance to other agents   118
Presence of R plasmids in the absence of drugs   119
Origin of drug resistance and R plasmids   119

Plasmids conferring pathogenicity   120

The need for restraint in drug usage   123

Summary   124

Chapter 7. Other Plasmids   125

Bacteriocins   125
Attachment of colicin to sensitive cells   126
Mechanism of colicin action   127
Gene expression in CloDF13   128

Degradative plasmids in pseudomonads   129

Tumorogenic plasmids of Agrobacterium tumefaciens   133

Streptomyces coelicolor *A3(2)*   135

Summary   135

Chapter 8. Prospects and Conclusions   137

The ubiquity of plasmids   137

Origin and role in evolution of bacterial populations   139

Plasmids in eukaryotes?   140

The impact of man   141

Genetic engineering   141
    Types of chimaera   142
    Vectors   142
    The host cell   144
    Benefits and risks   145
    Containment   147

Summary   148

References   149

Author Index   189

Subject Index   195

Preface

This book is an account of plasmids and the means by which they are studied. Although my main aim has been to establish the general principles, I have also tried to provide sufficient references for the reader who wishes to refer to the primary sources. To avoid weighing down the narrative unduly, often I have quoted only the initial report on a subject, to give historical perspective, and an up-to-date reference that can act as a source for intervening references. I have strongly preferred papers in common journals or reviews to reports in symposium volumes. I have sometimes not mentioned reports that show simply that a situation reported first for a given system applies also to others. Certain topics which I consider not directly relevant are not discussed; these include the biology of phage λ, the applications of conjugation in genetic analysis, and generally the details of the expression of plasmid functions apart from replication and transfer. However, insertion sequences and transposons and some aspects of 'genetic engineering' are treated in some detail. I have also given in outline the steps involved in particular methods, especially in the chapters on structure and medically important plasmids. These outlines should indicate how much effort is necessary to acquire useful information. Detailed procedures are not presented, since anyone wishing to do such experiments will in any case consult the primary sources. The reader in search of further definitions is referred to Novick *et al*. (1976).

I am deeply indebted to those who have read large parts or the whole of this book during its preparation. These include John Cullum, John Fincham, David Finnegan, Andrew Fraser, Stuart Levy, Alan Linton, Werner Maas, Claire MacLeod, Millicent Masters, Kurt Nordström, Robert Rownd, John Scaife, Ron Skurray, David Sherratt and Ken Timmis. I am also grateful for the patience shown by my publisher, John Gillman. This book is dedicated to Engelbert Broda and Bill Hayes, and to Cleo and Andrew.

I
Introduction

The use of drugs to combat bacterial infections became common after the Second World War. With time there arose strains that were genetically resistant to the original drugs, and infections were then treated with more recently discovered drugs. Often more than one was used in a single course of treatment, since any given pathogen was unlikely to have become resistant to more than one drug.

However, in 1963 there appeared a review in English (Watanabe 1963) of recent Japanese work that had demonstrated the existence of simultaneous resistance to two or more drugs in species of *Shigella*, which are a group of Gram-negative enteric bacteria that cause dysentery. It had been shown moreover that such resistances could be transferred together to other bacteria (Ochiai *et al*. 1959; Akiba *et al*. 1960). Such infectious multiple drug resistance was then also reported in Europe (Datta 1962). Over the years it has become ever more important, with respect to the number of pathogenic host strains, the range of drug resistances and the number of cases of infection in both human and animal populations (see Chapter 6).

Very soon (Mitsuhashi *et al*. 1960) the analogy was drawn between the agents of such transferrable drug resistance (later termed R factors) and the sex factor F of *Escherichia coli* K-12, which like the shigellae, is a member of the *Enterobacteriaceae*. A few years earlier F too had been recognized as a quite novel phenomenon, albeit one of academic interest only. Lederberg *et al*. (1952) and Hayes (1953) had found that F, the causative agent of gene transfer (conjugation; see Chapter 5) between strains of *E. coli*, appeared not to be part of the bacterial chromosome, and, like R factors, could spread through bacterial populations. It is now known that F and some R factors are indeed closely related (see Chapter 3).

What are plasmids?   F and R factors are plasmids; that is, autonomously replicating entities, or, in the original definition (Lederberg 1952), extrachromosomal hereditary determinants. Numerous other types of plasmid have also been described in many bacterial species (Table 1.1). All those so far isolated from bacteria exist as double-stranded DNA circles. Although plasmids have so far been studied mostly in bacteria, analogous entities exist in eukaryotes. However, because of the medical importance of R plasmids, and the importance of F and *E. coli* in the development of molecular biology, most work has been on plasmids in Gram-negative bacteria, as will become evident from this book.

Table 1.1
A range of plasmids in bacteria. Extensive lists of plasmids are given in Bukhari *et al.* 1977.

Original host	Plasmid	Phenotype recognized	Size (mega-daltons)	Conjugation
E. coli	F	transfer	62.5	+
	λdv	lambda immunity	8.6	−
	ColE1	colicinogeny	4.2	−
	Ent	enterotoxin	53	+
	15	cryptic	1.5	−
Shigella	Collb-P9	colicinogeny	61.5	+
	P1	phage; restriction	67	−
	R100	drug resistance	58	+
Salmonella typhimurium type 29	series of R factors	drug resistance	−	+,−
Pseudomonas aeruginosa	RP1	drug resistance	38	+
Pseudomonas putida	TOL	toluene degradation	78	+
Staphylococcus aureus	pI258	resistance to anti-biotics, heavy metals	19	−
Streptomyces coelicolor	SCP1	drug resistance and production	?	+
Agrobacterium tumefaciens	Ti	plant tumours	95–156	+

Successful plasmids must effect a balance between multiplying consistently faster than their host cell, as do viruses, and not multiplying as fast, and hence being diluted out during growth of the population (see Chapter 4). Plasmids and bacterial viruses can be related: thus λ is a bacteriophage ('phage') of *E. coli*, but λdv particles, which arise from λ by simple deletion of DNA, are plasmids. In the autonomous state phage λ kills its host and is then released in the form of infectious particles, but λdv is present in the cell in a fairly stable number of copies and does not kill its host. This is because although λdv particles contain the genes for replication and its control, they lack the genes that specify the protein coat and the lytic functions (Matsubara and Kaiser 1968). In its lytic state P1 is another phage of *E. coli*, but in its latent ('lysogenic') form it is a plasmid, since it replicates autonomously (Ikeda and Tomizawa 1968). Stability in copy number also distinguishes plasmids from coliphage M13, which multiplies and releases large numbers of daughter particles (with protein coats) but does not kill its host. Analogies with parasitism and symbiosis clearly exist at this sub-cellular level. Lederberg (1952) pointed out that the alternative views of plasmids as symbionts or as integral parts of the host's genetic complement depend upon the observer's concept of the scope of the host organism.

Many plasmids carry genes which specify functions that allow the plasmids to transfer themselves to other cells. In some cases plasmids can cross intergeneric boundaries with great ease (Chapter 5). With such potential for transfer, it will often be impossible to decide what was the original host of a particular plasmid, or even whether it arose in the bacteria.

Plasmids are studied for their own sake. The medical importance of plasmids is discussed in Chapter 6. Plasmids are also of great value as material for studying the structure and function of genetic material. They have two great virtues for this purpose. One is their relatively small size, generally in the range between 1.5 and 100 million daltons (megadaltons), which means that they are much easier to manipulate *in vitro* than are intact bacterial chromosomes. 1 megadalton is equivalent to about 1,500 base pairs (1.5 kilobases) of DNA, and therefore is sufficient to code for 1–2 average-sized proteins. Second, their host cells can usually survive without them. Therefore the properties conferred by a plasmid (for instance drug resistance) can be easily examined. Since such plasmid-specified functions can often be selected for, many genetic experiments are possible. Such studies are beginning to reveal details of their structure, replication and other functions, and to show their importance in bacterial evolution.

Plasmids are tools for molecular biology. Plasmids can also serve as experimental tools. Genetic analysis of bacteria involves exchange of genes between strains, and plasmids, in particular F, are important agents of transfer (see Hayes 1968, and Chapter 5). Certain plasmids that can transfer between different genera are being used extensively to introduce DNA into novel hosts. An example is the introduction of nitrogen fixation genes from *Klebsiella* to *E. coli* (Cannon *et al.* 1976) and to *Azotobacter* (Cannon and Postgate 1976) using hybrid ('recombinant') plasmids based on F and RP4 respectively.

Plasmid DNA can also be joined with fragments of alien DNA *in vitro*. Such alien DNA can come from any source, prokaryotic or eukaryotic, to make hybrid molecules that are unlikely to arise frequently in nature. Such 'chimaeras' can then be introduced into bacterial cells, where they can become established (Cohen 1975, Timmis *et al*. 1978e, and Chapters 3 and 8). Large amounts of hybrid DNA can then easily be purified from such clones. Such 'genetic engineering' makes possible many previously impracticable experiments and thus has transformed the prospects for the development and application of biology. It has also raised novel scientific-political problems (Chapter 8). Thus for several reasons the study of plasmids is no longer the preserve of a few people but is at the centre of the New Biology. In this book I try to take stock of this process and its consequences.

2
Isolation and Sizing of Plasmid DNA

Initially the demonstration of plasmids depended upon genetic experiments. For instance, the original evidence for the autonomy of F was threefold: its transfer between cells independent of other genetic material, its loss at rates higher than normal mutation frequencies, and the enhancement of this rate by incubation in the presence of acridine orange, which much later was shown to interfere with its replication (Hohn and Korn 1969).

The initial demonstration of R and bacteriocinogenic factors also generally depended upon the loss or transfer of some easily recognized phenotype (in these cases drug resistance and the ability to kill other strains of bacteria, respectively). However, not all plasmids are transferable, very few are susceptible to acridine orange, and many are cryptic (have no recognizable phenotype). The realization that plasmids are very common has come from the use of methods for their physical isolation and characterization.

Isolation of plasmid DNA
Use of density gradient centrifugation.   In 1961 Lavallé and Jacob showed that a number of plasmids, like the chromosome, were sensitive to ^{32}P decay, and concluded from this that plasmids contained DNA. Plasmid DNA was first isolated by Marmur *et el*. (1961). Their method involved the transfer of an F'*lac* plasmid (that is, an F factor also carrying genes that allow the cell to utilize lactose as the sole carbon source) from *E. coli* into cells of the Lac⁻ (= non-lactose-utilizing) bacterium *Serratia marcescens*, to obtain Lac⁺ (= lactose-utilizing) derivatives. This was done because *Serratia* has DNA that is denser than that of *E. coli* and of F'*lac* (1.718 g/cm³ compared with 1.709 g/cm³), as it contains a higher proportion of guanosine·cytosine base pairs. Therefore plasmid DNA could be detected in extracts of such strains following caesium chloride equilibrium density gradient centrifugation to separate the plasmid DNA from the host DNA (Table 2.1) The rationale of this method is as follows.

Table 2.1
Uses of centrifugation for the isolation of plasmid DNA.

Type of centrifugation	Contains	Basis of separation	Typical duration (hours)	*g* value ($\times 10^{-3}$)
Clearing spin	lysis mix	mass	0.25	12
Sedimentation velocity gradient	preformed sucrose gradient	mass and conformation	1	250
Equilibrium density gradient	(1) CsCl	density	48	100
	(2) CsCl and ethidium bromide	amount of intercalation of ethidium bromide in DNA	48	100

When a solution of caesium chloride is ultracentrifuged, a gradient of caesium concentration is set up that in time reaches equilibrium. The slope of this gradient is defined by the opposing effects of centrifugation of Cs ions towards the bottom of the tube (making the solution at the bottom of the tube denser), and by the random diffusion of these ions (tending to restore homogeneity within the solution). The particular virtue of CsCl is that concentrated solutions of it (e.g. 1.7 g/cm³) can be made and that, when spun, such solutions form steep and stable density gradients (e.g. from 1.6 at the top to 1.8 g/cm³ at the bottom). The caesium salt of DNA has a density of about 1.7 g/cm³ but, being of far greater mass than the Cs and Cl ions, it is much less subject than they are to random diffusion. Therefore in such a CsCl gradient DNA concentrates rather slowly in a narrow band at the appropriate density. Once formed, this band is very stable.

The distribution of the DNA in the tube may be determined with the naked eye. The DNA can then be removed with a syringe. Alternatively drops of isotopically labelled DNA can be collected through a small hole made in the bottom of the tube as a series of small samples and the radioactivity in each sample is then determined. In the experiment of Marmur *et al.* (1961), DNA from the Lac⁺ *Serratia* strain had a small extra band of DNA of a density characteristic of DNA from *E. coli*. In analogous experiments in which F'*lac* had been transferred to *Proteus mirabilis* (G·C = 39%), Falkow *et al.* (1964) observed that this peak disappeared in extracts from cultures of spontaneously arising Lac⁻ variants ('Lac⁻ segregants'). Therefore F'*lac*, and presumably F itself, contained DNA.

Isolation of intact plasmid molecules. In the early experiments, plasmid DNA was isolated as linear molecules. However, with the development of gentler methods of releasing DNA from cells, several plasmids were shown by electron microscopy to be circular molecules (Roth and Helinski 1967; Hickson *et al*. 1968; Freifelder 1968). This is the form in which most, if not all, plasmids are present in the cell.

Usually plasmids can be isolated efficiently from normal cells. However, for some purposes, minicells have proved useful. Minicells are aberrant products of cell division produced by certain mutants of *E. coli* and other bacteria. They do not contain chromosomal DNA but copies of some plasmids are segregated into them. Since minicells can be separated from normal cells by centrifugation or filtration, it is possible to obtain plasmid preparations free of chromosomal DNA (see Frazer and Curtiss 1975, for a review).

Lysis is achieved in two steps. First spheroplasts (cells without a rigid outer wall) are made by digestion with the enzyme lysozyme (lysostaphin is used with staphylococci) in the presence of sucrose, which protects the spheroplast from bursting by providing a high external osmotic pressure. The spheroplasts are then lysed with detergent, so that the DNA of both the chromosome and the plasmid is released gently. A number of methods can then be used to separate plasmid DNA from chromosomal DNA and other cell material (Table 2.2). Commonly a given procedure, developed for one plasmid, gives poor yields with another plasmid or strain. Hence, in investigating a new system, a number of procedures may have to be tested before a satisfactory one is found.

Many procedures involve a relatively slow and short centrifugation (for instance 15 min at 15,000 rev./min). Such a 'clearing spin' (Table 2.1) pellets most of the cell debris and chromosomal DNA, which remains intact or is only fragmented into a few large pieces; the (smaller) plasmid molecules, usually contaminated with small pieces of chromosomal DNA, remain in the supernatant, the 'cleared lysate'.

Another widely used method is velocity gradient centrifugation. Here the molecules move downwards through a pre-formed gradient of sucrose solution (a gradient from 5 per cent to 20 per cent would be typical) at rates that depend upon their mass and conformation. This is not an equilibrium gradient since in time all the DNA would reach the bottom of the tube. However, if the centrifugation is stopped before this happens, molecules of different mass will have reached different points on the gradient, and can therefore be resolved. A plasmid usually gives two bands because DNA circles can exist in two conformations, the covalently closed circle (ccc) or supercoil, in which the molecule is tightly twisted, and the open circle (oc),

Table 2.2
Summary of some procedures commonly used for isolating plasmid DNA.

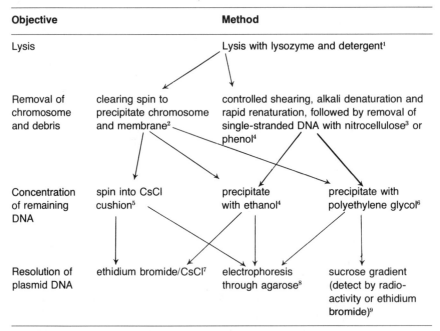

Objective	Method
Lysis	Lysis with lysozyme and detergent[1]
Removal of chromosome and debris	clearing spin to precipitate chromosome and membrane[2] · controlled shearing, alkali denaturation and rapid renaturation, followed by removal of single-stranded DNA with nitrocellulose[3] or phenol[4]
Concentration of remaining DNA	spin into CsCl cushion[5] · precipitate with ethanol[4] · precipitate with polyethylene glycol[6]
Resolution of plasmid DNA	ethidium bromide/CsCl[7] · electrophoresis through agarose[8] · sucrose gradient (detect by radio-activity or ethidium bromide)[9]

[1] Clewell and Helinski, 1970. This can be done by centrifugation through detergent. Minicells can sometimes be used (Frazer and Curtiss 1973).
[2] Prior treatment with high concentrations of salt may improve separation (Guerry *et al.* 1973).
[3] Sharp *et al.* 1972.
[4] Currier and Nester 1976a.
[5] Thompson *et al.* 1974.
[6] Humphreys *et al.* 1975.
[7] Radloff *et al.* 1967.
[8] Meyers *et al.* 1976.
[9] Hughes and Meynell 1977.

where, because at least one of the strands is nicked at least once, for one reason or another, one or more points of free rotation exist, and the super-coil is not maintained (Fig. 2.1). cccDNA molecules sediment more rapidly than ocDNA molecules of the same mass, because their more compact form makes their movement less subject to drag. In general plasmids are present in the cell in the covalently closed circular form, although replication involves unwinding (see Chapter 4).

Purification of covalently closed circular DNA.   Cohen and Miller (1969) denatured DNA in cell extracts with alkali, and then returned the pH to

Fig. 2.1. Covalently closed and open circular plasmid DNA. The molecules shown are of TP123, an R factor which has a mass of 123 megadaltons and belongs to the H1 incompatibility group (Grindley *et al*. 1973). (Photograph by courtesy of Henry Smith.)

neutrality. Since the two strands of plasmid cccDNA remain joined as interlocking rings, they renature much more efficiently than plasmid ocDNA and chromosomal DNA, where the complementary strands are lost to each other. Cohen and Miller were therefore able to separate the renatured cccDNA from other DNA using nitrocellulose, which binds single-stranded DNA preferentially.

Radloff *et al.* (1967) observed that linear and open circular molecules can bind more of the intercalating compound ethidium bromide than can covalently closed circular molecules. When this occurs in CsCl solution, Cs ions are displaced, and the DNA becomes less dense. Because of this difference in density covalently closed circular molecules can be separated from other DNA species on a CsCl–ethidium bromide equilibrium density gradient.

Simplified methods for plasmid isolation. The methods discussed so far are used for preparation of moderate amounts of plasmid DNA. Recently these have been supplemented by simpler methods that use fewer cells (Table 2.3). There have been at least four objectives: a wish to screen large numbers of clones, a need to avoid spending the time and money involved in CsCl centrifugation, the development of electrophoresis methods that can resolve plasmid molecules of up to at least 150 megadaltons, and the need to 'contain' possibly dangerous organisms (see Chapter 8).

Transformation and transduction. *E. coli* cells treated with $CaCl_2$ can be transformed with chromosomal DNA (Cosloy and Oishi 1973) and plasmid DNA (Cohen *et al.* 1972; Lederberg and Cohen 1974; for a review see Benzinger 1978). Methods for transformation in other organisms involve freezing and thawing (Holsters *et al.* 1978a) and treatment with polyethylene glycol (Bibb *et al.* 1978; Chang and Cohen 1979). Some of the factors that affect the efficiency of transformation of particular species of plasmid DNA are discussed by Canosi *et al.* (1978) and Contente and Dubnau (1979).

The possibility of introducing purified plasmid DNA into cells makes the demonstration that a given plasmid species is responsible for a given phenotype more rigorous than was hitherto possible. It is an essential part of the technology of genetic manipulation *in vitro* (see later). Plasmid DNA can also be treated with mutagens *in vitro* and then introduced into host cells (Humphreys *et al.* 1976; Hashimoto and Sekiguchi 1976). This is especially useful for the isolation of mutants of plasmids that are present in the cell in many copies. This is because whereas recessive mutations present in only one of many such copies will not be recognized, cells transformed with a single mutant molecule will give rise to clones containing only mutant plasmids.

Table 2.3
Some screening methods for detection and sizing of plasmid DNA from small bacterial cultures.

Procedure	Meyers et al. 1976	Barnes 1977	Telford et al.1977	Hughes and Meynell 1977	Hansen and Olsen 1978a	Eckhardt 1978
Starting material	30 ml ↓	single colony ↓	single colony ↓	50 ml ↓	40 ml ↓	single colony ↓
Principal subsequent steps	Lysis	Lysis	Lysis	Lysis	Lysis at 55° C, denaturation/ renaturation	Lysis in gel slot
	↓ clearing spin	↓ 70° C 10 min	↓ 60° C 30 min	↓ 50° C 8 min		
	↓ phenol extraction	↓ mild shear		↓ clearing spin	↓ SDS salt precipitation of chromosome	
	↓ ethanol precipitation				↓ ethanol or PEG precipitation	
Resolution[1]	↓ electrophoresis	↓ electrophoresis	↓ electrophoresis	↓ sucrose gradient	↓ electrophoresis	↓ electrophoresis

[1] In all cases visualization is by fluorescence of ethidium bromide in the presence of DNA.
SDS = Sodium dodecyl sulphate.
PEG = Polyethylene glycol.

Normally it is necessary to have a plasmid phenotype that can be selected, since the maximum efficiency of plasmid transformation (at least in *E. coli*) is only in the order of 10^{-3} per recipient cell. Transformation is due to the competence (ability to take up DNA) of only a minority of the cells, since some cells can receive two plasmids independently (Kretschmer *et al*. 1975).

Therefore one can nevertheless isolate transformants for cryptic plasmids. This is done by using a saturating concentration of a mixture of two plasmid preparations and then screening transformants of a selectable plasmid for the presence of the cryptic plasmid.

Conjugation (mating involving cell-to-cell contact—see Chapter 5) and transduction (gene transfer mediated by phages) have also been used to demonstrate the existence of plasmids. However, both of these methods are less rigorous than transformation, since plasmid DNA is not being isolated and because here also two physically separate plasmids can frequently enter a single recipient cell (see, for instance, Anderson 1969; Iordanescu 1977). Phage coats containing small plasmids contain more than a single copy's worth of DNA. Whether this extra DNA is of plasmid or chromosomal origin is unknown at the time of writing. An intact recombination system is needed to form such particles (Ubelaker and Rosenblum 1978).

The synthesis *in vitro* of proteins specified by plasmids such as ColE1 and F can now be studied (see later). This approach will sometimes reveal products not easily demonstrated *in vivo* (see, for instance, Miller and Cohen 1978).

The Sizes of Plasmid Molecules
Two methods were originally used to determine the molecular weight of plasmid DNA. Using sucrose gradients also containing particles with a known sedimentation coefficient (*s* value), the *s* value for a given plasmid DNA can be determined. Empirical equations exist for both cccDNA and ocDNA that relate such *s* values to molecular weight (Clowes 1972). The second method is the electron-microscopical measurement of the contour length of plasmid molecules (Lang and Mitani 1970). Phage λ DNA (30.8 megadaltons, Davidson and Szybalski 1971) and ColE1 DNA (4.2 megadaltons, Helinski *et al*. 1975) are examples of convenient standard molecules to include in the same preparation. Since ocDNA molecules are more easily measured than cccDNA molecules, cccDNA molecules are sometimes converted to ocDNA by X–irradiation, even though nicking of some molecules always occurs during purification and spreading on the electron microscope grid.

Determination of *s* values has now largely given way to sizing using agarose gels. This can be done with intact cccDNA (Fig. 2.2) or with fragments produced by cleaving all molecules in a preparation with site-specific endonucleases (see later) followed by summation of the sizes of the fragments. Here it is important to allow for different fragments having similar sizes; these are revealed by densitometry as bands of twice (for

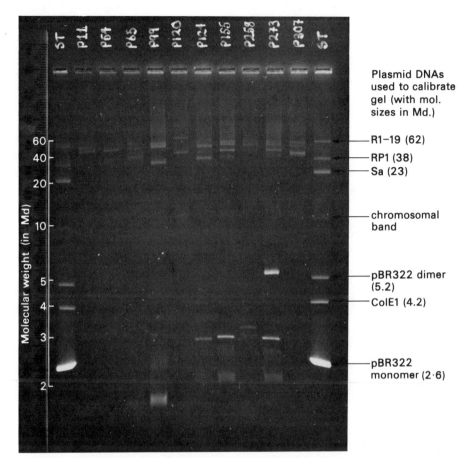

Fig. 2.2. Agarose gel electrophoresis of covalently closed circular plasmid DNA from *E. coli* strains isolated by H. Williams Smith. Each strain contains several plasmids. The method of Meyers *et al.* (1976) summarized in Table 2.3 was used, and was followed by purification by CsCl/ethidium bromide buoyant density centrifugation. The volumes of DNA applied were 20 microlitres. The gel was of 0.7 per cent agarose, and electrophoresis was for 5 hours. The diffuse bands of contaminating chromosomal fragments can just be discerned. The two side tracks contain mixtures of the plasmids named. (Photograph by courtesy of D. Morris.)

Strains carrying several different plasmid species provide convenient sources of covalently closed molecules of known size (see for instance Macrina *et al.* (1978).

doublets) the expected absorbance (Fig. 2.3). Also it must be shown that all fragments come from a single plasmid species.

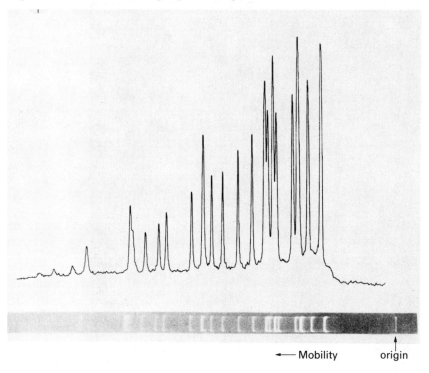

Fig. 2.3. **Densitometry trace of endonuclease-derived fragments of a 78-megadalton plasmid resolved on agarose, showing doublet bands (from Duggleby *et al.* 1977.)**

The sizes of many plasmids have been determined by such methods. One of the smallest known naturally occurring plasmids, a cryptic plasmid of *E. coli* 15 (Cozzarelli *et al.* 1968), has a mass of about 1.5 megadaltons, which is only sufficient to code for about two proteins of average size. Others of over 200 megadaltons have been described (Ohtsubo *et al.* 1974; Duggleby *et al.* 1977) and with improved isolation methods (e.g., Fennewald *et al.* 1978; Hansen and Olsen 1978a, b) still larger ones, for instance a class of large plasmids from pseudomonads, are being isolated. Many of the plasmids so far examined have either sizes around 3–6 megadaltons or 50–70 megadaltons, although many with other sizes also exist. Only the larger ones are self-transmissible; the smallest known naturally occurring self-transmissible plasmids have sizes of about 25 megadaltons (R6K: Kontomichalou *et al.* 1970; R931: Bryan *et al.* 1973). This suggests that autonomous replication needs few plasmid genes but that transfer needs many.

Cells may carry several plasmids. Many strains carry more than one type of plasmid. One such is the *Salmonella typhimurium* strain RT1, which is resistant to ampicillin, streptomycin, sulphonamide, tetracycline and furazolidone (Anderson 1969). The determinants for resistance to ampicillin (Ap) and streptomycin (Sm) were transferred independently to an *E. coli* strain at frequencies of about 0.01 per donor cell (Table 2.4) and sulphonamide resistance (Su) was always transferred with Sm, as if Ap was carried on one plasmid and Sm and Su were carried on another. Ap and Sm could be retransferred from most but not all of the appropriate progeny clones. Such transfer was the clue to the existence of a further plasmid, the sex factor Δ, which although itself transferred at high frequency (about 0.5) was not always found in the selected progeny. Strains previously unable to re-transfer Ap could do so once Δ was introduced into them. In contrast, although transfer of tetracycline resistance (Tc) from the original strain was extremely rare, its subsequent re-transfer was as efficient as that of Δ. All such second generation Tc$^+$ clones were fertile, as if Δ and Tc had become fused to give a new plasmid, Δ-Tc. Fu may be a chromosomally borne function, since its transfer has never been observed; Tc may also have been initially chromosomal.

Table 2.4
Transfer of drug resistance from *Salm. typhimurium* strain RT1 to *E.coli* K–12 in standard 16h matings (after Anderson 1969).

Progeny class	Approximate frequency (%)
Δ Ap	2
Δ Sm	1
Δ Ap Sm	0.1
Δ Tc	0.0001
Δ	50

These genetic conclusions were confirmed by physical experiments. Milliken and Clowes (1973) showed that the sizes of the Ap, Sm and Δ plasmids were 5.6, 5.6 and 61 megadaltons respectively, and that at least the great majority of plasmid molecules from preparations from Δ^+Ap^+ and Δ^+ Sm^+ strains were of these sizes. They termed this type of association of plasmids an 'aggregate', and contrasted it with the 'cointegrate' Δ-Tc, which is present as a unique species with a size of 67 megadaltons. However, since Tc has never been shown to have an independent existence, Δ-Tc does not conform to the current definition of a cointegrate (Novick *et al*. 1976). This is of 'a naturally occurring genetic element composed of two or more complete replicons in covalent linear continuity where the component replicons are known to be capable of physically independent replication'. According to the complementary definition, any plasmids present together in a cell constitute an aggregate. Anderson (1969) has pointed out that the Sm determinant appeared in type 29 of *Salm. typhimurium* (of which strain RT1 was a particular isolate) nearly two years before the Ap determinant.

Association and dissociation of plasmids. In other cases the resistance and transfer functions are on a single molecule. Examples are three closely related plasmids, R1, R6 and R100, in *E. coli*. R1 DNA has a density in CsCl of about 1.710 g/cm^3 and a molecular weight of about 65 megadaltons by contour length and s value measurements (Cohen and Miller 1969). However, in such DNA preparations there were also a few circles of about 11 megadaltons. A self-transmissible segregant (RTF for 'resistance transfer factor') was isolated that had lost the drug-resistance determinants for Ap, chloramphenicol (Cm), kanamycin (Km) and Sm; its DNA was 0.002 g/cm^3 less dense than that of R1 (Cohen and Miller 1970b). These two observations were brought together in the suggestion that R1 was composed of the RTF together with a smaller resistance determinant (r), of which the smaller circles were representatives. On the basis of similar results Silver and Falkow (1970 a, b) suggested that the resistance moiety of R1 absent in the RTF should have a density of about 1.716–1.718 g/cm^3 to account for the density of the composite molecule being greater than that of the RTF. These suggestions have been shown to be essentially correct (see below).

Although composite molecules of R1 predominate in *E. coli*, the related R factor 222 (R100, 222 and NR1 are synonyms used by different workers) was segregated and then lost more readily from *Salm. typhimurium* than from *E. coli* (Watanabe and Ogata 1970). Therefore the equilibrium between the RTF-r and the RTF + r states depends upon the host as well as the plasmid. A point of interest was that although the RTF segregants had lost Cm and Sm they retained Tc. Sharp *et al*. (1973) then showed by other methods that Tc is on the RTF moiety although the other resistance functions map within the r determinant region (Lane and Chandler 1977; Miki *et al*. 1978a).

At about the same time these plasmids were also being examined in *Proteus mirabilis*, where, as discussed earlier, the distinct density of the host DNA (1.700 g/cm^3) allows the clean separation of plasmid DNA from chromosomal DNA in CsCl density gradients. The state of the plasmids here was more complex than it was in *E. coli* (Rownd *et al*. 1966). On centrifugation of DNA from plasmid 222, Nisioka *et al*. (1969) observed three peaks of comparable sizes with densities of 1.708, 1.711 and 1.717 g/cm^3. The minority of molecules from these fractions that were circular had sizes of about 54, 68 and 12 megadaltons respectively. On the basis of both size and density, it therefore appeared that here too the largest molecules were composites of those from the two smaller size classes. But since in the gradient the peaks represented comparable amounts of DNA, it appeared that in this case aggregates as well as cointegrates were present in substantial numbers in the population. Cohen and Miller (1970a) described analogous results with R1.

'Transition' or amplification.   In the experiments described above (and most of the other earlier experiments) *Pr. mirabilis* was grown in antibiotic-supplemented medium to prevent the accumulation of R$^-$ segregants. However when *Pr. mirabilis* carrying NR1 is grown in drug-free medium for many generations the plasmid DNA forms a single band with a density of 1.712 g/cm^3, as it does in *E. coli* (Rownd and Mickel 1971). The amount of plasmid DNA is also comparable. When such a culture is then inoculated into medium supplemented with chloramphenicol or streptomycin (but not tetracycline) and serially subcultured, the DNA becomes heterogeneous in density, and there is a gradual 'transition' towards a greater amount of plasmid DNA, with a density strongly skewed towards 1.718 g/cm^3 (Fig. 2.4). The implied increase in number of r determinants is reflected in higher levels of resistance to chloramphenicol and streptomycin (Hashimoto and Rownd 1975). In contrast, the amount of 1.710 g/cm^3 (RTF) DNA does not change. On subsequent serial subculture in the absence of the antibiotic the amount of plasmid DNA declines and its density returns to 1.712 g/cm^3. This process is referred to as the 'back-transition'. Transition probably depends upon the occurrence in non-transitioned cultures of cells with an increased number of r determinants. Such cells grow faster than normal cells in the presence of chloramphenicol or streptomycin (Hashimoto and Rownd 1975) and are therefore selected for.

The state of the many r determinants in transitioned cells has been disputed (Clowes 1972; Rownd *et al*. 1975). Having observed both RTF-Tc and r molecules from *Proteus*, Clowes suggested that in transition these moieties are physically separate. The RTF-Tc molecule, replicated 'strin-

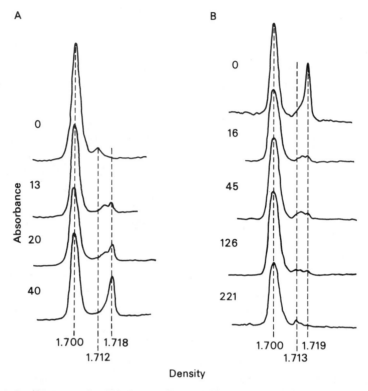

Fig. 2.4. Changes in density profiles of DNA prepared from a strain of *Pr. mirabilis* carrying NR1 after various periods of growth (A) in medium containing chloramphenicol and (B) after subculture of such a transitioned culture in drug-free medium. The numbers refer to the generations of growth from the initial cultures (top). (From Rownd and Mickel 1971 with permission.)

gently', would be present in a small and constant number of copies, whereas the r determinants, under 'relaxed' control, would be able to increase from a small number of copies to a very large number under such selective conditions. This view draws on an analogy with the ColE1 plasmid, which is present in many copies and is a model for 'relaxed' control of replication (see Chapter 4).

The alternative model (Rownd and Mickel 1971) postulates that the r determinants are arranged tandemly on large structures. The increase in number of r determinants per cell during transition would involve a lengthening of these tandem structures by some type of recombination. The question, therefore, is whether most of the r DNA in transitioned preparations is present as monomers. Although independent monomers clearly exist, in the preparations of Nisioka *et al.* (1969) they only accounted for about 10 per cent of the molecules and therefore 1 per cent of their mass. On the other hand, tandem structures would have to carry many r moieties to account for the observed density of 1.718 g/cm³. They would therefore be very difficult to isolate as intact structures. The resolution of this problem has depended upon improved methods for characterizing plasmid DNA.

Perlman and Rownd (1975) found that NR1 molecules from non-transitioned cultures were about 8 μm longer than those of an RTF-Tc derivative. This suggested that the r determinant had a length of 8 μm. In contrast, plasmid preparations from transitioned cultures consisted mostly of linear molecules of about 150 megadaltons. Since chromosomal DNA from the same lysate was also in the form of linear molecules of about 150 megadaltons, this length was determined by the extent of shearing in the extraction procedure, and was only a lower limit for the size of the bulk of the plasmid DNA. In addition about 5 per cent of the total plasmid DNA was present as 8-μm circles, which presumably were r monomers, and in another experiment a series of circular molecules with lengths that were multiples of 8.5 μm were observed (Table 2.5). These observations suggested that both r and poly(r) molecules can exist independently of the RTF-Tc moiety, but gave no information on the composition of the 150-megadalton molecules.

For this reason molecules intermediate in both density and molecular weight were isolated from cultures early in the transition or in the back-transition. These were found to include intact circles that had the lengths expected of RTF-Tc-(r)$_2$, RTF-Tc-(r)$_3$ and RTF-Tc-(r)$_4$ molecules (Table 2.5).

Perlman *et al.* (1975) tested the tandem model further using the denaturation mapping method. The pH at which DNA denatures is a function of its base composition, since G·C base pairs have three hydrogen bonds and A·T base pairs only have two. The more G·C-rich a sequence, therefore, the higher the pH required to denature it. Careful treatment and electron microscopy of a given molecule, such as phage λ (Schnös and Inman 1970), reveals a reproducible pattern of partial denaturation, yielding double and single-stranded regions. Since, as discussed above, the RTF-Tc and r moieties appeared to have quite different base ratios and therefore densities, they should be denatured to different extents at a given pH. By comparison of RTF-Tc and NR1 molecules Perlman *et al.* were able to assign the r moiety to a G·C-rich sequence, and to show that the linear molecules from transitioned cultures included RTF-Tc-(r)$_n$ molecules. The r moieties were contiguous and were arranged head to tail. The scheme proposed by Rownd *et al.* (1975) for r amplification is reproduced in Fig. 2.5.

More than one mechanism may operate in NR1 transition (Perlman and Stickgold 1977). With low concentrations of chloramphenicol (25–100

Table 2.5
Contour lengths of circular NR1 molecules in transitioned and non-transitioned cultures of *Pr. mirabilis* (from Perlman and Rownd, 1975).

R factor	Density (g/cm³) (approximate)	Contour Length (μm)	Number of molecules observed
RTF-Tc	1.710	28.7	18
Non-transitioned NR1	1.712	37.0	40
NR1 during back-transition	1.713	45.9	6
	1.715	53.8	8
	1.715	62.2	9
Transitioned NR1	1.718	8.2	7
	1.718	16.3	7
	1.718	24.4	1
	1.718	33.9	7
	1.718	42.0	1

μg/ml) transition depends upon the selection of the pre-existing partially transitioned cells mentioned earlier. But at a chloramphenicol concentration of 250 μg/ml and a cell concentration of 10^7/ml, when non-transitioned cells are unable to grow at all, there is a lag of 20–30 hours before growth is seen. Chloramphenicol is being inactivated during this period and growth only starts when its concentration falls below a critical level. But even before growth starts the amount of r determinant DNA starts to increase, and eventually the 1.712 g/cm³ band disappears. Much of the r DNA is seen in monomers, then in poly(r) molecules and finally in RTF-Tc-poly(r) molecules. Such amplification is occurring without growth, i.e., not by selection of existing cells, and continues even if the remaining chloramphenicol is removed towards the end of the lag period. It requires protein synthesis and only occurs if the combination of cell and chloramphenicol concentrations are such that the lag is more than 12 hours.

Transition also occurs in the Gram-positive organism *Streptococcus faecalis*. Yagi and Clewell (1976) have demonstrated gene amplification of plasmid-borne Tc resistance that depends upon the tandem repeat of a 2.8-megadalton segment.

In both systems amplification is thought to depend upon recombination between homologous 'IS' (for insertion sequence) regions (see next Chapter). According to the Campbell model (Chapter 3) this results in the amplified region being bounded by the two segments in the same orienta-

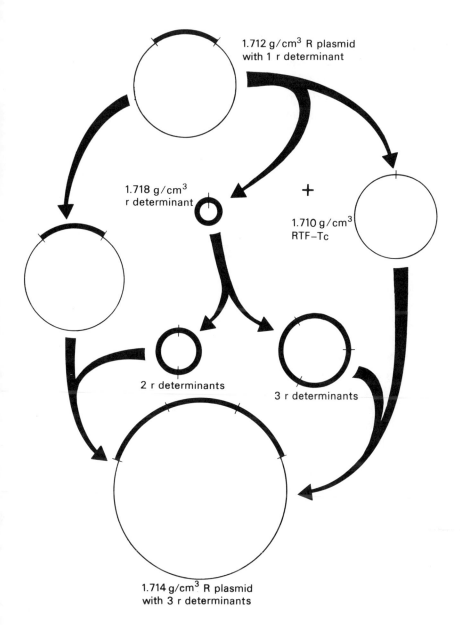

1.712 g/cm³ R plasmid
with 1 r determinant

1.718 g/cm³
r determinant

+

1.710 g/cm³
RTF–Tc

2 r determinants

3 r determinants

1.714 g/cm³ R plasmid
with 3 r determinants

Fig. 2.5.   Schematic diagram illustrating the dissociation and the reassociation of RTF-Tc and r determinants in *Pr. mirabilis* and the density increase that accompanies the incorporation of multiple copies of r determinants into individual R molecules to form poly(r)-determinant R plasmids. After the incorporation of a large number of r determinants, the poly(r)-determinant R plasmid has essentially the same density as r-determinant DNA (1.718 g/cm³), since most of the mass of the DNA is due to r determinants (from Rownd *et al*. 1975, with permission.)

tion. But the mode of amplification of NR84 (a plasmid related to NR1) in *Pr. mirabilis*, cannot yet be explained simply (Rownd *et al*. 1978). Here, in different experiments, even with the same selection, different unselected resistances were amplified. Molecular studies on these amplified plasmids revealed that many other regions within the r determinant could act as the ends of the amplified segment.

Why amplification of NR1 is observable in *Pr. mirabilis* but not in *E. coli*, *Salm. typhimurium* or *Serratia marcescens* (Rownd *et al*. 1975) is unclear. It is possible that for some reason the molecular interactions do not occur. An alternative is that only in *Pr. mirabilis* can a strong enough selection be exerted to reveal them. Perhaps in *E. coli* these antibiotic resistances are sufficiently expressed without amplification, or else such amplified plasmids are too great a burden upon the cell. In connexion with the former possibility, it is known that expression of genes from *E. coli* in *Pr. mirabilis* can be poor. A case of amplification of a (tetracycline) resistance plasmid in *E. coli* has now been reported (Mattes *et al*. 1979).

On the practical level, studies on amplification bring out the point that the structure (and ease of isolation) of a plasmid may depend upon growth conditions. Another case in which a plasmid is larger when selection is exerted for a plasmid-borne function is found with a toluene-degrading strain of *Pseudomonas* (Broda *et al*. 1978).

Summary

With the development of methods for isolating plasmid DNA, the ubiquity of plasmids in bacteria is being recognized. Methods exist for the preparation of relatively large amounts of pure plasmid DNA, and also for the economical isolation of small amounts. Plasmids exist as covalently closed circles. Transformation, transduction and conjugation all have value in relating a species of plasmid molecule to an observed phenotype. Some plasmids smaller than 1 megadalton are known, while others in excess of 200 megadaltons are being characterized. In some cases growth of a culture in the presence of a drug results in the selection of cells with plasmids in which the segment that specifies drug resistance is repeated in tandem fashion.

3
Structure and Evolution of Plasmids

Relationships between plasmids

With many plasmids being studied, a workable scheme for their classification is essential. At present the principal criterion is microbiological. If closely related plasmids (e.g. F and F'*lac*) are introduced into the same cell, one or other is eliminated during growth. Such 'incompatibility' (Datta 1975; Table 3.1) is thought to result from a close relationship of the mechanisms by which they regulate their numbers of copies per cell (Chapter 4). In a cell containing incompatible plasmids their replication is there-

Table 3.1

Classification of coliform plasmids into incompatibility groups (after N. Datta, personal communication).

1.	Transfer a second plasmid into cells of a culture already carrying a resident plasmid.
2.	Select for presence of incoming plasmid.
3.	Purify at least ten progeny clones.
4.	Test these for properties that characterize each plasmid.
5.	If the resident plasmid is eliminated from all clones, repeat test in opposite direction.
6.	If introduction of either plasmid always eliminates the other, the two plasmids are incompatible.
7.	If the resident plasmid is not eliminated from progeny clones, test 'doubles' for (a) stability and (b) separate replication of the two plasmids.
8.	Stability is shown by continued presence of markers of both plasmids after many generations in non-selective (e.g., drug-free) medium.
9.	Separate replication is suggested if the two plasmids are separately transferred when the double is used as a donor in a mating.
10.	If the two plasmids co-exist stably, and are separately transferable, they are compatible.

Possible problems:

1.	The plasmids may not have distinguishing markers; in this case mutants must be isolated.
2.	Surface exclusion (Chapter 5) may prevent a plasmid entering the recipient cell.
3.	Absence of surface exclusion may complicate the stability test through repeated infection.
4.	The presence of other plasmids may interfere with tests on one.

fore blocked until the total number of copies of the two together falls to the value that normally obtains for one alone. This is an unstable situation, especially for plasmids normally present only in a few copies, and eventually results in descendants that have lost one or other plasmid. In contrast, unrelated plasmids are compatible because their replication systems are different enough for them not to interact. Most plasmids of Gram-negative bacteria (e.g., enterobacteria and *Pseudomonas*) have been assigned to one or other of a manageable number (about 20) of incompatibility groups (Table 3.2.) although a few plasmids are incompatible with each of two plasmids belonging to different incompatibility groups (Smith *et al.* 1973a; Willshaw *et al.* 1978). As discussed below, it is thought that the classification arrived at is largely natural, in that incompatibility reflects evolutionary relationship at least of the replication functions.

Table 3.2
Incompatibility groups of plasmids that are transmissible to *E.coli* (mainly after Chabbert *et al.*, 1972, Datta, 1975, and Novick *et al.*, 1976). FI, FII and FIII, and I1 and I2, which are full incompatibility groups, are so named because the pili (see Chapter 5) which they produce are related.

Group	Sex Pili	Representatives
C	?	R40a, R55
FI	F	F'*lac*, R386, ColV2, P307
FII	F-like	R1, R100, R538–1
FIII	F-like	ColB-K98, MIP240
H	?	R27, R726–1
I1	I	R64, CoIIb-P9, *Δ*
I2	I-like	TP114, MIP241
J	?	R391
L	?	R471a, R831
M	?	R446b, R69
N	N	N3, R15
O	?	R16, R724
P	RP4	RP4, R702
S	?	R478, R477–1
T	E	Rts1, R401
W	W	S-a, R388

In addition, R factors of *Pseudomonas aeruginosa* have been assigned to at least ten incompatibility groups (Sagai *et al.,* 1976; Korfhagen *et al.,* 1978). Of these, P, W and a few N group plasmids can be transferred to *E.coli* (Jacoby, 1977). In analogous studies, using transduction as the means of transfer, a number of R factors of *Staphylococcus aureus* have been assigned to seven groups (Novick *et al.,* 1976).

Molecular hybridization. A more direct criterion of relationship is similarity of base sequence. This is tested using the techniques of molecular hybridization. Two strands of a DNA duplex that have been separated by mild treatment with alkali can reassociate when the alkali has been neutralized. If a mixture is made of the dissociated strands from two different sources, for instance two different plasmids, reassociation of complementary strands will occur as before to form 'homoduplex' DNA. However, if there are similarities in DNA sequence between the DNA from the two different sources 'heteroduplexes' will also be formed. Methods exist which allow the detection of even very small amounts of hybrid DNA among otherwise single-stranded DNA (see below).

The original method used for plasmids (Brenner *et al.* 1969; Guerry and Falkow, 1971) depends upon the different affinities for hydroxyapatite of single-stranded and duplex DNA. Labelled single-stranded DNA from one plasmid is incubated with a great excess of unlabelled single-stranded DNA from the other, under conditions that allow complementary DNA strands to form duplexes (Table 3.3). Because of the relative proportions of the labelled and unlabelled DNA, any homology between the two plasmids will

Table 3.3
A scheme for the determination of the degree of homology between two plasmids (after Guerry and Falkow, 1971). Phosphate buffers at pH 6.8 were used. The DNA is generally used as sheared fragments of about 0.2 megadalton (about 300 base pairs). If lower temperatures are used less perfectly matched but possibly still related sequences can reanneal.

Prepare sheared labelled DNA of plasmid 1   Prepare large amount of sheared unlabelled DNA of plasmid 2

Mix, denature and incubate in 0.12 M buffer at 75° C for 18 h to allow annealing
↓
Add mixture in same buffer to hydroxyapatite (HA); maintaining at 75° C, incubate for 5 min to allow binding of duplex DNA to HA
↓
Wash HA with 0.12 M buffer to remove single-stranded DNA
↓
Elute duplex DNA from HA with 0.40 M buffer. Determine the proportion of total label that is present in eluate

result in the labelled DNA entering into heteroduplexes rather than into homoduplexes. The mixture is then incubated briefly with hydroxyapatite to allow duplex DNA to bind to it. The single-stranded DNA is washed away, and the retained duplex molecules are then eluted from the hydroxyapatite. The proportion of the initial radioactivity which binds to the hydroxyapatite is an index of the extent to which the two plasmids are homologous.

Two simple and rapid alternatives for determining the amount of hybridization are also available. One uses the S1 endonuclease from *Aspergillus oryzae*; this enzyme only digests single-stranded DNA (Crosa *et al*. 1973; Barth and Grinter 1975). In the other, hybridization occurs on nitrocellulose filters coated with paraffin for the duration of the hybridization reaction (Roussel and Chabbert 1978). A further method uses hybridization in conjunction with endonuclease digestion (Heinaru *et al*. 1978) and will be discussed in the section on restriction enzymes.

Because homology is assumed to imply a common origin, hybridization and developments based upon it that will be described presently are much used for assessing relatedness between plasmids. In one such investigation Grindley *et al*. (1973) asked whether the genetic test of incompatibility did in fact reflect molecular relatedness. They tested 15 R factors that had been assigned to six incompatibility groups, in pairwise combinations (Table 3.4). Within incompatibility groups there was an average of about 85 per cent homology, whereas most pairs of compatible plasmids showed negligible homology. Thus incompatibility is indeed an indication of relatedness. However, the correlation was imperfect. On the one hand plasmid TP116 had insignificant homology with other H (or indeed any other) plasmids; TP116 is unrelated to the other H group plasmids on other criteria too (Taylor and Grant 1977). On the other hand, up to 22 per cent homology was observed between compatible plasmids.

Other reports (e.g., Guerry and Falkow 1971) also show that in general incompatible plasmids do have most molecular relatedness, but there are also further instances of incompatible plasmids with insignificant homology (Willshaw *et al*. 1978).

Electron microscopy of heteroduplexes. Simple hybridization does not show which parts of two related plasmids are homologous. Electron microscopy of heteroduplexes (Davis *et al.* 1971; Table 3.5.) overcomes this problem. It was first used on strains of phage λ and then applied to plasmids by N. Davidson's group. A mixture of the ocDNA molecules being tested is denatured in alkali, reneutralized and allowed to renature. Some of the duplex molecules are heteroduplexes. The molecules are mounted for elec-

Table 3.4
Hybridization efficiencies between plasmids belonging to different incompatibility groups (adapted from Grindley et al. 1973). A dash symbolizes experiment not done. Note the lack of homology between TP116 on the one hand and TP117 and TP124 on the other. Note also that the drug resistances carried by the plasmids within a group may differ, but that there is a correlation between molecular size and incompatibility grouping.

Compatibility group	Plasmid	Drug Resistances	Size (Mdalton)	Plasmid						
				240	Δ	TP 114	TP 118	TP 113	TP 116	TP 117
FII	240	Tc	41	100	4	0	1	7	1	5
	R1–19	ApCmSm	54	75	–	–	–	–	–	–
I1	Δ	–	59	12	100	2	0	25	3	0
	TP102	Km	59	9	78	3	–	27	–	–
	TP110	Km	65	–	83	6	–	–	–	–
I2	TP114	Km	41	1	0	100	1	3	1	0
N	TP118	ApSm	27	3	2	2	100	3	5	2
	TP120	ApSmTc	32	0	–	–	81	6	–	–
	TP122	ApSuTc	33	6	–	–	83	–	–	–
B	TP113	Km	57	11	19	3	10	100	4	2
	TP125	CmSmTc	64	–	18	–	–	88	–	–
H	TP116	CmSm	144	2	0	0	3	8	100	2
	TP117	Tc	112	10	0	1	0	0	3	100
	TP124	CmSmTc	120	–	–	–	–	–	2	97

tron microscopy by the standard methods for displaying DNA, modified to permit single-stranded and duplex regions to appear as extended filaments (Fig. 3.1). Lack of homology in an otherwise duplex molecule is revealed as two kinds of single-stranded loops. If the lack of homology is due to non-homologous sequences in the two strands, a 'substitution loop' is formed, whereas if a sequence of DNA is present on one strand for which there is no analogue on the other (as when one molecule has undergone an insertion or deletion) there is an 'insertion or deletion' (I–D) loop. I–D loops can be distinguished from substitution loops by inspection. Loops need only be about 50 bases long to be detected.

Table 3.5

Summary of methods of Davis *et al.* (1971) for heteroduplex formation.

---

1. Denature a few microlitres of DNA with NaOH and EDTA at room temperature for 10 min. The DNA must be either in the open circular or the linear form to allow strand separation. However, it should have as few nicks and double-strand breaks as possible since partial molecules complicate subsequent interpretation.

2. Neutralize NaOH with buffer.

3. Renature with formamide. 1 hour at room temperature allows about 50% of a preparation of molecules to renature. More complete renaturation results in more complex structures.

4. Chill and remove formamide by dialysis at 4° C.

5. Spread on electron microscope grid.

This technique has been used to determine the regions of homology of F and some R factors, and also the interactions between F and the bacterial chromosome that give rise to Hfr strains (in which F is inserted into the chromosome: see later) and then F' factors (Sharp *et al.* 1972; Davidson *et al.* 1975). Heteroduplexes showed that F and an F'*gal* (galactose-utilizing) plasmid, F8(N33), differed in four respects (Fig. 3.2): there was a large substitution loop due to (1) the gain by F8(N33) of chromosomal DNA and (2) the loss of 7,300 bases (7.3 kilobases) of the 94.5 kilobases that comprise F DNA. Also, (3) and (4), two small (1.3-kilobase) sequences not present in F itself were present within the F-derived portion of F8(N33). These small insertions were at specific distances from the ends of the substitution loop. Extensive use was made of these (and other insertions, deletions and substitutions in other plasmids) to establish a system of co-ordinates. In this way points on F could be placed unambiguously on a circular 94.5-kilobase scale, proceeding from an arbitrarily chosen point, one of the junctions of F and chromosomal DNA in another F'*gal* plasmid, F450.

F is partially homologous with ColV and R1.   Sharp *et al.* (1973) examined F, ColV-K94, R1, R6-5 (a derivative of R6) and R100 for homologous sequences. It was already known that all these plasmids are about the same size; that F and the colicinogenic plasmid ColV are incompatible (group FI); and that the R plasmids R1, R6 and R100 are incompatible (group FII). In addition, Guerry and Falkow (1971) had shown that R1 is partially homologous with F. Sharp *et al.* found that about 90 per cent of the DNA of one half of F (49.6–3 kilobases, reading clockwise) had regions homologous with R1 (and R6). But the other halves, including the r determinant region of R1, are unrelated (Fig. 3.3). It was known that F and the three R factors have closely related transfer systems (see Chapter 5), and the homologous region is that which codes for the transfer systems (see below). It was also striking that the R factors were largely homologous over their entire lengths

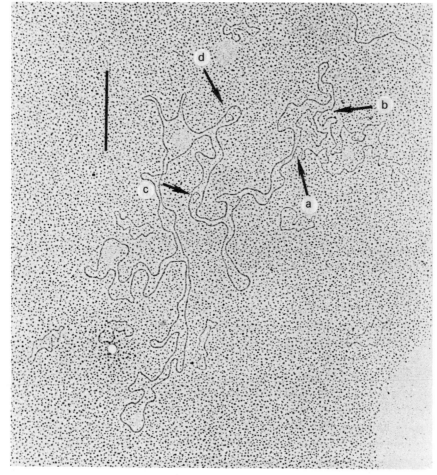

Fig. 3.1. Heteroduplex between F and the F'gal F8(N33). Single-stranded molecules of phage ϕX174 serve as internal standards. Arrows a and b are the junctions of duplex DNA with single-stranded DNA (at 8.5 and 15.8 kilobases on F respectively). Arrows c and d mark two I–D loops, at 91.0 and 34.9 kilobases respectively. The bar represents 1 μm. The diagrammatic interpretation is given in the next figure. (From Sharp et al. 1972, with permission of authors and publisher.)

(Fig. 3.4). R6-5 was almost identical to R100, but has three additional segments. R100 was also closely related to R1. Therefore although R6 was isolated in Germany, R100 in Japan and R1 in England they presumably had a common ancestor. This may have existed quite recently, since at least in laboratory stocks substantial evolution of plasmids can occur in relatively short periods without any intentional selection being exerted (Sharp et al. 1972; Timmis et al. 1978c).

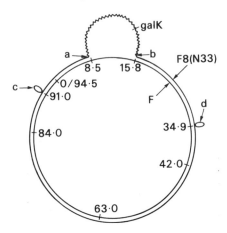

Fig. 3.2. The interpretation of the F/F8(N33) heteroduplex shown in Fig. 3.1. The sawtooth line is DNA of bacterial origin. (From Sharp *et al.* 1972, with permission of authors and publisher.)

ColV-K94 bore a similar relationship to F as did R factors. That is, there was considerable homology in the 46–94.5/0-kilobase region, and almost none in the other half-molecule. The relationship between the R factors and ColV was not tested directly.

The principal conclusion is that plasmids that are closely related over part of their sequence may have other regions that are quite unrelated. Clearly, therefore, the relationship between two plasmids cannot be adequately assessed on any single genetic criterion such as incompatibility or a phenotype conferred upon the host cell.

Other groups of related plasmids. Many bacterial strains have been isolated that carry plasmids specifying resistance to both streptomycin and sulphonamides. Such plasmids from a wide range of locations and host organisms (*Salmonella, Proteus, Providencia, Pseudomonas* and *E. coli*) were closely related (Barth and Grinter 1974; Grinter and Barth 1976). They were of similar size, usually 5.7 megadaltons, their DNA was largely homologous, they belonged to a single incompatibility group, and most had only a single site that is recognized by the endonuclease *Eco*RI (see later). Another study (Falkow *et al.* 1974) was concerned with plasmids producing I-like sex pili (see Chapter 5). Although these plasmids belonged to a number of incompatibility groups, DNA·DNA hybridization revealed a 'core' of common DNA that they shared with each other but not with other plasmids that were tested. It therefore appeared that these plasmids had

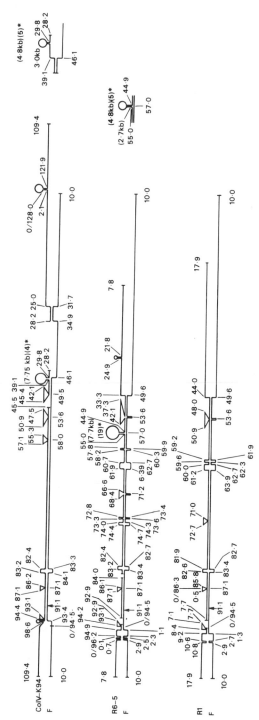

Fig. 3.3. Heteroduplexes of ColV-K94/F, R6-5/F and R1/F. The left and right end of each strand should be joined since the heteroduplexes are of circular molecules. Two close parallel lines indicate homologous DNA sequences. The triangular structures represent I–D loops with sizes that are shown by the horizontal arms of the triangles. The rectangular structures are substitution loops, and the round, stemmed, loops represent insertions bounded by inverted repeats (see later). Two different types of structure were seen at the asterisked positions in the ColV/F and R6-5/F heteroduplexes. In each case, the second structure is shown on the right, and the numbers of observed cases of the two types are given in parentheses. Right to left on these linear maps is clockwise on the conventional circular maps. Dimensions are given in kilobases. (From Sharp et al. 1973, with permission of authors and publisher.)

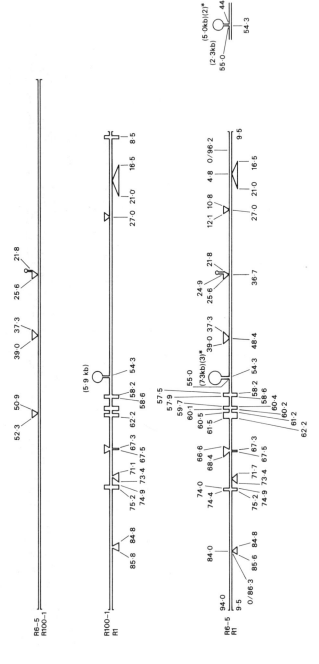

Fig. 3.4. Interpretation of heteroduplexes between R1, and R6-5 and R100-1. The asterisk and the second con-figuration in the R6-5/R1 heteroduplex are analogous to those described in Fig. 3.3. (From Sharp et al. 1973, with permission of authors and publisher.)

I-like pilus-synthesizing functions of common origin, but that other parts of the plasmids had arisen from other sources.

These, and other studies (e.g. Smith *et al*. 1973b, 1974; Heinaru *et al*. 1978) which will be described later, indicate that plasmids isolated from natural sources are often related to each other (see also section on transposons, in this chapter, and Chapters 6 and 7).

Physical mapping of plasmids

Physical mapping of F started with the examination of a series of transfer-defective mutants of F'8 (Sharp *et al*. 1972). Since F'8 itself is too large to be packaged within the head of phage P1, transduction and selection of Gal$^+$ progeny provides a strong selection for smaller (that is, deleted) plasmids. Previous genetic analysis of such plasmids (Ohtsubo 1970) had established that a number of genes determine the transfer function (see also Chapter 5). From the functions lost by the different deleted plasmids it had been possible to order the genes on the F' factor. Heteroduplex analysis of these mutant plasmids allowed the correlation of the genetic and physical maps of the transfer genes. These genes map in the 62–94.5/0-kilobase region (Sharp *et al*. 1972; Davidson *et al*. 1975). This is within the part of F that is homologous with R1, R6 and R100 and includes DNA sufficient for about 30 genes. Taken together with studies on other deletions of F and F' factors (Davidson *et al*. 1975), the results show that all parts of F except the 43–52-kilobase region can be lost without loss of the ability to replicate autonomously. The 43–52-kilobase region is therefore thought to code for all essential plasmid-specified replication functions (see Chapter 4).

The heteroduplex method was also used by Sharp *et al*. (1973) to map the resistance determinants on the R factors. An RTF derivative of R1 lacking the Ap, Cm, Km, Sm and Su determinants had lost the 16.5–39-kilobase sequence of R1, suggesting that the r determinant lies within this sequence. Moreover, the only apparent difference in the regions of R6-5 (which specifies resistance to kanamycin) and R100-1 (which does not) other than in the region homologous with F is the presence of an extra segment at 25.6 kilobases on R6-5 (Fig. 3.4). Km may therefore map in this loop.

In contrast to the other resistance determinants Tc was found to be in the F-like region. The first indication of this was that, unlike its parent plasmid R6, R6-5 does not confer resistance to Tc and also has an extra sequence at 52.3. Further, a derivative of R6-5 that had regained Tc resistance had lost this DNA sequence. The Tc function had been inactivated and then restored by precise insertion and excision of a special DNA sequence (see below).

The heteroduplex method has thus become central to studies on structural

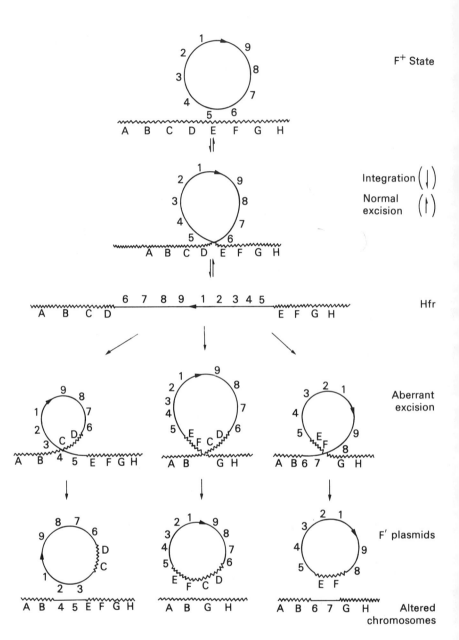

Fig. 3.5. The formation of (a) Hfr strains and (b) F′ factors by reciprocal recombination between (a) two circles and (b) two points on the Hfr chromosome (the Campbell model). The main points of difference between the F case and the formation of λ lysogens and transducing λ particles are: (1) λ enters the cell as a linear structure which then circularizes, whereas F is circular (2) F integration occurs at different sites on F and on the chromosome, whereas λ integration is by recombination between a single λ site and a single

changes in plasmids. There are at least four different processes which we would like to understand:

(1) the insertion and excision of DNA sequences such as the two encountered in F'8 and that in R6-5;

(2) the formation and dissociation of cointegrate plasmids;

(3) the transition phenomenon;

(4) the formation of Hfr strains from F⁺ strains, and of F' factors from Hfr strains.

Since what we know comes largely from investigating the last of these questions, we must first consider the earlier genetical work upon which such studies depended.

The Campbell model and Hfr and F' formation.   It has been known for over 20 years that F⁺ populations of *E. coli* contain variants that transfer the chromosome with high frequency. Each such Hfr (for high frequency of recombinant formation) strain transfers the chromosome in one direction from a characteristic point on the chromosome (the 'origin'). As the orders of genes transferred by different Hfr strains constituted a set of circular permutations Jacob and Wollman (1958) proposed that the *E. coli* chromosome is circular. Such circularity was later confirmed using an autoradiographic method (Cairns 1963). Jacob and Wollman also showed that the lysogenic state of phage λ of *E. coli* was due to its association with a particular region of the host chromosome, near the galactose (*gal*) region.

Campbell (1961) suggested that this association came about by physical integration, involving pairing and a reciprocal recombination event between the chromosome and a circular λ molecule. He also suggested that Hfr strains arose by recombination between the chromosome and a circular F molecule (Fig. 3.5). There is now considerable evidence that the Campbell model does indeed apply to both λ (Franklin *et al.* 1965) and F (Broda *et al.*

---

chromosomal site, except under special circumstances (Shimada *et al.* 1972). Therefore (3) the only markers that λ transducing particles arising from normal lysogens can carry are those adjacent to the attachment site (e.g., *gal* on one side and *bio* on the other). (4) There are 'headful' constraints on the amount of DNA in phage λ, whereas a single F' factor can carry chromosomal DNA originating from each side of the integrated F (Broda *et al.* 1964).

The polarity of transfer of an Hfr strain is determined by the polarity of the pairing event between the autonomous F and the chromosome. If integration and excision are truly reciprocal, there should be no gain in homology between chromosome and the F' factor (Broda *et al.* 1964). However, the same F' factor will have homology with the chromosome of other cells. This is revealed by chromosome mobilization with the same orientation as in the parent Hfr strain.

1964; Ippen-Ihler *et al*. 1972; Freifelder 1968). It is now known that λ can also integrate at further sites, with a lower probability (Shimada *et al*. 1972). F integration occurs at a moderate number of specific sites (Broda 1967) albeit with a lower efficiency.

The excision of integrated λ and F is usually by a simple reversal of the integration event, but occasionally it occurs between other sequences so that the autonomous particles may include chromosomal DNA that can be recognized genetically (see Fig. 3.5). In the case of λ the first-studied such particles carried the adjacent *gal* genes. The amount of DNA that can be included into the λ coat is limited. Such particles are therefore defective, since they lack genes needed for the formation of infective phage. They are therefore termed λdg particles for λ defective, *gal*. In the case of F no such constraint applies. Thus although some F' factors have lost F DNA (Type I factors) it is also possible to isolate F' factors that carry chromosomal DNA from both sides of the integrated F factor (Type II).

Hotspots in Hfr and F' formation.   Each of a set of F' factors examined by Sharp *et al*. (1972) lacked some of the original F DNA. Therefore if the whole F factor had been integrated in the parent Hfr strains, these F' factors must have arisen by Type I excision events. A common portion of F is absent in F'1, F'450 and F'*lac* but F'8 lacks a different part. Fig. 3.6 summarizes the conclusions drawn. These were that:
(1) although the formation of Hfr 2 and Hfr 3 involved the insertion of F at different points in the bacterial chromosome the F locus (94.5/0 kilobases) was the same;
(2) the excision events by which Hfr 3 gave rise to F'1 and F'450 and Hfr 2 gave rise to F'*lac* all involved the 3-kilobase region;
(3) although such 'hotspots' exist they are not the only sites since the 8.5 and 15.8-kilobase regions were involved in the formation of Hfr 8 and then F'8.

Insertion sequences and transposons
Inverted repeats.   When single-stranded plasmid DNA is submitted to renaturing conditions in dilute solution, reassociation between molecules is rare. Under these conditions any homology within a strand will result in the formation of duplex regions that can be detected by electron microscopy. R6, R100-1, ColV and F8(N33) all gave such self-annealing that was revealed as single-strand loops on a short duplex stalk (Sharp *et al*. 1972, 1973; Fig. 3.7). Such pairs of sequences are termed 'inverted repeats'; that is, the original DNA carries a sequence twice, with each strand carrying one 'Watson' sequence and also its 'Crick' complement. Direct repeats (two

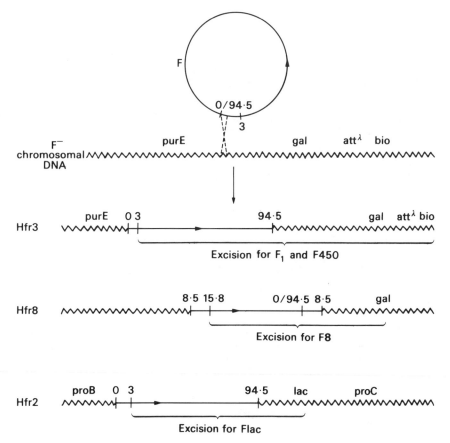

Fig. 3.6. Probable insertion and excision processes leading to the formation of Hfr strains 2,3 and 8, and then of the F′ factors F′1, F′450, F′8 and F′*lac*. The recombination process giving Hfr 3 is shown explicitly. The proposed structures of Hfr strains 2, 3, and 8 are also shown. (After Sharp *et al*. 1972, with permission of authors and publisher.)

'Watsons' on one strand) are also known (see later) but would not be detected by this method (Fig. 3.8). The lengths of the duplexes were 1.4 kilobases in some cases and 0.7 kilobase in others. Inverted repeats of about 1.3 kilobases have also been demonstrated in chromosomal DNA (Deonier and Hadley 1976).

The single sequence by which R6-5 differs from R6, which causes the Tc-sensitive phenotype, is one such inverted repeat (Sharp *et al*. 1973). While R6 has a pair of sequences close together that on single-strand renaturation form a duplex stalk of 1.3 kilobases and a loop of 6.0 kilobases, R6-5 yields loops of two sizes, 7.9 and 5.0 kilobases. This is due to insertion between the pair of sequences of a third copy of this sequence (Fig. 3.8).

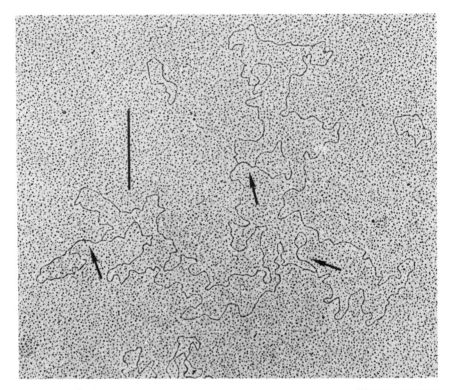

Fig. 3.7. Loops formed by inverted repeats in single strands of ColV-K94 DNA (Sharp *et al*. 1973). The arrows point towards the three duplex regions. The bar represents 1 μm. (Photograph by courtesy of P. Sharp, and reproduced with permission.)

Therefore in different self-annealed molecules either the original complement or the newly inserted sequence can provide half of the duplex. The Tc-resistance-determining derivative of R6-5, discussed earlier, behaves as R6 because it has lost this third copy. Similar sequences have appeared at 34.9 kilobases on F8(N33) (one of the small I–D loops that differentiate this plasmid from F) and other F' factors. As mentioned earlier, they provide valuable reference points for heteroduplex analysis. Their mobility was very reminiscent of sequences of similar size that had been described in λ transducing phages, the insertion (IS) sequences. The subject of insertion sequences and transposons (see later) is covered in detail by Starlinger and Saedler (1976) and in the book edited by Bukhari, Shapiro and Adhya (1977).

Insertion sequences. It had been observed that some mutations in operons carried by λ transducing phages were due to insertion of alien DNA (Shapiro

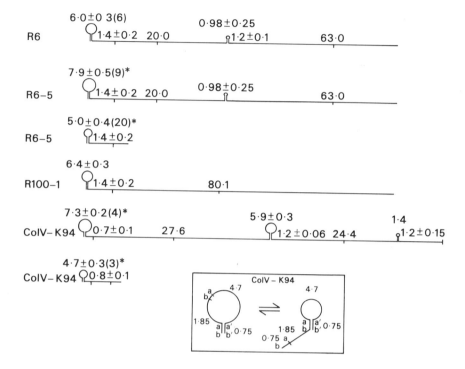

Fig. 3.8. Inverted repeats in single strands of DNA of R6, R6-5, R100-1 and ColV-K94. Lengths are given in kilobases. The positions where two different loop sizes were observed are asterisked. The number of loops observed for each size is given in parentheses. The inset presents an interpretation of the two sizes of loop in ColV-K94 in terms of a non-tandem direct repeat (a'b') and its inverted complements (ab). (From Sharp *et al.* 1973, with permission of authors and publisher.)

1969; Jordan *et al.* 1968; Fiandt *et al.* 1972; Hirsch *et al.* 1972). In such mutants gene expression 'downstream' from the point of insertion was blocked, i.e., they were polar mutations. The termini of these sequences can also serve as the end points in the formation of deletions, although the IS sequence itself is not lost (Reif and Saedler 1975). Five apparently unrelated IS sequences have so far been described in *E. coli* and λ (Bukhari *et al.* 1977; Guyer 1978) in addition to mini-insertion derivatives of one of them (Ghosal and Saedler 1977). Saedler and Heiss (1973) concluded from molecular hybridization experiments that IS1 and IS2 are present in the *E. coli* chromosome in about 8 and 5 copies respectively, and that about one copy of IS2 is also present on F. Analysis of heteroduplexes of F and the R factors with λ phages carrying the appropriate IS sequences has shown that some of their previously designated integration and excision sites (Table

3.6) correspond to IS1, IS2 and IS3. It therefore appears that these sequences are involved in these processes too.

The sequence of the 768 base pairs comprising IS1 has been determined (Ohtsubo and Ohtsubo 1978). About 30 bases at its ends are themselves present in an invertedly repeated order. IS1 is absent from F but occurs twice on R6—and by implication on R1 and R100, since the regions of R6 containing these IS1 sequences are homologous with R1 and R100 (see Fig. 3.4). It is also present in P1 DNA (Iida *et al.* 1978). Since the two IS1 sequences in R6 are directly repeated, they did not show up in the self-annealing experiments just described but could be demonstrated using DNA of IS1-containing λ phage. They map at the points at which RTF DNA adjoins r DNA (Sharp *et al.* 1973), and presumably recombination between these IS regions is the basis for the formation of these moieties. They are also involved in the duplication of the r determinant in the amplification of NR1 in *Pr. mirabilis* (Tanaka *et al.* 1976; see Fig. 2.5). Repeated sequences have also been demonstrated at the termini of the amplifiable region of the streptococcal plasmid studied by Yagi and Clewell (1976, 1977).

IS2, which has been described in λdg derivatives, corresponds to $\varepsilon\zeta$, the region of F at 16.3–17.6 kilobases (Fig. 3.9; Hu *et al.* 1975b). It is also present in R6 and R100 (Table 3.6). Recombination between two copies, one on the chromosome and the other on F, gave rise to Hfr 13. This can be inferred because IS2 is present at both boundaries between F and chromosomal DNA on F'13 (Hu *et al.* 1975a), which was probably formed by a Type II excision event from Hfr 13 (Broda *et al.* 1964). IS2 has also been implicated in the formation of F'8 (Davidson *et al.* 1975).

IS3 corresponds to the plasmid sequence $\alpha\beta$ (Hu *et al.* 1975c). It is repeated directly in F at 93.2–94.5/0 and 13.7–15 kilobases (Ohtsubo *et al.* 1974) and also is a site for both Hfr and F' formation (Sharp *et al.* 1972; Table 3.6). Moreover, it was by IS3 insertion into the Tc gene that R6-5 arose from R6 (see earlier). The chromosomal portion of F'13 also contains three copies of IS3 (Hu *et al.* 1975a). A number of Hfr strains have their origins within this region of the chromosome, and it has been suggested that the sites at which F is integrated in these strains (as judged by the genes that they transfer) can be explained in terms of integration involving these IS sequences (see also Deonier *et al.* 1977). Deonier and Davidson (1976) have shown directly (i.e., using Hfr chromosomal DNA rather than F' DNA) that the inserted F in chromosomal DNA from two Hfr strains is bounded by two IS3 sequences, and that these Hfr strains arose by integration at the same chromosomal IS3 site.

IS4 has not been shown to be present on F or the R plasmids, but another F sequence involved in Hfr formation and F' formation ($\gamma\delta$: Sharp *et al.*

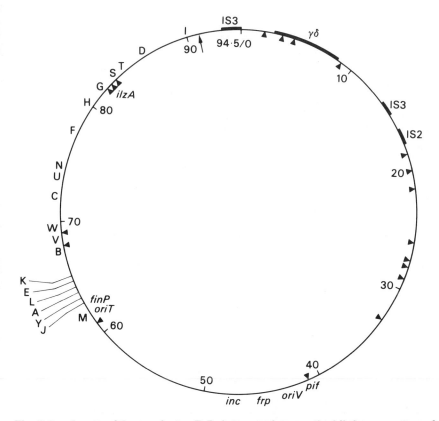

Fig. 3.9. A map of the sex factor F. Points are given on the kilobase system of Sharp *et al*. 1972. The single capitals refer to the midpoints of the locations of the corresponding *tra* genes. On the basis of the known and suspected sizes of the corresponding proteins, the DNA required for these genes ranges from 4.5 kilobases for *traI* and more than 2 kilobases for *traD* to less than 0.5 kilobase for *traL*, *traA* and *traY*. *traS* and *traT* are genes for surface exclusion (see text). Other symbols are *oriT*: origin of transfer; *oriV*: origin of replication; *ilzA*: immunity to lethal zygosis; *inc*: incompatibility; *pif*: phage infection inhibition (Palchaudhuri and Maas 1977b); *frp*: F replication; *finP*: fertility inhibition product. The site of an insertion into *traI* of F8(N33), described by Sharp *et al*. (1972), is shown at 91 kilobases.

An *Eco*RI cleavage map of F (19 fragments) and a partial *Bam*HI map (11 fragments) are given in Skurray *et al*. 1978, together with the composition of some *Eco*RI-based chimaeras. The triangles represent the *Eco*RI sites. The composition of some λ*tra* phages is given by Willetts and McIntire (1978).

1972) has recently been shown to be an (as yet un-named) IS sequence (Guyer 1978). γδ is directly repeated at the two junctions of F and chromosomal DNA in the Type II F′ F′14 (Ohtsubo *et al*. 1974). Interestingly, preparations of F′14 DNA (311 kilobases) also contained molecules of F (94.5 kilobases) and other molecules composed entirely of the

Table 3.6
Occurrence and role of IS sequences in F and R factors. The IS designation is that given to the sequence as first observed in derivatives of phage λ; the Greek symbols refer to sequences observed in plasmids.

Sequence and size (kilobases)	Copies per chromosome (approx.)	Site on F	Role	R factors	Role
IS1[1] 0.8	8[1]	−	−	R1[2] R6, R100-1	RTF-r ⟶ RTF +r[3,4]
IS2; $\varepsilon\zeta$[2,5] 1.4	5	16[2,3]	⟶ F8[6] ⟶ Hfr13[7]	R6[2] R100-1	−
IS3; $\alpha\beta$[8] 1.3	>3	93.2[9,8]	⟶ HfrP3	R6[10]	R6 ⟶ R6-5[3,8]
$\gamma\delta$[9,11] 5.8	?	2.8[9]	⟶ HfrAB313[9] F from F14[9] ⟶ F100 (F_1gal)[6] ⟶ F142 (F_2gal)[6] ⟶ F42 (F*lac*)[6]	−	−

[1] Saedler and Heiss 1973. [2] Hu *et al*. 1975b. [3] Sharp *et al*. 1973. [4] Chandler *et al*. 1977a. [5] Saedler *et al*. 1974. [6] Sharp *et al*. 1972. [7] Hu *et al*. 1975a. [8] Hu *et al*. 1975c. [9] Ohtsubo *et al*. 1974. [10] Ptashne and Cohen 1975. [11] Guyer 1978.

chromosomal DNA (217 kilobases). Each of these products had one $\gamma\delta$ sequence.

Hu *et al*. (1975c) have estimated the frequencies at which IS sequences might be translocated. Their estimates were that the probability of appearance of an insertion is about 4×10^{-9} per gene per generation, and that an IS has a residence time in any one locus in the genome of about 2.5×10^6 generations. Thus although movement is fairly rare, it is frequent enough to provide variation within bacterial populations for selection to act upon and indeed it accounts for a large proportion of spontaneous mutations (Starlinger and Saedler 1976).

IS sequences are probably involved in two kinds of recombination.
1. Recombination between pairs of homologous sequences, as in Hfr and F′ formation. This requires the host's recombination system, since both Hfr formation (Cullum and Broda 1979a) and normal F excision (Deonier and Mirels 1977) are strongly dependent on the *E. coli recA* function.

2. Translocation, as in insertion and excision that lead to polar mutations and their relief. This can occur in the absence of the *recA* function but requires at least one other chromosomal function (Nevers and Saedler 1978). Chromosomal integration of F′ factors (and some Hfr formation) can also occur in *recA*⁻ strains (Broda and Meacock 1971; DeVries and Maas 1971; Cullum and Broda 1979a) but it is unknown whether such interactions are between homologous sequences. In *recA*-independent excision non-homologous sites (that is, one IS sequence and another sequence) tend to be used (Deonier and Mirels 1977). The breakdown of F′14, due to recombination between the two $\gamma\delta$ sequences, is apparently also *recA*-independent (Ohtsubo *et al.* 1974). So too was a case of fusion between two F′ factors (Palchaudhuri *et al.* 1976).

The mechanisms involved in IS translocation are unknown at the time of writing. One intriguing fact to be taken into account is that IS1 inserted at different locations is flanked by different directly repeated sequences of nine bases (Grindley 1978; Calos *et al.* 1978; Kühn *et al.* 1979). The explanation proposed is that integration involves the introduction of two nicks nine bases apart, and the covalent attachment of the 3′ ends of the IS1 element to the free and protruding 5′ ends that are created. The two single-stranded gaps of nine bases would then be filled in by DNA synthesis.

Transposition of ampicillin resistance.   Another sequence found on other-wise unrelated replicons is that specifying resistance to penicillins in different bacteria. Most penicillin resistance is due to β-lactamases (penicillinases) of one or other of two general types, termed O and TEM. Whereas there is considerable variation in the substrate specificity profiles of O enzymes from different strains, the TEM enzymes are all very similar in their action and are immunologically related, suggesting that they have a common origin (Hedges *et al.* 1974). The TEM function could be transferred between plasmids (Datta *et al.* 1971). It was then found that a series of plasmids, each of which had acquired the TEM determinant from the plasmid RP1, were larger than their parent plasmids, and were able in turn to transfer TEM to other plasmids (Hedges and Jacob 1974). The same penicillin resistance can also be transferred between chromosome and plasmid DNA (Richmond and Sykes 1972; Bennett and Richmond 1976). The transposable element involved, termed transposon A (TnA) or Tn1 (Cohen 1976), occurs natur-ally as a sequence of 3 megadaltons in plasmids of at least eight incompatibil-ity groups (Heffron *et al.* 1975b). Heteroduplexes revealed the transposon as an insertion bounded by an inverted repeat sequence that was thought to be about 140 bases in length, but has now been shown to contain fewer than 40 bases.

Transposition of TnA does not depend on the *recA* function in *E. coli* and results in integration at a number of sites on a plasmid with either orientation (Rubens *et al.* 1976). TnA is mutagenic in both orientations but only insertions in one of the two directions caused polar mutations in the plasmid (Rubens *et al.* 1976) implying that transcription through or from the transposon is possible in the other orientation. Moreover, TnA provides a specific endpoint for deletions. This process is also *recA*-independent, but leaves the transposon itself intact (Nisen *et al.* 1977). In all these respects it is similar to IS elements. There are also analogies with phage Mu, which can apparently insert between any two bases in the DNA of *E. coli* and its plasmids (Bukhari and Zipser 1972). Indeed Mu is regarded as a type of transposon.

On translocation the whole TnA element, including both of the sequences present as inverted repeats, is found at the new location. Therefore excision and integration do not occur through simple Campbell-type reciprocal recombination events between these repeated sites. Further, acquisition of one transposon by a plasmid was far more frequent than its demonstrable loss from the donor plasmid (Bennett *et al.* 1977; see also Berg 1977 for Tn5). One possibility is that transposition involves duplication of the transposon. Another is that excision normally results in the destruction of the donor replicon.

The repeated ends and also some internal regions are necessary for transposition. To establish this, Heffron *et al.* (1977a) generated a set of mutants *in vitro* by partial digestion of plasmid molecules with DNAase I, exonuclease III and S1—respectively these enzymes nick, remove bases from the nicked strands, and remove the single-strand regions that are produced—to yield linear molecules which recircularized after reintroduction into *E. coli* by transformation. Deletions of Tn1 that extended into either of the repeated sequences were translocation-defective and so were some of the purely internal deletion mutants. Among the latter class were some that could be complemented in *trans* by a co-resident Tn1 or Tn3 element (Gill *et al.* 1978).

Since TnA can move readily between replicons, why does it not serve as a more potent mutagen of the *E. coli* chromosome? There seem to be ways in which a chromosome can be protected, since Tn3 (TnA from plasmid R1) appeared in the chromosome at least one thousand times less frequently than it appeared in two other plasmids (Kretschmer and Cohen 1977). Plasmids already containing TnA are much less susceptible to the translocation of a further TnA unit than are related TnA-free plasmids. However, other cohabiting plasmids are still susceptible. In genetical terms this 'immunity' is therefore a *cis*-acting function (Robinson *et al.* 1977). Plasmids carrying two copies of TnA constructed *in vitro* carry both copies stably (Robinson *et al*. 1978).

Other transposons. The various transposons so far studied have little in common except that their movement is *recA*-independent (Kopecko and Cohen 1975; Barth *et al*. 1976; Rubens *et al*. 1976; Table 3.7). For instance Tn5 is bounded by inverted repeat sequences of 1.5 kilobases, whereas Tn9 is bounded by direct repeats. The terminal repetitions of Tn9 are homologous with IS1 (MacHattie and Jackowski 1977). Moreover, Tn9, like IS1, generates a 9 base pair repeated sequence during integration (Johnsrud *et al*. 1978). Therefore, although it is not known here whether such repeated sequences can translocate independently from these sites, two homologous IS sequences can together mediate translocation of intervening DNA (see also So *et al*. 1979).

Table 3.7
Some properties of transposons (partly after Kleckner, 1977).

Name	Syno-nym	Functions trans-posed[1]	Size (kilo-bases)	Length of repeat	Trans-location frequency[2]	Number of integra-tion sites	Refer-ence
Tn1,2,3	TnA	Ap	4.8	0.04; inverted		many	a, b, c,
Tn4	–	ApSmSu	20.5[3]	?; inverted		many	d
Tn5	TnK	Km	5.2	1.5; inverted	10^{-3}	many	e
Tn6	TnK	Km	4.1	?			
Tn7	TnC	SmTp[4]	13.5	?		few	f
Tn9	TnC	Cm	2.5	0.8; direct[5]	10^{-5}		g
Tn10	TnT	Tc	9.5	1.4; inverted	10^{-6}	medium	h, i
Tn402	–	Tp	7.5	?			j
Tn501	–	Hg^{2+}	9	?			k, l
Tol	–	toluene	58	?			m, n, o
Tn951	–	lactose	16.6	? inverted			p

(a) Heffron *et al.* 1975a; (b) Heffron *et al.* 1975b; (c) So *et al.* 1975c; (d) Kopecko and Cohen 1975; (e) D. Berg *et al.* 1975; (f) Barth *et al.* 1976; (g) Gottesman and Rosner 1975; (h) Kleckner *et al.* 1975; (i) Foster *et al.* 1975; (j) Shapiro and Sporn 1977; (k) Stanisich *et al.* 1977; (l) Bennett *et al.* 1978; (m) Jacoby *et al.* 1978; (n) Chakrabarty *et al.* 1978; (o) Nakazawa *et al.* 1978; (p) Cornelis *et al.* 1978.
[1] Utilization of toluene and lactose; the others are resistances.
[2] From infecting phage.
[3] Contains Tn3.
[4] Tp = trimethoprim.
[5] Homologous with IS1.

Whereas there may be preferred integration sites for Tn1 (Heffron *et al.* 1975a) and Tn10 (Kleckner 1977), Tn5 could integrate into the *lacZ* gene of *E. coli* in many places (Berg 1977). With Tn3, insertion sites on the recipient plasmid genome were clustered. One such region already contained the IS1 sequence, as if IS1 itself provided the recognition site.

Like phage Mu (Bukhari *et al.* 1977), transposons are used to generate insertion mutations. These can be easily selected for because of the antibiotic resistance acquired (Dougan *et al.* 1978; Inselburg 1977a, b; Barth *et al.* 1978a; Kleckner *et al.* 1977; Hernalsteens *et al.* 1978). Moreover, using heteroduplex analysis or endonuclease digestion and subsequent gel analysis (see below), the site of insertion can be accurately determined (see, for instance, Inselburg 1977a, b; van Embden *et al.* 1978; Andreoli *et al.* 1978). Each such insertion can be used to generate a family of deletion mutations, in which the initial insertion site defines one end. These families of mutants can then be used to correlate regions of the parent plasmid's DNA with proteins produced, for instance in minicells (Inselburg and Applebaum 1978). In addition, transposons can be used to 'label' conjugative plasmids that do not themselves have a readily identifiable phenotype (So *et al.* 1978b).

Because insertion sequences and transposons are means of joining unrelated segments of DNA ('portable regions of homology') they are likely to have played a major role in plasmid evolution (Cohen 1976; Kopecko *et al.* 1976; Heffron *et al.* 1977b). The evolution of plasmids will be discussed more fully in Chapter 8.

Endonucleases and plasmid structure
Restriction enzymes.　　When phage λ grown on cells of strain C of *E. coli* infects cells of *E. coli* K-12 its DNA is degraded ('restricted') by enzymes that recognize it as foreign to that cell. The recipients' own DNA avoids such degradation by being chemically 'modified' by methylation of particular adenine or cytosine bases. The small proportion of the incoming DNA that escapes restriction yields phage that are modified and can therefore reinfect *E. coli* K-12 cells normally. Many such restriction systems are now known. Since they could attack any foreign DNA not modified in the same way they may have a protective function in nature.

Restriction enzymes are endonucleases that recognize specific sequences of different lengths (see Table 3.8). The more complex the target sequence, the less likely it is to occur on a given piece of DNA. Enzymes of one class attach at a target but then break the DNA fairly randomly; these enzymes do not concern us here. Enzymes of the other class (Type II) cleave the DNA at the target site itself. Thus *Eco*RI cleaves F into 19 fragments (Skurray *et al.*

1976b), while *Hin*dIII (enzyme III from *Haemophilus influenzae* strain d) cleaves it into 13 fragments. Such fragments can be resolved electrophoretically on an agarose gel; the larger the fragment, the less its mobility. By analysing the gel patterns given by differently deleted F' factors it has been possible to assign unique positions on the F genome to independently isolated fragments. Such gel patterns can also be used as a simple test of identity for related plasmids. Thus although R1 and R6 are known to be very closely related, on the basis of the heteroduplex studies described above, digestion and electrophoresis gave only a few common bands (Thompson *et al*. 1974). In an adaptation of this method regions of homology of less closely related plasmids can be localized (Heinaru *et al*. 1978). Here DNA fragments are transferred in the single-stranded form from such gels onto the same relative positions on a nitrocellulose filter, and are allowed to hybridize with radioactively labelled single-stranded DNA of a 'probe' plasmid. Hybridization is then revealed by autoradiography.

Generation of chimaeras. The target sequences of all Type II enzymes so far determined have a twofold axis of symmetry (Table 3.8). The cleavage can yield either a clean break, or else a staggered break, resulting in fragments with single-stranded ends, generally of two or four bases, that may have either a free 3' or 5' end. Where this sequence is unambiguous, all such single-stranded ends will be complementary to all others in the digest, because of the twofold symmetry (see Table 3.8). These ends can therefore join by hydrogen bonding. Depending on the concentrations of the fragments, this will lead to the formation of circles and/or linear or circular combinations of two or occasionally more fragments. Such hydrogen-bonded associations can be converted to covalent linkages *in vitro* by the action of 'ligases'; the ones generally used are those coded for by *E. coli* and phage T4. Where there is ambiguity in the single-stranded sequences, not all combinations of fragments are possible. Techniques also exist for the addition *in virto* of a single-stranded scgments of poly(dA) or poly(dT) to the products of those Type II enzymes which produce clean breaks.

Hybrid ('chimaera') molecules are formed if endonuclease-digested DNA from a plasmid and a different source (which can be prokaryotic or eukaryotic) are mixed, become associated by hydrogen bonding and are ligated (Table 3.9). Formation of recombinants mediated by endonucleases may also occur at low frequency *in vivo* (Chang and Cohen 1977). Hybrids formed *in vitro* can be introduced into bacterial cells (e.g. *E. coli*) by transformation (Cohen *et al*. 1972) and those containing the plasmid's replication functions may be maintained as plasmids. Because the exogen-

Table 3.8
Recognition sequences and points of breakage in duplex DNA for some restriction enzymes. The bases in the upper strands run in the 5′ to 3′ direction. The broken line indicates the position of the axis of twofold symmetry. The arrows indicate positions at which phosphodiester bonds are broken, to leave a 5′ phosphate, and the asterisk indicates bases methylated by the homologous modification enzymes. R and Y refer to 'purine' and 'pyrimidine' respectively. N represents any nucleotide. A recent compilation of known enzymes together with their recognition sequences may be found in Roberts (1978).

Source	Enzyme	5′ Target sequence 3′
Anabaena variabilis	*Ava*I	–NCYCGRGN– –NGRGCYCN–
Bacillus amyloliquefaciens	*Bam*I	–NGGATCCN– –NCCTAGGN–
Escherichia coli 'R1'	*Eco*R1	–NGAATTCN– –NCTTAAGN–
Haemophilus influenzae d	*Hin*dII	–NGTYRACN– –NCARYTGN–
	*Hin*dIII	–NAAGCTTN– –NTTCGAAN–
Haemophilus parainfluenzae	*Hpa*I	–NGTTAACN– –NCAATTGN–
	*Hpa*II	–NCCGGN– –NGGCCN–
Xanthomonas malvacearum	*Xma*I	–NCCCGGGN– –NGGGCCCN–

Table 3.9

An outline procedure for generating chimaeric molecules *in vitro*.

1. Digest DNA from two sources separately with endonuclease; run control gels to ensure that digestion is complete.
2. Mix the two types of digested DNA; incubate at 30° C for 15 min, to open up self-circularised molecules.
3. Dilute DNA to final concentration of about 15 μg/ml. Incubate at 0° C for 24 h.
4. Add ligase 'cocktail' and ligase. Incubate at 10° C for 3–6 h, and then hold at 0° C. Purity and activity of the ligase must be carefully checked.
5. Introduce molecules into host strain by transformation,. This involves holding cells in 0.1 M CaCl$_2$ at 0° C for 30 min, giving a heat shock (e.g., 2 min at 42° C), and holding for a further 90 min at 0° C, before plating.
6. If possible there should be a selection for chimaeric transformants or some simple screening method for detecting them. A period of incubation before selection may be necessary to allow expression of the chimaeric functions.

ous DNA will often be more easily analysed in this form than in its original state this has far-reaching consequences (see Chapters 4, 5 and 8).

Use of endonucleases in mapping plasmids. Endonucleases are also widely used for making physical maps of the genomes of viruses and small plasmids (see below). Such maps can then be made into genetic maps, for instance by observing how the parent plasmid differs from deletion mutants, or from derivatives where insertion of a transposon has inactivated a plasmid function. Such studies also allow the specificity of integration of transposons to be determined. Another way of matching a region with a genetic function has been with cloned fragments. Examples of such functions are replication (Chapter 3) and transfer (Chapter 4). It may then be possible to determine the messenger RNA and protein products that such chimaeras specify.

Two main approaches have been used to order fragments. In one, the plasmid is cleaved with two enzymes simultaneously, and the sizes of the products are compared with those from the two single digestions. In simple cases (i.e., where there are only a few breaks) it is possible to infer the order of fragments. This is because only certain combinations of fragments given by one enzyme will together be of sizes matching those given by the other digestions. The next level of complexity requires that the products of one digestion are separated by electrophoresis and then individually extracted and digested with the second enzyme; this operation is normally performed both ways round. This approach is analogous to one using proteolytic enzymes to order peptides from proteins.

Alternatively or in conjunction, a single enzyme can be used to produce a partial digest. The different products are separated and extracted as before, and fragments are then digested to completion with the same or different enzymes, and the product sizes are determined (see for instance Danna *et al.* 1973; Tanaka *et al.* 1976).

The number of fragments (n) that are obtained will determine the feasibility of such approaches. Including singly cleaved and fully digested molecules, a total of n^2 products can be generated from a circle; which ones predominate will largely depend upon how far the digestion is allowed to proceed. However, advantage can be taken of the fact that some enzymes, such as *Bam*, *Hin*dIII and *Sal*, produce relatively few cuts because the target sequence has four rather than two bases (see Table 3.8). Moreover, certain plasmids have unexpectedly few target sites; thus RP1 (38 megadaltons) has only one *Eco*RI and one *Hin*dIII site, compared with 19 and 13 sites respectively for F (62.5 megadaltons). The extremely wide host range that RP1 possesses may be correlated with this fact in some way.

With larger plasmids other methods have been used. The digestion pattern of F was determined by comparing its products with those of an array of mutants with deletions that together covered most of the F genome. Another way is to use chimaeras from partial or complete digests for further ordering of fragments and to relate particular fragments to particular genetic functions, as was done by Skurray *et al.* (1976b) for F, and Timmis *et al.* (1978a,b,d) for R6 and R6-5. In this type of approach association of non-adjacent fragments in newly formed chimaeras is a possible source of artefacts. Other methods of ordering fragments have been described by Parker *et al.* 1977, Chilton *et al.* 1978b, and Villems *et al.* 1978.

It emerges from this discussion that the analysis of plasmid structure has depended mainly upon biochemical analysis of native plasmid DNA and variants obtained *in vivo* and *in vitro*. In contrast purely genetic approaches (e.g., genetic crosses for linkage analysis) have made only a minor contribution. The following chapter assesses the respective roles of these two approaches in the study of plasmid replication.

Summary

The most convenient classification of plasmids is into incompatibility groups. This is an index of related replication functions, and generally also reflects substantial homology between the plasmids. The fact that plasmids of *E. coli* fall into only a moderate number of groups implies evolutionary relationships. Heteroduplex analysis showed that homology exists between F, ColV and three R plasmids, plasmids specifying different phenotypes, and that this homology is of large segments, with other segments being quite unrelated. Heteroduplex analysis also showed that Hfr and F′ formation, and also dissociation of R plasmids, depended upon insertion sequences. The ampicillin resistance determinant carried by a range of R plasmids is part of a transposon. Transposons specifying other properties have also been discovered. Transposons are related in function (and sometimes in structure) to IS sequences. They, and endonucleases, are very valuable for the genetic manipulation of plasmids, *in vivo* and *in vitro* respectively.

4
Replication

Over a dozen proteins involved in replication in *E. coli* have been identified by genetical and/or biochemical methods. The activities that they promote include helix destabilization, helix unwinding, DNA polymerization, DNA ligation and the synthesis and erasure of RNA primer. It is possible that the complexity of the process is dictated by the need for a level of fidelity that prevents more than one error per 10^9 to 10^{10} bases (see Kornberg 1974, and Alberts and Sternglanz 1977, for treatments of the subject of replication). To what extent these functions are required for plasmid replication, and whether plasmids provide functions of their own, will be considered later.

We may also ask 'morphological' questions such as:
(1) Is there a unique origin of replication?
(2) If so, does it also serve as the terminus?
(3) If not, is replication to the terminus symmetric or asymmetric?
(4) What are the structures of the replicative intermediates?
(5) Is there a relation between the segregation of plasmid DNA and chromosome DNA?

Lastly we can ask how plasmid replication is controlled so that it keeps step, but no more, with that of the host. The main questions here are:
(1) How many copies of a plasmid are there per chromosome?
(2) How is this number regulated?
(3) How can this number change with changes in the cellular environment?
(4) What mechanisms ensure that both daughter cells receive plasmids?

Our present knowledge on all these questions comes from work with only a few plasmids, notably ColE1 and F. In particular, ColE1 has four great advantages as the subject of replication studies.
(1) It is small, and electron micrographs of its replicative intermediates are therefore relatively easy to interpret.
(2) It is easily isolated separate from chromosomal DNA.

(3) On chloramphenicol treatment (see later) the number of copies per cell becomes very large.

(4) It has one *Eco* RI site; the utility of this fact will emerge shortly.

Modes of replication

Replication is semi-conservative.   Bazaral and Helinski (1970) showed that ColE1 replicates semi-conservatively. That is, a complete new strand is made as the complement of each old strand, so that daughter plasmid molecules each consist of an old strand and a newly synthesized strand. This had been demonstrated for the *E. coli* chromosome by Meselson and Stahl (1958). Bazaral and Helinski grew ColE1$^+$ bacteria in dense (^2H_2O, $^{15}NH_4Cl$) medium, and after transferring them to normal (H_2O, NH_4Cl) medium, they took samples at intervals, isolated the plasmid DNA and examined its density profile by density gradient equilibrium centrifugation. The first-replicated plasmids were hybrid in density; these were followed by ones that were light. Since other density classes were not observed, the hybrid molecules presumably consisted of one older strand and one newly replicated strand. Such ColE1 replication proceeded rapidly. Similar conclusions were drawn for NR1 in *Pr. mirabilis* (Rownd 1969). All plasmids are now assumed to replicate semi-conservatively.

Replicative intermediates.   At least once in the replication of each covalently closed circle a nick must occur in one of the strands to allow the eventual separation of the daughter molecules. Three possible intermediates (Fig. 4.1) that are formed by semi-conservative replication and nicking are as follows.

(1) The 'Cairns intermediate'; this is an open circular structure with two Y forks. At least one fork is a replication site, and the other can be either a second replication fork (when replication is bidirectional) or the origin of replication.

(2) A similar structure, but one in which the unreplicated region remains supercoiled. Replicative intermediates of the monkey virus SV40, polyoma virus and mitochondrial DNA are of this type. Nicking and closure of the nick(s) would occur as replication proceeds.

(3) In a 'rolling circle' (Gilbert and Dressler 1968) one strand is attached to a site, and is elongated using the other as a template. The circular portion may be supercoiled. The daughter monomers would be covalently linked in a tandem structure.

Inselburg and Fuke (1970, 1971) and Fuke and Inselburg (1972) presented electron micrographs of replicating ColE1 molecules that seemed to correspond to each of these types of intermediate, though molecules of types

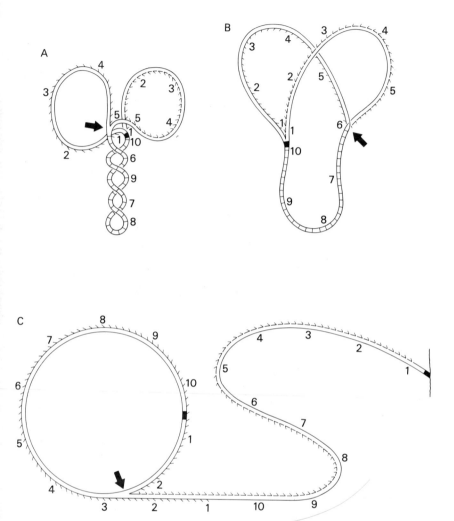

Fig. 4.1. Three possible modes of unidirectional plasmid replication. The rectangle represents the origin of replication and the large arrows the replicating fork. The unreplicated portions in A and B are represented by the linked parallel lines. The arrows on the continuously and the discontinuously synthesized new strands represent the directions of synthesis. A: intermediate in which the unreplicated portion is supercoiled. B: intermediate with no supercoiling. C: rolling circle intermediate, with attachment site.

(1) and the open form of (3) could also have been formed by nicking during extraction (Fig. 4.2). Oka and Inselburg (1975) showed later that ColE1 replication mainly occurs in molecules in which the unreplicated portion is supercoiled as in (2). Crosa *et al.* (1976b) reported similar results with respect to RSF1040, a derivative of R6K, but Sheehy and Novick (1975)

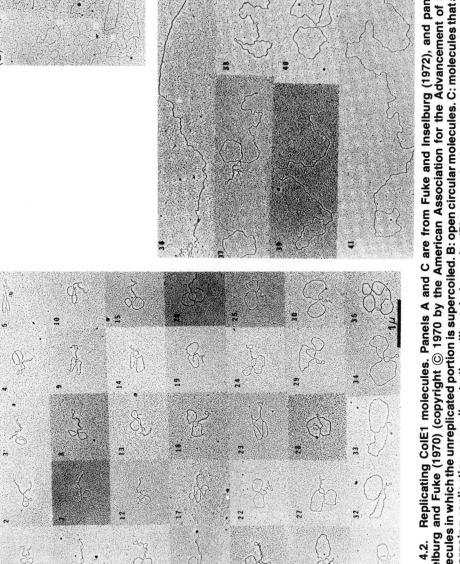

Fig. 4.2. Replicating ColE1 molecules. Panels A and C are from Fuke and Inselburg (1972), and panel B is from Inselburg and Fuke (1970) (copyright © 1970 by the American Association for the Advancement of Science). A: molecules in which the unreplicated portion is supercoiled. B: open circular molecules. C: molecules that are probably undergoing replication according to the rolling circle mode. (Photographs by courtesy of J. Inselburg.)

failed to observe such partially covalently closed circular intermediates in the replication of a *Staph. aureus* plasmid.

A later replicative intermediate structure observed with R6K and with three staphylococcal plasmids (Kupersztoch and Helinski 1973; Novick *et al*. 1973) has two complete plasmid copies, one in the open circular form and the other in the covalently closed circular form. A still later intermediate is the covalently closed (that is, lacking single-strand nicks) monomer into which supercoils have not yet been introduced. Such molecules have a density in CsCl/ethidium bromide solution that is greater than that of superhelical molecules (Timmis *et al*. 1976, Crosa *et al*. 1976a). The supercoiling of such molecules would require successive nicking and sealing reactions (see below).

Origin and direction of plasmid replication. If replicating ColE1 molecules are cleaved with *Eco*RI, the two Y forks of intermediates (1) and (2) can be related to the reference point provided by the single cleavage site. Inselburg (1974) concluded that ColE1 replication starts between 14 per cent and 20 per cent of the distance from the cleavage point, and that most replication proceeds along the longer arm, at least initially, although a limited amount in the other direction was not excluded. Similar observations were made by Tomizawa *et al*. (1974), who used an *in vitro* system, and by Lovett *et al*. (1974b), who placed the origin 18 per cent of the distance from the cleavage site (Fig. 4.3). The latter authors observed some molecules where replication of the longer arm was complete; among these, a variable amount of the other end had also been replicated. This is consistent with a unidirectional mode, rather than with one in which replication proceeds from the origin first in one direction, and then for a substantial distance in the other direction.

The origins and directions of replication of several other plasmids have been reported; different modes occur in related plasmids, and even in the same plasmid. R6K is larger than ColE1 (26 megadaltons), and it has two *Eco*R1 sites. From it, Crosa *et al*. (1975; 1976b) isolated the deletion mutant RSF1040 (17.3 megadaltons), which has only one cleavage site. The replicative intermediates of RSF1040 were of both the twisted and the (open) Cairns types. Early replicative forms that had been cleaved had loops starting at two positions, at about 23 per cent and 39 per cent from one end. It was clear that two independent origins exist, since about 5 per cent of the molecules were replicating from both sites simultaneously. In this plasmid replication from each site apparently proceeds bidirectionally, but at different rates in the two directions.

It might seem unduly cautious to conclude that these results only tell us

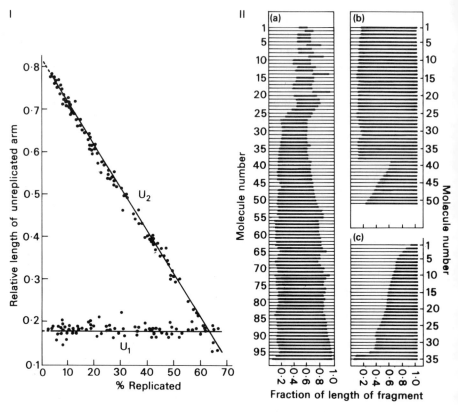

Fig. 4.3. Two ways of plotting the data from which origins of plasmid replication are inferred. In each case the relative lengths of the unreplicated and replicated portions were determined after cleavage of replicative intermediates with the enzyme *Eco*RI. I: ColE1. One arm (18 per cent of the total length) remains unreplicated, suggesting that replication proceeds away from it. II: the two fragments of R6K. Fragment A (panel c) has no origin of its own. Replication of B proceeds first in the leftward direction, and then stops, still within fragment B (panel a). Replication of the right arm of B (panel b), all of A and the leftmost portion of B then proceeds from the same origin, but in the other direction. (Reproduced from Lovett *et al.* 1974b, 1975, with permission of authors and publishers.)

about replication in RSF1040, and not necessarily about replication in its parent. However replication of R6K itself proceeds bidirectionally, first in one direction and then in the other, from a single site (Lovett *et al.* 1975; Fig. 4.3). Such replication is asymmetric. Since Crosa *et al.* (1975) have shown by heteroduplex methods that R6K and RSF1040 are completely homologous except for the deleted region, the relations between the two replication origins and the manner in which the initiation of replication is controlled are clearly of great interest. In the same way the finding that the mini-F plasmid pML31, derived from F'*lac*, replicates bidirectionally from a point which is at 42.6 kilobases on F should not be taken uncritically as establishing the mode of replication of F itself. Termination in pML31 occurs opposite the origin (Eichenlaub *et al.* 1977).

Perlman and Rownd (1976) used denaturation mapping to establish that non-amplified NR1 in *Pr. mirabilis* (under conditions of thymine limitation) replicated from two origins, one in the r moiety and the other in the RTF moiety. From each origin replication was sometimes bidirectional, but in other cases it was unidirectional, in either direction. There appeared also to be a preferred terminus for replication from the RTF origin. Although the r region may be used preferentially (Perlman 1978), it is not yet known whether autonomous r and poly(r) can replicate, and if so whether the same origin is used.[1] In contrast, Silver *et al.* (1977), using R100 in *E. coli*, observed unidirectional replication in a single sense, from a single origin in the RTF region. Ohtsubo *et al.* (1977) also observed unidirectional replication in three miniplasmids derived ultimately from R100.

The base sequence at the origins of replication of ColE1 (Tomizawa *et al.* 1977) and its derivative pBR345 (Bolivar *et al.* 1977a) and of phage λ, and therefore possibly the plasmid λdv (Denniston-Thompson *et al.* 1977), have been determined. Not enough is yet known of the mechanism of initiation, at this level of resolution, for it to be evident why it is at these particular sites that replication starts.

Relaxation complexes and replication. When ColE1 cccDNA is treated with heat or agents that include alkali, the proteolytic enzyme pronase, and ionic detergents such as sodium dodecyl sulphate, it yields open circular molecules (Clewell and Helinski 1969; 1970). Such 'relaxation' is due to the activation of an attached nuclease which nicks one strand. Relaxation complexes (cccDNA molecules capable of such relaxation) are known for other plasmids in *E. coli* that include F, R100, Δ and ColI (Helinski *et al.* 1975; Humphreys *et al.* 1972; Womble and Rownd 1977). They were also found for some but not other plasmids from *Staph. aureus* (Novick 1976). Generally more than half of the plasmid molecules are in the complexed form (Helinski *et al.* 1975).

The suggestion that relaxation complexes have a role in replication came from the finding (Lovett *et al.* 1974a) that relaxation of ColE1 occurred at a point which was almost the same distance from the *Eco*RI cleavage site as was the origin of replication. Alkaline denaturation of relaxed ColE1 DNA that had been cleaved with *Eco*RI (4.2 megadaltons) yielded one intact

---

[1] The data of Lane *et al.* (1979) indicate that they can not.

single strand (2.1 megadaltons) and two fragments, of 1.7 and 0.39 megadaltons. The possibility that the two sites are 19 per cent in from opposite ends of the cleaved molecule was rendered less likely by the observation that in R6K also there was a similarity in the distances of the origin of replication and the relaxation site from an end of one (the smaller) of the two *Eco*RI fragments (Kupersztoch-Portnoy *et al*. 1974; Lovett *et al*. 1975). Since the relaxation site here coincided with the origin rather than the terminus of plasmid replication, it also appeared that nicking was required for initiation rather than termination of replication.

It was then found that ColE1 cccDNA was not pure DNA, but contained three salt-dissociable proteins. In relaxation the two smallest proteins were released but the largest protein became covalently bound to the DNA, near to the 5' end of the nicked strand (Blair and Helinski 1975; Lovett and Helinski 1975; Guiney and Helinski 1975). Because dissociation of the proteins with salt does not result in relaxation it is thought that relaxation involves nicking itself, rather than the release of proteins that maintain the twisted configuration in an already-nicked structure. Partially supercoiled replicative intermediates are resistant to relaxation (Womble *et al*. 1976).

However, it now appears that relaxation may not after all be related primarily to replication, for two reasons. The base sequence for the origin of ColE1 replication is different from that at the relaxation site (Bastia 1978), and these two sequences are 300 bases apart (Tomizawa *et al*. 1977). Also mini-ColE1 plasmids exist that lack the relaxation site, and are unable to be relaxed (Inselburg 1977a). Since such mini-plasmids, unlike ColEl itself, can not be transferred by an Hfr strain, the main function of relaxation may instead be to provide a free end for conjugational transfer (Inselburg 1977b; Warren *et al*. 1978; see also Chapter 5). One possibility is that transfer involves a rolling circle mechanism and that in those molecules that do replicate vegetatively by this mode (Fuke and Inselburg 1972) initiation is also at this site.

Plasmid copy-number. In discussing models for replication and segregation (see later) it is important to know how many copies of a plasmid are present. Jacob and Monod (1961) found that the amount of β-galactosidase produced by a fully induced *lac*⁻/F'*lac*⁺ strain was about three times that produced by haploid Lac⁺ bacteria. This led them to suggest that such cells harbour about three F*lac* copies per nucleus. However, it is now known that the relation between gene dosage and gene expression is not always simple. A series of mutants of R1, present in different numbers of copies per cell, gave a stoichiometric relation between gene dosage and ampicillin resistance, but no such stoichiometric relationship in resistance to either chloramphenicol or streptomycin (Uhlin and Nordström 1977).

Physical methods are now generally used to measure the proportion of a cell's DNA that is of plasmid origin. If the sizes of the chromosome and the plasmid are known the copy number can then be calculated from this ratio. This approach requires plasmid and chromosome DNA to be isolated with equal efficiency or at least with known efficiencies.

Frame and Bishop (1971) prepared pure plasmid DNA and transcribed RNA from it *in vitro* with RNA polymerase. This plasmid-specific RNA was then hybridized against the DNA preparation being tested; it was taken to hybridize only to that fraction which was plasmid DNA. Collins and Pritchard (1973) and Rush *et al*. (1975) have employed DNA·DNA hybridization to obtain plasmid copy numbers. Hybridization methods do not require plasmid DNA to be purified from the host DNA of the cells on which the determination is being made, except when host and plasmid have sequences in common, as with F' factors.

In another method, the proportion of the total DNA that is in the covalently closed circular form is determined. However, this method, although simpler and more widely used, only gives minimum estimates since it depends upon the efficient extraction of plasmid DNA as covalently closed circular molecules, and indeed assumes that in the cell all the plasmid DNA is in this form. Alternatively, sucrose gradient centrifugation can be used to resolve both covalently closed circular and open circular plasmid DNA from chromosomal DNA. In the special case of NR1 in *Proteus mirabilis* plasmid and chromosomal DNA could be separated simply on the basis of their different densities (Rownd *et al*. 1966).

What emerges is that some plasmids, such as F, are present in only a few copies per cell whereas others, such as ColE1 and λdv, are present in many (it is not yet clear whether all plasmids fall so neatly into one of these two classes). Precise calculations depend upon knowing the amount of DNA per nucleus. This in turn depends upon the average form of the chromosomes, which, except in resting cells, are forked. The average number of forks per chromosome depends upon the growth rate (Sueoka and Yoshikawa 1963; Donachie 1968; Helmstetter *et al*. 1968) although the ratio between the number of origins and cell mass remains constant. It is therefore essential in such determinations for the growth rate of the culture to be recorded.

Copy-number mutants. Plasmid copy-number mutants have been isolated in several laboratories, for instance by Nordström *et al*. 1972 (R1-19), Morris *et al*. 1974 (NR1), and Veltkamp and Nijkamp 1976 (CloDF13).

The mutant R factors were obtained by screening populations for clones that are resistant to high levels of antibiotics; those of CloDF13 were recognized by their increased production of cloacin. The mutations are generally plasmid-borne, though chromosomal mutations affecting F′ copy-number have also been reported (Cress and Kline 1976). The plasmids are generally of similar size to their parents, and DNA synthesis proceeds at a similar rate. It is likely that the affected function is the initiation of replication. Each mutant has a characteristic copy-number, though cultures carrying plasmids derived by mutation from R1-19 and found in more than four times the parental concentration tended to throw off plasmidless cells (Uhlin and Nordström 1975). Some copy-number mutations of R1-19 are of the temperature-sensitive or amber types. In temperature-sensitive (ts) mutants the altered protein functions adequately at low ('permissive') temperatures and the cells multiply normally. At higher temperatures (e.g., 42° C) the protein adopts a different, non-functional, conformation. Amber mutations result in the synthesis of the complete protein in permissive ('Su⁺') hosts only. Therefore at least one protein is probably involved in copy-number control of R1-19 (Gustafsson and Nordström 1978; Uhlin and Nordström 1978).

Secondary plasmids.   When cccDNA was isolated from an *E. coli* strain that was *dnaA* ts (see later) and carried a copy-mutant of R1, a set of small plasmids, ranging from 5.1 to 13.4 megadaltons, were found (Goebel and Bonewald 1975). Such plasmids could be transformed into a plasmid-free host, in which they had copy numbers as high as 100. These plasmids had arisen from R1; restriction endonuclease treatment and gel electrophoresis showed that two out of four plasmids examined were composed of a continuous segment that included the replication region of R1, while the other two lacked an internal portion of this segment (Luibrand *et al*. 1977). Mickel and Bauer (1976) and Taylor *et al*. (1977) observed analogous plasmids from another copy-mutant, in this case R12, itself a derivative of NR1. In this case the host strain was *dnaA*⁺. The DNA of these plasmids comes from the RTF-Tc rather than the r region of R12, with one end being close to or at one end of one of the IS1 regions separating the two moieties. The formation of such small plasmids seems to depend upon the presence of transposons and/or insertion sequences (Mickel *et al*. 1977; Ohtsubo *et al*. 1978). The significance of these observations with respect to the regulation of copy-number is as yet unclear. A related observation (Chandler *et al*. 1977c) is that upon integration of R100-1 into the chromosome (in 'integrative suppression' of a *dnaA* ts strain—see later) plasmids arise that may correspond to the r moiety of the R factor. However, unlike those described above, they could not be transformed into novel hosts, and it is unlikely that they are capable of truly autonomous replication.

Segregation

A successful plasmid-host relationship requires that plasmidless cells ('segregants') do not arise frequently during the growth of the culture. Two complications can make it difficult to determine the true segregation rate of a plasmid. One is that with transmissible plasmids, segregants may be re-infected by other cells in the population. The other is that the parent and its plasmid-free segregants may grow at different rates.

One way of ensuring that a plasmid is not lost is for it to be maintained in enough copies for random apportionment to daughter cells to ensure that the great majority receive at least one copy. Thus if there were about 20 copies per cell of ColE1 at the moment of division, one would expect a segregation frequency per generation of about 2^{-20} (10^{-6}). For larger plasmids, which are present in fewer copies (see later), a more specific method of apportionment seems essential. This point was made by Jacob *et al.* (1963) in their classic paper on the control of plasmid replication. They argued that this required a structural mechanism and that the cell membrane could be the structure. A prediction of this model is that there is ordered co-segregation of different replicons (the chromosome and a plasmid or of two plasmids). Two experiments indicated that strands of DNA of the chromosome and an F′ factor, made in the same replication cycle, do indeed co-segregate (Cuzin and Jacob 1967b).

In one, a *lac⁻*/Fts *lac⁺* (an F′*lac* with a temperature-sensitive replication or segregation function) strain was grown at 25° C in ³²P medium, so that in most cells both strands of the plasmid and the chromosome were radioactive. The ³²P was then removed and the bacteria were grown at 42° C in the presence of non-radioactive (³¹P) phosphorus. Because the F′*lac* molecules cannot replicate, they segregate unilinearly after the first division of the generally binucleate cells. The question was: do all the F′*lac*-carrying cells that exist after several generations also carry a radioactive chromosome, indicating co-segregation? After 0, 0.8 and 3.8 generations samples were removed and frozen in liquid nitrogen. ³²P decay, which is independent of temperature, cleaves DNA so that ³²P-containing bacteria are killed. Samples were thawed and assayed for viability and for the presence of F′*lac* in the surviving cells. In the earlier samples the Lac⁺ and the total populations declined at the same rate, but after 3.6 generations the rate of killing of Lac⁺ cells (the same as that in the 0.8 generation sample) was far higher than that of the general population (Fig. 4.4). This indicated that F′*lac* remained with the ³²P-labelled chromosomes.

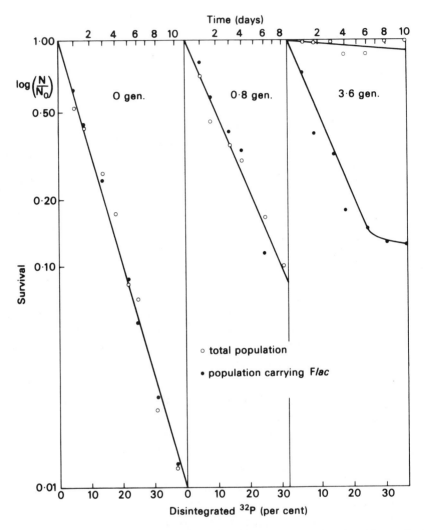

Fig. 4.4. Survival of an *E. coli lac⁻*/Fts *lac⁺* strain labelled with ³²P, washed and then subcultured in ³¹P medium for the intervals shown, before sampling and freezing (see text). At intervals, samples were then thawed and assayed for the numbers of viable cells and of cells still carrying Fts*lac⁺*. (From Cuzin and Jacob 1967b, with permission of authors and publisher.)

The second experiment also involved pre-labelling DNA of the same strain, this time with [³H]thymidine. This experiment depended on the fact that mutants which do not produce galactose epimerase lyse in the presence of galactose. After pre-labelling at 25° C the bacteria were transferred to non-radioactive medium at the same temperature, and grown for one generation, at which point each plasmid and each chromosome should consist of one labelled and one unlabelled strand. The temperature was then raised to 42° C so that only chromosome replication takes place. Eight generations later, the culture was challenged with a β-galactoside; those cells containing F'*lac* hydrolyse it to produce galactose and therefore undergo lysis. Most of the radioactivity was released, as if the unreplicated F'*lac*$^+$ particle and the labelled strand of the chromosome had co-segregated. Much later (1978) Liebowitz and Fox showed that either chromosomal strand can be involved in such serial co-segregation.

In analogous experiments Hohn and Korn (1969) showed that in F 'curing' by acridine orange the process affected is not co-segregation, which is conserved, but replication itself.

All these experiments involve an F plasmid, the replication of which is inhibited in some unknown way. We therefore do not know whether F and the chromosome co-segregate when both (rather than just the chromosome) are replicating normally. Also there is no proof that the membrane is involved. However, since F co-sediments with the intact chromosomes after gentle lysis and centrifugation they are probably physically associated in some way (Kline and Miller 1975; Kline *et al.* 1976).

Several studies have been made of segregation of multicopy plasmids in systems where plasmid replication is temperature-sensitive. If such replication is stopped, one would expect plasmid-free cells to appear sooner if segregation is random than if daughter cells always receive equal numbers of plasmid molecules (Novick *et al.* 1975). Durkacz and Sherratt (1973) estimated the copy number of ColE1 from the segregation of plasmid-free cells in a strain that was temperature-sensitive for *polA* (see later). It is not possible to make a rigorous test of the mode of segregation from their data, since there was substantial residual plasmid replication. However, later experiments with non-leaky replication mutants of pSC101 (Hashimoto-Gotoh and Sekiguchi 1977) supported the equal number model. Also, Della Latta *et al.* (1978) showed that a naturally temperature-sensitive *Staph. aureus* plasmid, pT169, is stably maintained in some strains at high temperature, even though the copy number is reduced from about 15 copies per cell to 2–3 per cell. The implication seems to be that here too apportionment is regular.

A clue to the control of segregation might come from the observation that different plasmids are segregated into minicells with very different efficiencies (see Frazer and Curtiss 1975), though this problem has not yet been pursued.

Role of host functions in plasmid replication
Plasmids depend largely upon their hosts for their replication, since host

replication mutants generally also affect plasmid replication. Expression of replication deficiency usually prevents cell growth, so usually replication is studied by using conditional mutants of the temperature-sensitive type. Some mutations (like *dnaA*) affect the initiation of new rounds of replication, so that when a growing culture is shifted to the non-permissive temperature rounds of replication that have been initiated can be completed, but no new ones start. In contrast 'sudden stop' mutations, like *dnaB* and *dnaE*, affect DNA chain growth.

Effect of pol *mutations.*   Three DNA polymerases, polI, polII and polIII, are known in *E. coli*. They are coded for respectively by the *polA, polB* and *dnaE* genes (see next section). Some non-conditional mutations exist in the *polA* gene; the fact that they are non-lethal is presumably because some of the functions of this enzyme can sometimes be performed by other enzymes in the cell. When these functions are defective as well, as in double mutants such as *polA⁻, recA⁻* and *polA⁻, lig*(ligase)⁻, the cell becomes non-viable. The known functions are: (1) the 5′ to 3′ polymerizing activity, (2) the 3′ to 5′ exonuclease activity (the 'proof-reading' function) and (3) the 5′ to 3′ exonuclease activity, which allows nick translation (the removal of RNA primer ahead of the filling in with new DNA). This last function is argued to be indispensible for normal growth and viability of *E. coli* (Konrad and Lehman 1974).

F′ factors could be maintained in a viable *polA⁻* strain (Gross and Gross 1969); so too could other self-transmissible plasmids (Kingsbury and Helsinki 1973a). But neither ColE1 or ColE2 could exist stably, although they persisted in *polA⁺* revertants of the *polA⁻* strain. The defect was one of maintenance of ColE1 rather than of its entry since when *polA⁺* strains already carrying ColE1 were made *polA⁻* by P1 transduction ColE1 was lost (Kingsbury and Helinski 1973a). However, ColE1 could replicate in *polA⁻* strains mutant only in the nick translation function (Tacon and Sherratt 1976). Although maintenance of the mini-plasmid from *E. coli* strain 15 (Goebel and Schrempf 1972a) was also *polA⁺* dependent, other small plasmids replicated efficiently in *polA⁻* strains (Grindley and Kelley 1976). Therefore no clear distinction between large and small plasmids can be drawn with respect to their dependence on DNA polymerase I.

Like *polA⁻* mutants, a *polB⁻* mutant was able to support the replication of F and a series of R factors (Hirota *et al.* 1972). However, its effect upon the replication of small plasmids has not been reported.

Effect of 'sudden stop' mutations.   Where plasmid replication does not depend upon a given host function, it should continue in a conditional mutant at high temperature after chromosome replication has ceased. However, the absence or reduction of plasmid replication does not show true dependence, since it could be due, instead, to an overall impairment of cellular function in the absence of chromosome replication. Thus it is known that ColE1 replication is somewhat abnormal at high temperatures, even in wild-type cells; catenated molecules accumulate (Goebel 1971; Goebel and Kreft 1974) and DNA is degraded (Goebel 1970a).

The primary enzyme for the replication of the *E. coli* chromosome is apparently DNA polymerase III, the function specified by *dnaE* (Gefter *et al*. 1971). Goebel (1972) made a series of *dnaE*ts strains carrying a large plasmid (ColV-K30,ColIb-P9 or Hly) or ColE1. At the restrictive temperature (45° C) replication of both the chromosome and the large plasmids decreased to less than 1 per cent of the 30° C value. ColE1 replication was only reduced to about 10 per cent of its former value; since the residual synthesis of ColE1 was semi-conservative in mode, it was thought to be true replication rather than a form of repair synthesis. It was therefore concluded that ColE1 can replicate without using DNA polymerase III, whereas replication of the larger plasmids requires this enzyme. Taken together with the findings that only ColE1 replication requires DNA polymerase I, this suggested that more than one basic mechanism of DNA replication may operate among *E. coli* plasmids. A comparable lack of dependence on the *dnaE* function was reported for two other small plasmids, that from *E. coli* 15 (Goebel and Schrempf (1972a)), and CloDF13 (Veltkamp and Nijkamp 1974). However, it may nevertheless be that normal ColE1 replication requires DNA polymerase III as well as DNA polymerase I (Collins *et al*. 1975). In any event ColE1 replication is sufficiently similar to that of the *E. coli* chromosome for both to have 'Okazaki fragments' as intermediates (Inselburg and Oka 1975). The conclusion here too is that the differences in the mechanisms of replication of large and small plasmids may not be as basic as was once thought.

To avoid using cells functioning so abnormally in studying F replication, Thompson and Broda (1973) used a strain with a particular *dnaE*ts mutation that had the additional property of being mutagenic at the permissive temperature. The DNA polymerase III molecule here is presumably making mistakes in the selection of the nucleotide precursors that it adds to the nascent DNA chain. This could be detected as an enhanced reversion rate of a point mutation in the *trpA* gene (involved in tryptophan synthesis) to *trp*+. Since there is also a greatly enhanced reversion rate for the *trpA* gene when carried on an F' factor, the plasmid was also being replicated by DNA polymerase III.

An essential feature of DNA synthesis of bacteria and of small viruses *in vivo* is the use of an RNA primer in the initial stages. This renders such DNA synthesis sensitive to rifampicin, a specific inhibitor of RNA (but not DNA) polymerase. Replication of ColE1 (Clewell *et al*. 1972) and F (Bazzicalupo and Tocchini-Valentini 1972; Kline 1973) is also inhibited by rifampicin. There is also the following direct evidence for a role for RNA in plasmid replication.

When ColE1$^+$ cells are incubated in the presence of chloramphenicol (which prevents new protein synthesis), ColE1 DNA continues to accumulate long after chromosome replication has ceased. It can reach 3000 copies per cell (Clewell 1972). Much of this DNA is in the covalently closed circular form, but is abnormal in being susceptible to nicking by RNAase or alkali, showing that RNA forms part of the covalently closed circular structure (Blair *et al*. 1972; Williams *et al*. 1973). In contrast to the situation in relaxation complexes, these nicks can occur in either strand. These structures appear to be true replicative intermediates, in that DNA synthesis is required to generate them, and they disappear when protein synthesis resumes. Also, rifampicin prevents their accumulation. It is suggested that this RNA is primer which is normally removed on the completion of replication; such a gap would then be filled with DNA and sealed with a DNA ligase. This RNA is probably present at other sites as well as at the origin of replication (Tomizawa *et al*. 1977).

The synthesis of RNA primer is the function of the *dnaG* gene (Bouché *et al*. 1975). ColE1 replication is dependent upon *dnaG* and also upon the 'sudden stop' *dnaD* (=*dnaC*) mutant studied by Collins *et al*. 1975 (see also Veltkamp and Nijkamp 1974).

ColE1, minicircular DNA and CloDF13 can replicate in *dnaB*ts strains at high temperature (Goebel and Schrempf 1972c; Veltkamp and Nijkamp 1974). However, at least ColE1 replication is abnormal in that catemers are formed (Goebel 1970b) which may not be true replicative intermediates (Sakakibara *et al*. 1976). The replication of F (and three other plasmids, ColV, Hly and lysogenic P1) does require the *dnaB* function (Goebel and Schrempf 1972c). On the other hand, it may be that some conjugative R plasmids specify their own *dnaB*-like functions (Wang and Iyer 1978). Other experiments (Marinus and Adelberg 1970; Vapnek and Rupp 1971; Fenwick and Curtiss 1973) also showed that the *dnaB* function is necessary for vegetative replication of F but not for transfer (which normally involves replication—see next chapter).

Effect of initiation mutations: integrative suppression.   Genetic experiments have shown that F either has a *dnaA*-like function of its own or does not need one for replication. Nishimura *et al*. (1971) found that about 0.006 per cent of cells of a *dnaA* ts mutant, plated at 42° C, formed colonies if F was present. These colonies were Hfr clones (that is, carried integrated F) and still had the *dnaA* mutation. In the F'*lac* strain (where integration would occur more often because of the extensive homology between the plasmid and the chromosome) the frequency was enhanced to about 0.1 per cent. The formation of such colonies depended upon an intact *recA*$^+$ function. The suggestion was made that, following integration into the chromosome, F provides a *dnaA*-like initiation function that allows further chromosome replication. Because autonomous F cannot effect such 'suppression' such a function could not be a soluble product; that is, it would be '*cis*-acting'. An alternative is that F itself requires no such function at all. 'Integratively suppressed' strains are sensitive to acridine orange at 42° C but not at 30° C. Since acridine orange inhibits autonomous F replication (Hohn and Korn 1969), but has no apparent effect upon normal chromosome replication, it was inferred that at 42° C the chromosome is replicated as part of the F replicon, but that at 30° C F is replicated as part of the chromosomal replicon.

All of a series of F-like plasmids, including R100-1, suppressed the *dnaA* lesion (Nishimura *et al.* 1973; Moody and Runge 1972; Goebel 1974). Although several ColI-related plasmids did not (Moody and Runge 1972), integrative suppression has now been reported for two I-like plasmids (Datta and Barth 1976). Phage P2 (Lindahl *et al.* 1971) and P1 and P7 (Chesney and Scott 1978) also gave integrative suppression. However, ColE1 replication requires the *dnaA* function (Goebel 1974).

Integrative suppression has been the means by which many Hfr strains have been isolated, using both F factors and de-repressed R and ColV2 factors (Nishimura *et al.* 1973). R' factors have in turn also been isolated.

Do integratively suppressed strains, like normal Hfr strains (Masters and Broda 1971; but see Chandler *et al.* 1976), retain the origin and bidirectional mode of replication, or does replication proceed from the site of F integration? The poor growth generally observed for such strains has made it difficult to establish this for F, but two R100.1-suppressed strains, grown at the non-permissive temperature, replicated bidirectionally from the integrated plasmids in at least some of the cells (Bird *et al.* 1976), but from the normal origin at 30° C (Chandler *et al.* 1977b).

Insertion alone seemed insufficient for suppression, since most Hfr strains isolated from the F$^+$ *dnaA*$^-$ strain at the permissive temperature did not grow at 42° C (Nishimura *et al.* 1971). However, Hfr strains isolated by others, when incubated at 40° C, did replicate in glucose-minimal medium, and gave colonies on glucose-minimal agar but not on rich medium such as that used by Nishimura *et al.* (Tresguerres *et al.* 1975). The reason why growth of such *dnaA*⁻ Hfr strains does not occur on rich medium at 42° C is unknown. Suppressed strains do replicate their DNA rather slowly, especially at high temperatures, as if F-controlled replication is relatively inefficient. This would be consistent with the findings of Stadler and Adelberg (1972) that on growth of *E. coli* at higher temperatures, under conditions where re-infection between cells is minimized, F'*lac* is segregated out.

Another unresolved question is why, in the great majority of integratively suppressed Hfr clones, F is integrated in the lower left quadrant of the conventional *E. coli* map (Nishimura *et al.* 1971; see also Iida 1977). This may, however, also have nothing specifically to do with suppression, since a similar non-random distribution of sites was observed among about 150 Hfr strains isolated from a *dnaA*⁺ parent (Broda, unpublished results).

Another initiation function, *dnaC*, is required for maintenance of F'*lac* (Zeuthen and Pato 1971; Goebel 1973; van Brunt *et al.* 1977) and ColE1 in *E. coli* (Goebel 1973; Collins *et al.* 1975). Integrative suppression has not been observed for *dnaC* (Goebel 1974), or for any of the sudden-stop mutations.

Supercoiling. Two *E. coli* functions (*cou* and *nalA*) specify the subunits of DNA gyrase, which introduces supercoils into replicated DNA (Higgins *et al.* 1978). If a mixture of complementary single-strand rings is annealed and then treated with this enzyme, the DNA circles completely renature to form cccDNA. This must be done by the introduction of transient single-strand breaks (Champoux 1977). Enzymes such as this, which must certainly be involved in plasmid replication, may well turn out to be involved in recombination and transposition as well.

Other functions affecting plasmid replication

Do plasmids also specify proteins required for their own replication? Such proteins might include the enzyme that nicks the double strand close to the origin of replication, and proteins that regulate copy-number and for the attachment of plasmids to cell structures (see later). Plasmids as small as 0.7 megadalton have been reported (Oka 1978; Kollek *et al.* 1978; Bolivar *et al.* 1977a); here there is a strict upper limit to the number of possible functions. In the case of F, heteroduplex analysis of deletion mutants showed that everything except the 43–52-kilobase region (Fig. 3.9) was dispensable (Anthony *et al.* 1974). Fragments of F'*lac* and R6-5 generated with endonucleases have also been used to determine which regions are essential. Timmis *et al.* (1975) isolated chimaeras containing one fragment each from *Eco*RI-cleaved extracts of these plasmids and an ampicillin-resistance fragment derived from a staphylococcal plasmid. The *E. coli* host transformed with the R6-5Ap^r chimaera contained a single R6-5 fragment of 12 kilo-bases. The analogous single F'*lac* fragment was of 9 kilobases (Skurray *et al.* 1976a). Thus rather small regions can provide origins of replication and whatever plasmid functions are required for replication, unless some of these came from the Ap region, which seems unlikely. Since the *Eco*RI fragment covers the 40.3–49.3-kilobase segment of F (Lovett and Helinski 1976; Guyer *et al.* 1976) such functions had to be within the 43–49.3-kilobase interval.[1]

In the case of λ*dv* plasmids too, the essential region is small. Some such plasmids contain only 7 per cent of the DNA of the parent λ genome. The indispensable region includes the O and P replication genes and the operator–promoter region from which their messenger RNA is transcribed (Berg 1974; Matsubara 1976; Fig. 4.5). It has recently been found that the origin of replication upon which the O and P products act overlaps the O

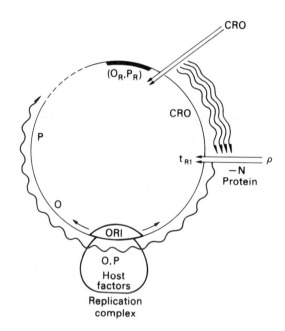

Fig. 4.5. A model for the transcriptional control of λ*dv* replication. The level of transcription (wavy arrows) from the rightward promoter is regulated by the inhibitory effects of the *cro* product (here shown arbitrarily as acting near the promoter) and of the bacterial termination factor rho (ρ). (From Berg 1974, with permission of author and publisher.)

[1] The segment carrying all DNA required for controlled replication of R6-5 (including an origin of replication) and expression of its incompatibility functions is no larger than 2.6 kilobases (Andrés *et al.* 1979).

gene. Analogous deletion mutants exist of P1; such mini-P1 plasmids replicate as precisely as the lysogenic parental plasmid, suggesting that the
plasmid and lytic cycle modes of P1 replication are regulated by separate
mechanisms (Austin *et al*. 1978).

Donoghue and Sharp (1978a) and Kahn and Helinski (1978) have suggested that no plasmid-specified proteins are needed for ColE1 replication.
This was because a ColE1 derivative introduced into a cell unable to synthesize protein could replicate normally. Yet such a plasmid apparently
cannot replicate when introduced into a ColE1$^+$ strain. It is not known
whether this is due to competition for replication components or to inhibition of its replication by the resident plasmid. The derivatives employed here
were *in vitro* hybrids of temperate phages (λ and P4 respectively) with
ColE1 derivatives. These could be packaged in phage coats, and introduced
with high efficiency, as phage particles ('phasmids'), into recipient cells. This
property gives such particles great potential as tools for the analysis of
plasmid functions (see also Hayakawa and Matsubara 1979; Couturier *et al*.
1979).

Replication mutants.   Since replication is an essential function, isolatable
mutants affecting plasmid replication normally need to have special properties. The host cell should be less affected by them than the plasmid, to allow
the effect on the plasmid to be studied, and they should be conditional
mutations, so that the plasmid can be maintained and demonstrated in
a host cell. However, it is now also possible to maintain replicons with
absolute defects, using chimaeras. In practice mutations affecting replication are generally difficult to distinguish from those causing irregular
segregation.

Jacob *et al*. (1963) described a series of ts mutants in a chromosomally *lac*$^-$
strain carrying an F'*lac*$^+$ plasmid. Whereas at 30° C the strains remained
Lac$^+$, Lac$^-$ colonies accumulated at 42° C. Since this was due to loss of F'*lac*,
either replication or apportionment of the F' factor to daughter cells was
defective. Some of the mutations mapped on F'*lac*, so that this plasmid does
indeed specify replication or segregation functions (the use of one such
mutant was described in the section on Segregation). Others mapped at
chromosomal loci so that, although cell growth itself was apparently normal,
the host chromosome also carries functions involved in this process.

The point that both plasmid-borne and chromosomal mutants arise was
reinforced by Kingsbury and Helinski (1973b), who isolated many clones in
which ColE1 replication was temperature-sensitive. The particular problem
in isolating such mutants is that ColE1 is present in the cell in about 20
copies, which makes it more difficult to isolate clones carrying only mutant

plasmids. However, use of two variants of a method that destroyed replicating plasmids yielded strains with, respectively, chromosome-borne and plasmid-borne mutations. The chromosomal mutations fell into three classes.

(1) At 42° C Class I mutants could not maintain any of a number of plasmids (ColE1, ColV, F'*lac*, ⊙-19, ColIa, ColIb and R64).

(2) Class II mutations affected ColE1 and fewer plasmids (F'*lac*, ColV and R1-19).

(3) Class III mutations only affected ColE1 maintenance. Some of these were mutations in *polA* (Kingsbury and Helinski 1973a).

Of the ColE1-borne mutations some could be complemented by F'*lac*.

Another way of isolating mutants depends upon the observation that mutations caused by N-methyl-N'-nitro-N-nitrosoguanidine tend to be clustered at replicating forks (Guerola *et al.* 1971). Using N-methyl-N'-nitro-N-nitrosoguanidine Koyama *et al.* (1975) obtained plasmid mutants, including maintenance mutants, with high efficiency among Trp$^+$ revertants of a ColVB*trp* plasmid that carried a point mutation in the *trpA* gene. Many of the mutants caused slow growth, and some caused cell filamentation. Although the mode of mutagenesis made it likely that some of the mutants were due to multiple mutation, in some cases revertants could be isolated, indicating that only a single mutation was involved (Koyama and Yura 1975).

Other mutants in which plasmid replication and/or segregation are affected have been described for *E. coli* (Hathaway and Bergquist 1973; DeVries and Maas 1973; Hashimoto-Gotoh and Sekiguchi 1977), *Staph. aureus* (Novick 1974) and *Pseudomonas aeruginosa* (Chang and Holloway 1977). However, apart from the *polA*$^-$ mutants affecting ColE1 replication only in one case has a specific function been assigned to a mutation; a chromosomal mutation affecting F'*lac* fell within a gene specifying a ribosomal protein (Yamagata and Uchida 1972). The significance of this observation is unclear. A more intelligible observation (Kingsbury *et al.* 1973; Koyama and Yura 1975) is that many maintenance mutants were temperature-sensitive in the presence of deoxycholate. This suggested that the cell envelope is altered, and therefore that it has a role in plasmid maintenance (see also Nakamura 1974).

The situation regarding plasmid replication functions is therefore confusing. Several genes have been implicated but only some of the chromosomal genes and none of the plasmid genes are well characterized. In some cases the connexion between the lesion and plasmid replication may well be indirect. Complementation between plasmid replication functions has only been reported by Kingsbury and Helinski (1973b), in the case mentioned above, Wyman and Novick 1974 (for *Staph. aureus* plasmids) and for the O and P genes of phage λ.

Plasmid replication in vitro. *In vitro* systems are now being developed. Sakakibara and Tomizawa (1974) observed a complete round of semi-conservative ColE1 replication in cell-free extracts, and Tomizawa *et al.* (1975) extended these observations to a mixture of an extract from a ColE1-less strain and added ColE1 DNA. The conversion of open circular ColE1 DNA to covalently closed circular molecules *in vitro* by DNA gyrase has also been demonstrated (Gellert *et al.* 1977). In addition, the base sequence of the replication origin of ColE1 has been partially determined (Tomizawa *et al.* 1977; Bolivar *et al.* 1977a). Most of the first-formed DNA has one or more ribonucleotide bases attached (Bird and Tomizawa 1978). Both DNA polymerases I and III are necessary for the replication of ColE1 *in vitro* and another small plasmid, RSF1030, in *E. coli* extracts (Staudenbauer 1976). For RSF1030 replication, at least, the DNA polymerase I step precedes the DNA polymerase III (Staudenbauer 1977), *dnaB* and *dnaC*-dependent steps (Staudenbauer *et al.* 1978).

In vitro systems are also being developed for R6K (Inuzuka and Helinski 1978) and R1 (Bezanson and Goebel 1979).

Incompatibility

Incompatibility is observed if the replication of two plasmids is subject to a common regulation and if both are present in a cell. One or other will then be lost. Such 'incompatibility' operates between autonomous plasmids (e.g. F' factors) and also between incoming F' factors and the integrated F factors of Hfr strains (Scaife and Gross 1962; Maas and Maas 1962; Cuzin 1962; Maas 1963). As discussed in Chapter 3, the incompatibility test is a principal criterion for deciding whether two plasmids are related.

When F'*lac*$^+$ was introduced into a Lac$^-$ Hfr strain, the level of β-galactosidase that could be induced in the culture remained constant over at least eight generations growth (Dubnau and Maas 1968). This suggested that F'*lac* was neither being replicated nor broken down, but was being inherited unilinearly. When F enters an F$^+$ or Hfr cell it is converted normally to the covalently closed circular duplex (Saitoh and Hiraga 1975). However (in an analogous case in which R factors were used), membrane-bound replicative intermediates of the superinfecting plasmid accumulated (Hershfield *et al.* 1973). Therefore incompatibility in these cases seems to operate by inhibiting replication. For this reason it has been studied as a probe on replication and its control (see also later). Attempts have therefore been made to isolate mutant strains in which two incompatible plasmids can now cohabit. Another reason for isolating such 'Inc⁻' mutants has been that incompatibility is an obstacle to performing complementation tests on those plasmid-borne replication mutants that have been isolated. Such tests would make it possible to decide whether a series of mutations all fall within the same gene.

Strains carrying two F factors could be of three types: with two autonomous F factors (F_a–F_a), with two integrated F factors (F_i–F_i) and with one of each (F_a–F_i). In attempting to isolate F diploids of the F_a–F_i type Maas and Goldschmidt (1969) found that the efficient establishment of F'*his* (for histidine synthesis) in an Hfr strain required an intact recombination system. It was therefore likely that the different replicons had become covalently linked. The rare His⁺ clones that arose in the corresponding cross with a *recA*⁻ recipient strain had with one exception lost the transfer function of the integrated F, indicating that they were deletion mutants (DeVries and Maas 1973). In the exceptional clone also the mutation was in the integrated F factor, although F' factors isolated from the integrated F were incompatible with other F' factors. This was because Hfr strains isolated in turn from these F' factors were again mutant (DeVries *et al.* 1975; Pfister *et al.* 1976). Thus the incompatibility barrier that had been overcome for the F_a–F_i situation still held for the F_i–F_i situation. This raises the possibility that different mechanisms may be under study in the two situations.

The earliest attempts at isolating F_a–F_a Inc⁻ strains (Echols 1963; Cuzin and Jacob 1967) employed F'*lac* and F'*gal* and *rec*⁺ strains. A minority of the recipient cells could be isolated as Gal⁺Lac⁺ clones, and F'*lac* and F'*gal* could be recovered from them. However, these too were probably transiently tandem structures. When *recA*⁻ strains were used, the few derivatives carrying markers from the two F' factors were generally single fused structures that were smaller than the sum of the separate sizes (Palchaudhuri *et al.* 1972; Willetts and Bastarrachea 1972; Palchaudhuri *et al.* 1976). However, San Blas *et al.* (1974) and DeVries *et al.* (1975) have reported cases of apparent loss of F_a–F_a incompatibility. The difficulties involved in interpreting such results are discussed by these authors and by Jamieson and Bergquist (1976; 1977). It should be remembered that if F is indeed present in only one copy per nucleus (Frame and Bishop 1971), compatibility would require an enhanced overall copy number.

In analogous experiments with *Staph. aureus* the formation of a 'double' was due to irreversible integration of one plasmid into the host chromosome. This plasmid was able to complement ts replication mutants of related plasmids but not of unrelated plasmids (Wyman and Novick 1974).

The F_i–F_i case had been considered by Clark (1963), who isolated a 'double male' Hfr strain in a cross between two Rec⁺ Hfr parents. This strain throws off F′ factors at an unusually high rate (Clark *et al*. 1969), although both F factors are apparently carried on a single chromosome, rather than on separate linkage groups (Falkinham and Clark 1974). Other such strains have been reported by Kaney and Atwood (1972) to revert to the singly Hfr strain at high frequency.

Deletion mutants of Hfr strains have been used to map the '*inc*' function(s) of F, at least for the F_i–F_a situation, approximately within the replication region (Willetts 1974a). At least part of the *inc* region was thought to lie within the 46.4–48.6-kilobase segment, since only this region is common to F and a number of plasmids that are incompatible with it (Palchaudhuri and Maas 1977a). It is distinct from the origin of vegetative replication (42.5 kilobases). Recent results from experiments with cloned fragments of F have led to the proposal that there are two *inc* loci, *incA* being the one described above, and *incB*, mapping in the 43–46-kilobase segment (Manis and Kline 1978).

In ColE1 derivatives that have lost a particular region the expression of incompatibility is greatly reduced (Inselburg 1977b). This also suggests that replication (which is indispensable) and incompatibility are separate functions. For the *Staph. aureus* system it is further suggested that incompatibility depends upon the distribution of the replicas to different daughter cells rather than upon an inhibition of replication (Novick and Schwesinger 1976).

One can predict a rate of segregation for different models for incompatibility (Ishii *et al*. 1978; Novick and Hoppensteadt 1978; Cullum and Broda 1979c). Such calculations show that the rate for a given copy number is about twice as high under a random pool model as under a democratic model.

Control

The plasmid molecules that are used as the templates for replication might be chosen in different ways:

(1) A single plasmid molecule is the template for the synthesis of all new plasmid molecules;

(2) The templates are taken randomly from a pool, as happens in the multiplication of the virulent coliphages T2 and T4 (Visconti and Delbrück 1953). Some plasmids will then undergo two or more cycles of replication while others will remain unreplicated;

(3) A mechanism exists that ensures that each copy is replicated once and once only per cell cycle.

Mechanisms (2) and (3) are comparable to the random pool and specific mechanisms for segregation, as discussed earlier. Two 'classic' models exist for control. On the model of Jacob *et al*. (1963) (which was formulated with particular reference to F but can also be applied to multicopy plasmids) copy number depends upon the number of available membrane attachment sites. Only when new sites become available can replication occur. They proposed also that each replicon carries two determinants: (a) a structural gene controlling the synthesis of a specific initiator and (b) a site, the replicator, upon which this initiator would act, allowing the replication of the replicon. As stated, this is a model for positive control of replication.

On the principal alternative model (Pritchard *et al*. 1969) a plasmid-specified repressor exerts a negative form of control. This repressor would be produced briefly during plasmid replication, so inhibiting further plasmid replication. As the cell grows, the concentration of repressor molecules would fall below a critical value, so that a new round of plasmid replication can be initiated. This model does not deny that the membrane may be important in replication and segregation, but merely the idea that membrane-borne sites determine plasmid copy-number. Some attempts to distinguish between these hypotheses are described later.

Relaxed and stringent control. If, as has been thought to occur for plasmids present in few copies per cell, each copy is replicated once per generation, all plasmid DNA in a cell population would be replicated once before any is replicated a second time. An analogous situation is that observed by Meselson and Stahl (1958) for chromosome replication. The converse of such a 'democratic' mode has been observed for the multicopy plasmid ColE1 (Bazaral and Helinski 1970). Here some molecules are replicated twice in the time it takes to replicate only half the chromosome, while about a third had still not been replicated at all after 1.5 generations. The data are consistent with the random selection from a pool of those molecules that are to be replicated. Similar conclusions had been drawn earlier by Rownd (1969) for NR1 in *Pr. mirabilis* grown in chloramphenicol-supplemented medium, where it was thought to be present in several copies (but see Chapter 2).

These observations provided the initial basis for the division of plasmids into those with 'relaxed' and those with 'stringent' control of replication. However, in time these words have unfortunately been taken to represent at least three only partially related ideas.

(1) The definition of 'relaxed' adopted by Novick *et al*. (1976) states that such replication is not coupled in an obligatory manner to chromosome replication. The initial basis for this criterion was that ColE1 can replicate in the absence of chromosome replication, after addition of chloramphenicol. This has since been found not to be the case for some other

multicopy plasmids. Another condition in which replication of the two replicons (ColE1 and the chromosome) was uncoupled was in *polA*⁻ mutants (see earlier). The replication of two small-copy-number plasmids (R28K: Kontomichalou *et al*. 1970; *Δ*: Milliken and Clowes 1973) was considered to be stringently controlled because they provide constant proportions of the total cellular DNA in exponential growth and the stationary phase. This was contrasted with the behaviour of two relaxed and multicopy plasmids (R6K: Kontomichalou *et al*. 1970; NR1 in *Pr. mirabilis* grown in the presence of chloramphenicol: Kasamatsu and Rownd 1970) where the proportion increases greatly. The proportion of the total cellular DNA that is provided by NR1 can rise from 10 per cent to 60 per cent.

(2) Stringently controlled replication should be according to the democratic mode whereas in relaxedly controlled replication there is random selection from a pool, with a spread in initiation times, as with ColE1 (see above). But if the period during which initiation of plasmid replication is possible is short, relative to the time needed for plasmid replication to be completed, a multicopy plasmid would appear to replicate 'democratically'. Such a case has not been observed.

(3) The stringently replicating plasmids are present in one or a few copies per nucleus. Thus NR1 would be a special case, being under relaxed control in *Pr. mirabilis* but under stringent control in *E. coli*.

However, the determination of the replication mode for plasmids present in few copies gave a surprising result. Abe (1974) and Gustafsson and Nordström (1975) reported for P1 and R1 respectively that replication is according to the random mode. Our current view may therefore be too simple. One possibility is that estimates of copy number are systematically too low. Another is that these plasmids are replicated as a pool in the cell, rather than in association with particular nuclei. If so, it may be that the 'unit of segregation' formed of a chromosome and a plasmid, and demonstrated with non-replicating plasmids only (see earlier) does not apply to replicating plasmids.

At present the mode of multicopy plasmid replication seems uncontroversial, but that of small-copy-number plasmids is quite unclear. The latter point emerges independently from the next experiments to be described.

Replication and the cell cycle.   How does the timing of replication fit in with events in the cell's growth cycle? Although the machinery for chromosome and F factor replication has common features (e.g. *dnaB*, *dnaC* and *dnaE*, and possibly a common segregation mechanism), other features (e.g., *dnaA*) may be different, and therefore the signals for initiation may be different.

Collins and Pritchard (1973) and Pritchard *et al.* (1975) determined the relation between growth rate and the amount of F'*lac* DNA as a proportion of total DNA. They found that this proportion declines as cells grow faster. This was also found for R1 (Engberg and Nordström 1975). Put another way, the average number of plasmids per chromosome origin increases as the growth rate decreases. Therefore initiation of replication of these plasmids is not related in a simple way with the initiation of chromosome replication. Nor has coupling between F replication and any other stage of the replication cycle of the host chromosome or cell division been observed. F replication is not related to the cell's surface area either (Collins and Pritchard 1973; Pritchard *et al.* 1975). For prophage P1, there is no coupling between initiation and either initiation or termination of chromosome replication (Prentki *et al.* 1977).

Such attempts to relate plasmid replication to the cell cycle were based on the idea that plasmid replication in all cells in the population occurs at the same cell age. Other workers have tested this point using synchronous *E. coli* cultures; that is, populations in which all cells are about the same size and age, and divide at the same time. In each case, *lac⁻*/F'*lac⁺* strains were used to follow the doubling of β-galactosidase activity; the enzyme level and therefore presumably the plasmid number in the growing population did increase by twofold jumps, as if replication occurs at a specific time in the cell cycle. But there were differences in the further interpretation of these rather indirect experiments. On the one hand Zeuthen and Pato (1971) concluded that F'*lac* replicated at a fixed stage in the division cycle of cells grown at a variety of rates. On the other hand Cooper (1972) and Davis and Helmstetter (1973), who obtained synchronized cells from previously induced cultures, found that replication occurred relatively earlier in faster-growing cells. Plasmid replication here took place at about the same time as the initiation of chromosomal replication. Yet Finkelstein and Helmstetter (1977) suggested that replication of F'*lac* occurs at the same time as that of the homologous (*lac*) region of the chromosome.

In other experiments the idea that plasmid number for a small-copy-number plasmid increases in a stepwise manner is itself challenged. Apparently ColBM*trp lac* grown in synchronous populations did not increase in this way (Zeuthen *et al.* 1972); nor does R1-19 (Gustafsson *et al.* 1978) or F'*lac* (Andresdottir and Masters 1978). The important points about the last papers were that the cultures used were not disturbed by synchronization, and that amounts of cccDNA as well as enzyme levels were determined.

In conclusion, it is unclear whether there is indeed a stepwise increase in copies of small-copy-number plasmids, still less what the timing of any such event might be. The author is unaware of analogous experiments having been done with any multicopy plasmid.

The mechanism of control.   The simplest model for control is that copy number is limited solely by the availability of replication substrates and enzymes. This would require neither sites nor repressors (see below). However, this is unlikely to be the case with the examples discussed below. More generally, even when eight different plasmid species were present in a cell the copy number of each was apparently the same as when that species was present alone (Barth *et al.* 1978b).

Because so much is known about phage λ, the regulation of λdv replication is understood better than that of any other plasmid. Two genes that are not essential for controlled replication are those for the λ repressor and the N protein (which antagonizes the ρ factor—see below) since λdv plasmids need not carry these genes. On Berg's model (Fig. 4.5) replication is controlled through the regulation of transcription of the O and P genes in two ways. The first is through the *cro* (or *'tof'*) product, which is in effect inhibiting its own further synthesis, and is therefore acting as a repressor of plasmid replication. The other is through the bacterial termination factor ρ, for which there is a target (tR) between *cro* and the O and P genes. Only with a proportion of the messenger RNA molecules will transcription continue as far as O and P. The control here is negative, with the *cro* product and ρ acting as repressors. The C_I product (the repressor responsible for λ immunity) is not involved. Matsubara and Otsuji (1978) have presented evidence that the *cro* gene and the promoter–operator region pROR upon which it acts are also responsible for the determination of incompatibility between different λdv plasmids.

The Jacob, Brenner and Cuzin 1963 and the Pritchard, Barth and Collins 1969 models (see below) have dominated thinking on the mechanism of control. Timmis *et al.* (1974) and Cabello *et al.* (1976) have attempted a test of these models. For this purpose they constructed *in vitro* a hybrid, pSC134, that was composed of complete copies of plasmids of ColE1 and pSC101. Plasmid pSC101 was thought to be a small derivative of the small-copy-number plasmid R6 (but see Cohen and Chang 1977). Their observations were that:

(1) pSC134 normally replicates from the ColE1 origin.

(2) The copy number per genome (16) was similar to that for ColE1 in the same host strain (18) and greater than that for pSC101(6).

Points (1) and (2) suggest that pSC134 is replicated by the ColE1 replication system. However:

(3) pSC134 is incompatible with genetically marked derivatives of pSC101 as well as of ColE1.

(4) In a *polA⁻* background, in which ColE1 is unable to replicate, only the pSC101 origin is used, and the copy number falls to a value typical for pSC101.

Points (3) and (4) suggest that the pSC101 replication system is also functioning.

The Jacob, Brenner and Cuzin model postulates regulation of replication by means of availability of membrane attachment sites and competition between incompatible plasmids for available sites. Since both ColE1 and pSC101 replication origins and functions are available for pSC134 replication, this model predicts that some plasmids should replicate using each type of site, and that the copy number should depend upon the sum of the numbers of the ColE1 and the pSC101 sites (in this case 24 copies per genome); this appeared not to be the case. If instead the fact that only ColE1-type replication of pSC134 is occurring is taken to imply that only ColE1 sites are being used, it is not clear why pSC134 should be incompatible with pSC101.

In the Pritchard, Barth and Collins model, control is through a repressor (see earlier). The number of repressor molecules would be determined by the number of plasmid copies. In pSC134, therefore, repression of the pSC101-type of replication should only be lifted when the copy number falls to pSC101-type levels. Long before this time, however, ColE1-type replication would have become initiated. That is, the plasmid which by itself is present in more copies should provide the replication system that is triggered in the hybrid plasmid. As we have seen, the ColE1 system is used to replicate pSC134. Nevertheless, if the pSC101 repressor is still being produced (in abnormally high amounts, since the pSC134 copy number is higher than the normal pSC101 copy number), pSC101 should be unable to cohabit with pSC134. It was found that clones carrying pSC101 and pSC134 were indeed particularly unstable.

The experiments of Uhlin and Nordström (1975) also support a repression model. Here, the loss of plasmids was studied in clones starting from cells carrying R100(= Tcʳ) and a series of copy mutants of R1(=Apʳ), which are incompatible. In all cases the rate of loss of the two types were different than in the case of clones with R100 and the parental R1 plasmid, when there was a segregation frequency of about 8 per cent per cell division with respect to each plasmid. Thus the control of copy number and incompatibility are related aspects of replication control (the same point emerges from studies on ColE1 derivatives by Warren and Sherratt 1978). Further, while some of the copy mutants caused R100 to be lost more frequently, others, though also present in more copies than R1 itself, were themselves lost more frequently than R100. On an operator–repressor model of the Jacob-

Monod type, copy mutants could arise through having an operator less able to bind normal repressor or by production of less effective repressor. Those mutants that cause R100 to be lost more efficiently could then be operator mutants, producing increased amounts of normal repressor through being present in more copies. On the other hand, those lost more rapidly in the presence of R100 could have normal operators, subject to R1 repressor, but repressor reduced in amount or effectiveness. The action of R100 upon the latter class of mutant seems more difficult to explain on a site model than on a repressor model.

Summary

Plasmid replication is semiconservative and is catalyzed by host functions. Replicative intermediates can be isolated. These have shown that some plasmids replicate from a single origin, while others have more than one origin. Both unidirectional and bidirectional replication have been observed. Replication is generally from true circles rather than rolling circles. Some plasmids are present in only few copies per genome; for such plasmids the rules for initiation of replication and for apportionment into daughter cells must be strict. There are few replication functions that are plasmid-specified. One such is incompatibility, which is an aspect of replication control. What controls the frequency of initiation of replication, and how far different plasmids are subject to common mechanisms, is still unclear.

5
Conjugational Transfer

Three types of gene transfer, conjugation, transformation and transduction, have been described in bacteria. Many plasmids can effect conjugation, although it has not been detected in some groups of bacteria, for instance the staphylococci. All known bacterial transfer systems that depend upon cell contact are plasmid-dependent.

The study of conjugation is interesting for several reasons.

(1) Conjugation provides an important route for genetic exchange and therefore genetic analysis in bacteria.

(2) It is important to understand the basis of plasmid transmissibility because of its epidemiological implications (see next chapter).

(3) Conjugation is itself a good example of a defined complex function.

We can conveniently divide any conjugation process into three stages: collision leading to effective contact formation, transfer of DNA, and the processing of the DNA in the recipient cell. The first (Lederberg and Tatum 1946) and much the best-studied transfer system is that mediated by F, and the account that follows is primarily of this system (see also Table 5.1).

Contact formation

Conjugation requires physical contact (Davis 1950); however, a rigorous demonstration of contact has often been omitted in the characterization of conjugative plasmids. As expected from a collision-dependent process, in *E. coli* matings higher yields of progeny are obtained at high cell concentrations, and with motile compared with non-motile cells. However, the probability of successful transfer per collision is highest at low concentrations (when it becomes exceedingly efficient), and it may also be that male cells seek out female cells, following some chemotactic gradient (Collins and Broda 1975). At higher cell densities, mating complexes may be composed of more than two cells (Lederberg 1956; Achtman 1975; Achtman *et al*. 1978b). However, the aggregates that are observed microscopically in mat-

Table 5.1

Conjugation techniques (after Willetts, personal communication). In all, a counterselection against the donor strain, for instance with streptomycin, is necessary.

1. Replica plating: used for screening many clones. Patch colonies with sterile toothpicks onto nutrient plates. Grow for 6 h. Replicate onto selective agar spread with 0.1 ml of a suspension of the recipient strain. This can be from an overnight broth culture, spun and concentrated ×10 in buffer.

2. Cross-streak matings: used for fewer clones than above. Can use overnight broth cultures. Streak a full loop of recipient strain down centre of plate. After it has dried in, cross streak with loopfuls of donor clones.

3. Quantitative liquid mating: grow donor and recipient cultures in broth to about 2×10^8 cells/ml. Mix 1 vol. of donor and 10 vol. recipient in tubes or flasks. Incubate at 37° C for 30 min for plasmid transfer, 90 min for chromosome transfer. Plate dilutions for viable counts of donor, recipient and progeny colonies. Calculate efficiency per donor cell.

4. Qualitative plasmid transfer: use 0.1 ml each of broth overnight cultures of donor and recipient, in 0.8 ml broth. Incubate for 60 min and streak on selective plate.

5. Mobilization of plasmid B by plasmid A. Mix exponentially growing A$^+$ strain (sensitive to phage T6) and overnight culture of B$^+$ strain (resistant to T6). After 40 min incubation, kill donor with T6. After 20 min further incubation, add exponentially growing second recipient strain. After 40 min incubation, plate for second recipient clones that have become B$^+$. If plasmids A and B are easily distinguished, killing with T6 is unnecessary.

In addition, semiautomatic methods have been devised for conjugational tests on large numbers of colonies in parallel (Achtman 1971; Burman and Ostensson 1978).

---

ing mixtures, at least involving Hfr donors, may be largely the result of growth and division, followed by failure to dissociate, rather than being due to accretion of new cells (Broda and Collins 1978). It now seems that specific pair formation does not require active energy metabolism (Curtiss and Stallions 1967).

Pili. Common pili or fimbriae are appendages present in many Gram-positive bacilli; they may be as long as the cell itself (see Ottow 1975, for a review). F$^+$ and Hfr cells of *E. coli* have in addition 'sex pili' or 'F pili' with lengths of about 1–2 μm (Brinton *et al.* 1964; see Tomoeda *et al.* 1975, for a review). The mean number of F pili per cell, taking together data from different strains in exponential growth, was 1.4 for cells grown with aeration and 2.7 without aeration (Curtiss *et al.* 1969). F-pili have a diameter of about 9 nm and an axial groove of about 2.5 nm. They are composed of many molecules of a single protein, pilin, which has a molecular weight of about 10,750 (Helmuth and Achtman 1978). This is a hydrophobic protein lacking arginine, cysteine, histidine and proline, and associated with it are a glucose molecule and two phosphate residues (Brinton 1971). A large pool of unpolymerized pilin exists within the outer membrane of the cell (Beard and Connolly 1975).

There are five lines of evidence for sex pili having a role in conjugation.

(1) They are found in F+ but not F– cells. They are best seen under the electron microscope after absorption of the small male-specific RNA phages Qβ or MS2. These attach to the sides of the sex pilus but not to common pili (see Fig. 5.1).

(2) Such absorption occurs efficiently to cells carrying F-like R factors de-repressed for transfer (i.e. pilus producing), but not in those carrying the corresponding repressed R factors (where the great majority of cells do not carry pili).

(3) All pili-less mutants of donor strains so far examined are transfer-deficient.

(4) Phages that absorb to the pilus tip (Fig. 5.1), such as the small filamentous single-stranded DNA phage f1, prevent mating, whereas Qβ and MS2 (see above) do not.

(5) Mating cells (subsequently demonstrated as such by recovery of recombinant cells by micromanipulation) which move together, but some distance apart, have been observed microscopically (Ou and Anderson 1970). The pilus might provide the invisible connexion. This observation does not necessarily mean that close cell-to-cell contact is not required for transfer, since most mating cells had come close together by the time that transfer could be demonstrated.

Their precise role is not understood. One suggestion is that pili serve as conduction tubes (Brinton 1971). Another is that they bring mating cells together (Curtiss 1969; Marvin and Hohn 1969). Retraction does occur after treatment with cyanide or heat (Novotny and Fives-Taylor 1974; 1978), or infection with phage f1 (Jacobson 1972).

Surface exclusion.   Male cells mate less efficiently with other males than they do with females. This is because of 'surface exclusion', which (see later) is an F-specified function quite distinct from incompatibility (Sheehy *et al.* 1972; LeBlanc and Falkow 1973). An intact mucopeptide layer in the donor cell is necessary for its expression (Beard and Bishop 1975), although intact pili are not. It is no known whether it acts by preventing contact formation, subsequent transfer or both. Surface exclusion is reduced in cells in stationary phase, such as those in vigorously aerated cultures (F– phenocopies: Lederberg *et al.* 1952).

When F– cells are mated with a high mulitiplicity of Hfr cells (but not F+ cells), many are killed ('lethal zygosis'). However, male cells are immune to such killing, owing to another F-specified function, *ilz* (immunity to lethal zygosis), which is genetically distinct from surface exclusion (Skurray *et al.* 1976c). It is possible that the normal function of *ilz* is to effect active disaggregation of F+ and F– cells once F has been transferred into the

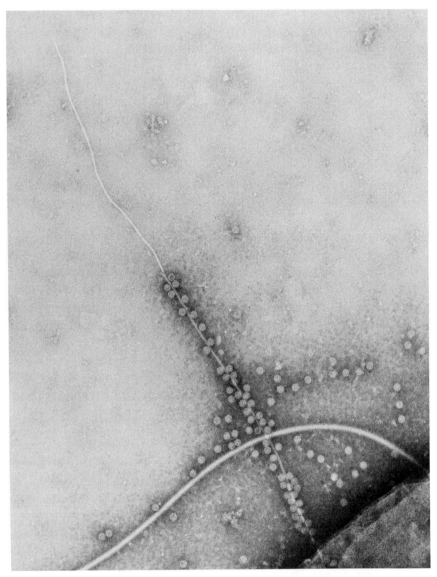

Fig. 5.1. Absorption of male-specific phage MS2 and f1 to the sides and end respectively of sex pili of *E. coli* K-12. A flagellum is also visible. (Photograph provided by courtesy of E. Boy de la Tour and L. Caro.)

recipient. Such disaggregation is reported to occur in matings with F′ but not with Hfr donors (Achtman *et al*. 1978b). If the *ilz* gene is not in the part of F transferred early by Hfr cells such disaggregation would not occur; this might be the explanation for killing by Hfr cells.

Role of the female in contact formation. At least 95 per cent of cells in an F⁻
population can act as recipients (Cullum and Broda 1979b). Mutants of F⁻
strains that are deficient in conjugation (Con⁻) have recently been
described. Such a deficiency has been correlated in different mutants with
the loss of a number of cell envelope functions. These include synthesis of
lipopolysaccharide (Monner *et al.* 1971; Manning and Reeves 1975;
Schweizer and Henning 1977; Achtman *et al.* 1978c), phage absorption and
appearance of protein components (Skurray *et al.* 1974; Achtman *et al.*
1978c), phage absorption (Reiner 1974) and carbohydrate fermentation
(Falkinham and Curtiss 1976). These last authors have divided their mutants according to the step at which transfer is prevented. These are (1) initial
union formation, (2) effective union formation and/or DNA transfer and (3)
stable establishment of the plasmid in the recipient. Strains in this last class
can form recombinants in matings with Hfr strains. Conjugation-deficient
mutants of recipient cells are of great interest to those studying the organization of the cell envelope.

DNA transfer

Contact formation presumably generates a signal for the synthesis or activation of enzymes involved in the transfer of DNA, perhaps including the
nicking of F to provide a linear structure. Since Hfr strains always transfer
from F, with a defined polarity, this opening-up must involve a specific site
on F. Such a site ('*oriT*': Willetts *et al.* 1975) has been mapped genetically
(Willetts 1972), at a different site from the origin of vegetative replication
(see previous chapter). Therefore which F genes are transferred early
depends upon the site at which F integration occurred to give the different
Hfr strains (Guyer and Clark 1977).

A unique strand is transferred. When an Hfr strain that is lysogenic for
phage λ is mated with a non-lysogenic recipient strain the λ DNA is excised
from the donor chromosome that enters the recipient, and multiplies and
kills the recipient cell ('zygotic induction'). Rupp and Ihler (1968) and Ohki
and Tomizawa (1968), who used an F'*gal* carrying a phage λ prophage,
performed such matings with radioactively labelled donor strains and
unlabelled recipient strains, and recovered the λ phage that were eventually
released. In any particular cross only a particular strand of the λ DNA was
radioactive and had therefore come from the donor cell. This was shown
using a method for separating the strands of λ from each other on the basis of
their differential binding to poly(U,G) due to a difference in base composition (Hradecna and Szybalski 1967). Therefore only one strand of the
integrated F and the chromosomal DNA was transferred. Hfr strains trans-

ferring λ from opposite directions transferred complementary labelled strands, indicating that the F strand transferred was always of the same polarity. Since the orientation of λ DNA in the chromosome was already known, it was possible to conclude that the transferred strand had a 5' end rather than a 3' end at its origin. Two R factors, one F-like and the other I-like, also transfer a specific strand (Vapnek *et al*. 1971).

Is replication a necessary concomitant to transfer?   Jacob *et al*. (1963) had proposed that replication is the driving force for transfer. Vegetative replication is not however involved, since *dna*ts mutants that can replicate neither chromosomal nor plasmid DNA vegetatively at 42° C can transfer DNA at this temperature (Bonhoeffer *et al*. 1967; Marinus and Adelberg 1970; Stallions and Curtiss 1971; Vapnek and Rupp 1971; Fenwick and Curtiss 1973; Sarathy and Siddiqi 1973). Nevertheless donor cells normally do synthesize DNA, presumably to replace the single strand being transferred to the recipient cells. DNA polymerase III is required for the synthesis in the recipient of the strands complementary to the single strands of F'*lac* and ColI that are transferred (Wilkins and Hollom 1974).

The question of the mode of replication—whether or not it obeys a rolling circle mechanism (see previous chapter)—is undecided (see, however, Kingsman and Willetts 1978, who present a modified rolling circle model for transfer based on results with F'*lac* plasmids mutant in different transfer functions—see below). The rolling circle model predicts that plasmid DNA will be transferred in longer than monomer sizes. Such moieties have been reported for F (Ohki and Tomizawa 1968; Matsubara 1968), but Fenwick and Curtiss, using R64–11 (1973), Falkow *et al*. (1971) and Boulnois and Wilkins (1978) (ColI) only observed monomers. However, such monomers could still be derived from longer molecules.

The first transferred plasmid DNA detectable as covalently closed circular molecules is bound to the membrane (Falkow *et al*. 1971). The mechanism of circularization is not yet understood. It does not depend upon the *recA* function, since F' factors can be established in *recA*⁻ strains (Clark and Margulies 1965); nor does it need the transfer region (McIntire and Willetts 1978). On the rolling circle model one would envisage a staggered scission, like that creating the 'sticky ends' of phage λ, to provide a means of circularizing.

In chromosome transfer the final step is integration of DNA into the recipient chromosome by recombination. Using a density and radioactivity-labelling protocol Siddiqi and Fox (1973) found that only one incoming strand is integrated, becoming covalently bound to newly replicated recipient DNA. A *dnaB*ts F⁻ strain accumulated single-stranded Hfr DNA when mating was carried out at 42° C. The number of generations that elapse before genetically pure progeny cells emerge depends upon the Hfr strain (Wood 1967).

Genetic analysis of the F transfer system

The genetics of the F transfer system have been analysed using F'*gal* (Ohtsubo 1970; Ohtsubo *et al.* 1970) and F'*lac* (Willetts 1972b; Achtman 1973b). In both analyses mutants were obtained after mutagenesis. Mutant F'*gal* plasmids were also isolated after challenge with male-specific phage, and deletion mutants were obtained by 'transductional shortening' with phage P1, the head of which is too small to carry a complete F'*gal* plasmid (Chapter 3).

The main technical problem was that complementation analysis, to establish whether two mutations fell within the same gene, could not be performed between two F' plasmids cohabiting in a cell, because incompatibility prevents them from coexisting stably. Therefore Ohtsubo *et al.* (1970) made use of the previously demonstrated similarity between the transfer systems of F and R100-1 (which can cohabit) to test for complementation between F mutants and a set of transfer-defective mutants of R100-1 isolated earlier. Achtman and Willetts performed their complementation analysis using transient F'-F' diploids obtained in two different ways:
(1) by infecting cells of a plasmid-carrying strain with a phage P1 lysate grown on the second strain (Willetts and Achtman 1972);
(2) by transferring (by conjugation) one of the amber conditional mutant plasmids that they isolated from cells of a permissive ('Su⁺') strain into cells of an F⁻ phenocopied non-permissive ('Su⁻') strain carrying the other plasmid (Achtman *et al.* 1972).

By such means 13 transfer (*tra*) genes were defined. They were subsequently ordered by deletion mapping (Ohtsubo 1970; Ippen-Ihler *et al.* 1972). More recently some other genes have been described (*traM*: Achtman *et al.* 1978d; *traN*, *traU*, *traV* and *traW*: Miki *et al.* 1978b; *traY*: Willetts and McIntire 1978). Sharp *et al.* (1972) used the heteroduplex method to correlate the genetical and physical maps (Fig. 3.9). All the *tra* genes are contained within the 62–93.2-kilobase region of F (Davidson *et al.* 1975). This is within that region of F shown by Sharp *et al.* (1973) to be homologous with regions of R100-1 and ColV–K94, explaining why R100-1 can complement most F *tra* mutations (Ohtsubo 1970; Willetts 1971). Subsequent work (Skurray *et al.* 1976b; Kennedy *et al.* 1977; Achtman *et al.* 1978d; Willetts and McIntire 1978) using deletion mapping, chimaeras and λ transducing phages carrying parts of the *tra* region, established the location of the *tra* genes more accurately (Fig. 3.9). On the basis of their likely sizes these genes still do not account for all the region's coding capacity. Probably still more genes await discovery, since *in vitro* and in minicells the different chimaeras direct the synthesis of protein species that are not specified by the known *tra* genes (Kennedy *et al*. 1977). Most of these proteins are strongly associated with the cell envelope.

Experiments with polar mutations (Helmuth and Achtman 1975) showed that at least 13 *tra* genes (all those described until then except *traJ* and *traI*: Willetts and McIntire 1978) fell within one large operon, which would code for a messenger RNA molecule of about 7×10^6 daltons. Just the transcription of such a messenger might take about 6 min, so that synthesis of all the transfer proteins *de novo* would take even longer.

Mutations in any of eight contiguous genes (*traJ* to *traH*, and, oddly, part only of *traG*), resulted in the absence of pili and consequent resistance to male-specific phages. These genes are therefore presumably involved in the synthesis or positioning of the pili. Why so many genes are needed is not understood, since pilin itself is the product of the *traA* gene alone (Minkley *et al*.1976). Functions have also been proposed for some other *tra* genes. Reeves and Willetts (1974) tested a number of plasmids for their ability to effect the transfer of deleted derivatives of F'*lac* from its transfer origin. ColV2 and ColVB*trp* could initiate such transfer, but R100-1,R1-19 and R538-1 could not. Since the former but not the latter plasmids could also supply a function that could act in lieu of the F'*lac traI* function, it was suggested that the origin of transfer is the site of action of the *traI* function, which would then be an endonuclease. This origin has been mapped by genetical methods and termed *oriT* by Willetts (1972a). *traM*, which maps at the other end of the *tra* region, near *traJ*, gives a similar phenotype to *traI* (Willetts and Maule 1979).

Among the deletion mutants of F'*lac* were some which had lost the surface exclusion function. The genes responsible for this function, *traS* and *traT*, map within the *tra* operon (Fig. 3.9; Willetts 1974a; Achtman *et al*. 1977) although surface exclusion is not essential for transfer, as point mutants in *traS* are transfer-proficient (Helmuth and Achtman 1975). An outer membrane protein associated with the expression of surface exclusion by the *traT* gene has now been identified (Minkley and Ippen-Ihler 1977; Achtman *et al*. 1977).

Regulation of tra *expression.* There are two levels at which the transfer functions of the F-like plasmids are controlled. *traJ* provides a positive control for the expression of the *tra* operon, and *traJ* expression itself is under the (negative) control of the *finOP* system (Fig. 5.2). The initial evidence for these controls was genetic, but it is now supported by evidence

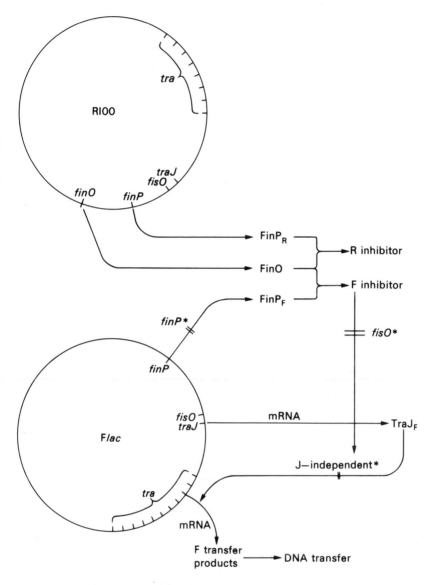

Fig. 5.2. A model for the regulation of F transfer (Finnegan and Willetts, 1973; Willetts, personal communication). The R factor FinO product and the F factor FinP$_F$ products interact to form the F transfer inhibitor. This acts to prevent the synthesis of the product (TraJ$_F$ of the F gene *traJ*) the absence of which in turn prevents the synthesis of all the transfer operon gene products. The operator for *traJ* (formerly *traO*) is now termed *fisO*; *finO* was previously *fin* and *finP* was previously *traP*. F mutations which relieve transfer inhibition are asterisked. An analogous scheme for inhibition of R100 is not shown.

from *in vitro* studies using λ phages carrying portions of the *tra* region (Willetts 1977b).

(1) In *traJ* strains messenger RNA for the other *tra* functions (i.e., those in the major *tra* operon) is not produced (Finnegan and Willetts 1973; Willetts 1977b). The isolation of J-independent mutants, which transfer at low levels in the absence of the *traJ* product, shows that this control can be by-passed (Achtman 1973a).

(2) In populations of strains carrying other F-like plasmids, such as R100, only a minority of the cells are (transiently) competent donors (Broda 1975). However, all cells in populations of strains carrying 'derepressed' mutants, such as R100-1 from R100 and R1-19 from R1, are competent donors. F is unusual among plasmids in being naturally 'derepressed'. However, in cells carrying both F and R100, R100 also inhibits F fertility. The molecular basis of such 'fertility inhibition' is the prevention of *traJ* transcription by the products of two further R100 genes, *finO* and *finP*, which map close to *traJ* (Willetts 1977b). F also has a functional *finP* gene (Fig. 3.9) but no demonstrable *finO* gene. The majority of F-type plasmids possess interchangeable *finO* products; F fertility can be inhibited by fi^+ plasmids because these act on the F *traJ* gene. In contrast the *finP* product is more plasmid-specific, so that the only plasmid so far known to inhibit the fertility of $F'lac^+finP^-$ plasmids is ColV2. Even the *finP* products of the very closely related plasmids R100 and R1 (see Chapter 2) are not interchangeable.

Fertility inhibition has been used as a means of classifying plasmids in enterobacteria. Those that inhibit F fertility (fi^+ plasmids) are presumed to have F-related transfer systems (see Meynell *et al*. 1968, for a review). But it now appears that at least one group of plasmids that inhibit F fertility do so by a different mechanism from that of R100 (Gasson and Willetts 1976).

Plasmid spread through populations

When a ColI$^+$ strain was incubated overnight with a recipient strain, there were two main effects: first, the plasmid spread through the recipient population in an 'epidemic' fashion, and second, although only about 0.02 per cent of the original ColI$^+$ strains were competent donors, under optimum conditions most of the newly ColI$^+$ cells, when challenged with fresh recipient cells, were competent (Ozeki *et al*. 1962; Stocker *et al*. 1963). Such a preparation is termed an HFCT ('for high-frequency colicinogeny transfer') culture. However on growth in the absence of such recipient cells competence returned to the original level within seven generations. Therefore transfer is generally due to a physiological escape from repression, rather than a mutational event. Apparently those few plasmids that are initially transferred from cells of a repressed culture can then re-transfer before their own repression mechanisms can take effect (Willetts 1974b; Cullum *et al.* 1978b). The analysis of such systems is complex, since they involve rounds of both primary transfer and re-transfer from newly formed donors, and also growth which, by changing cell densities, will affect cell physiology and the frequency of encounters between cells.

The progress of spread (once transfer has started) is similar for R100 and R100-1 (and F'*lac*), so that the *finOP* system seems to have no role in this process. Further, the kinetics are similar for the I-like plasmid R64 and its derepressed derivative R64-11 (Cullum *et al.* 1978b). There are two main constraints upon 'epidemic spread' of these plasmids. After the initial transfer from virgin donors to virgin recipient cells, subsequent rounds of transfer can only occur at about 30-min intervals, during active exponential growth, and less frequently in slowly growing cultures. In addition, it takes about 60–90 min for the descendants of newly infected cells to become proficient donors. Therefore in mixed cultures progeny do not increase dramatically more rapidly than does the total viable count (Cullum *et al.* 1978a, b; Fig. 5.3).

Viewed in population terms the control of transfer in a plasmid-containing population is biologically very efficient. Repression has the effect that most cells in a population do not make pili and other transfer proteins. This is economical and they are then not susceptible to phages that absorb to pili. However, the few cells that at any time are competent can set off the transfer process once a receptive recipient population has been encountered. This process can proceed unimpeded by the *finOP* system, because this takes some time to take effect within newly infected cells.

Plasmid mobilization by other plasmids.   All the small plasmids of *E. coli* are non-autotransmissible; the smallest known transmissible plasmid, a derivative of R6K (Crosa *et al.* 1975), has a size of 17 megadaltons. This suggests that all transfer systems require a relatively large number of genes. Of the smaller plasmids many can be transferred by other plasmids. Thus F can mediate ColE1 transfer. With the others, the possibility always exists that a mobilizing plasmid will be discovered. All of a number of F*tra* functions are required for ColE1 mobilization, with the exception of *traI* (Willetts 1971). If *traI* is an endonuclease (see earlier), this could mean that ColE1 provides its own nicking function to provide a leading end for transfer. Consonant with this, the presence of ColE1 in the same cell results in the transfer of transfer-deficient and relaxation-deficient ColE1 mutants (Inselburg 1977b), presumably by providing a diffusible product that acts upon a site which is probably the relaxation site (Warren *et al.* 1978). There

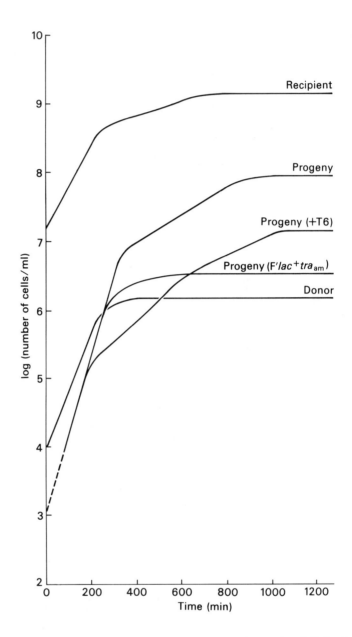

Fig. 5.3. Spread of F'*lac* and an amber-conditional transfer-deficient mutant F'*lac* through a recipient population. The donor strain was permissive and sensitive to phage T6. The recipient strain was non-permissive and T6-resistant. After the first hour, T6 was added to half of each culture. (Adapted from Cullum *et al.* 1978b.)

are DNA sequence data that suggest that F and ColE1 have related sequences that could provide recognition sites for nicking enzymes (R. Thompson, personal communication).

Another case of mobilization is of A and S by $\varDelta$ (Anderson 1969 and Chapter 2). It is unlikely that in such cases the replicons become physically associated during transfer, since F mutants unable to transfer themselves can mobilize ColE1 and also CloDF13 (van de Pol *et al*. 1978). However, Olsen (1978) has described a case in which mobilization was greatly enhanced when there was homology (in the form of a common transposon) between two plasmids.

Chromosome transfer

F⁺ strains. The mobilization of the *E. coli* K-12 chromosome by F is a further case of transfer of one replicon by another. At least some of the low level of fertility of F⁺ strains for all chromosomal markers is due to Hfr clones arising in the population (Jacob and Wollman 1956), but other authors (Broda 1967; Curtiss and Renshaw 1969a, b and Curtiss and Stallions 1969) have suggested that such clones cannot account for all the fertility observed; there may also be more transient interactions. Thus Hayes (1952) found that F⁺ strains had an enhanced fertility after ultraviolet irradiation, but that this enhancement was very rapidly lost on growth. It was suggested (Evenchik *et al*. 1969) that in the repair of ultraviolet damage the chromosome and F become associated in a few of the cells, to yield Hfr-like chromosomes that can be transferred but cannot be replicated, so that the cells are inviable. Another possibility is that an F product nicks at chromosomal loci rather than at the F *ori* site, and that transfer can be effected without any covalent linkage between the two replicons. Many other plasmids can effect chromosomal transfer in different bacteria (Levinthal 1974; Holloway 1979). Such plasmids are referred to generically as 'sex factors'. However, it is not known whether chromosome transfer is important in nature.

Hfr transfer. Hfr transfer is regarded as F self-transfer, in which the bacterial chromosome is inserted into F. Its special interest lies in its continuing use as a probe for chromosome structure (see Bachmann *et al*. 1976) and as a tool in many experiments in molecular genetics. The process was analysed in most detail by Jacob and Wollman (1958). Their experiments were of two kinds.

(1) If Hfr and F⁻ strains are mixed, and samples plated at intervals on different selective media, the yields of the different recombinant classes increase with time until a plateau is reached. Since this time was similar for

the curves for the different markers, it was thought to represent the time required before all those cells that are competent to mate had formed mating pairs. The final yields of recombinants for the different markers depended upon which Hfr strains were used. The mode of transfer became clearer through the second type of cross.

(2) Here samples from the cross were taken at intervals, and mating was interrupted by killing the donor strain with phage T6, to which it, but not the recipient strain, was sensitive, or by shearing apart mating complexes by agitation.

Those markers that in given crosses in (1) were transferred with the highest frequency were in (2) transferred after the shortest mating times. Each marker had a characteristic 'time of entry' (the time at which the marker started to enter the recipient cell). At later times more progeny are formed, until, as in the other type of cross, a plateau is reached, indicating that all competent donors had transferred that region of the chromosome. However, in this type of experiment, the plateau is reached at a different time for each marker.

Each type of cross can be used to construct a genetic map. The differences in time of entry and yield for different markers are both consequences of the fact that DNA transfer proceeds from a fixed origin within the sex factor (see earlier) until perhaps the DNA strand is broken (either spontaneously or by the experimentalist), so that those regions closest to the inserted F will be transferred most efficiently. Only when the whole chromosome is transferred (which happens from only about 0.01 per cent of the donor cells) is the remaining portion of F transferred. Only then can the progeny become Hfr.

Other conjugation systems

F-like plasmids.   A number of plasmids, belonging to several incompatibility groups, have related transfer systems to that of F. The same phages can absorb to their pili, albeit at different efficiencies, but the other components of their transfer systems are related in a complex way (Table 5.2). The best-studied examples of these plasmids are R100-1 and R6-5. There is both genetic (Ohtsubo *et al.* 1970; Willetts 1971; Foster and Willetts 1977; Achtman *et al.* 1978a) and physical (Sharp *et al.* 1973) evidence that their transfer systems are closely related to that of F.

Other transmissible plasmids in E. coli.   Transmissible plasmids have been assigned to about 20 incompatibility groups (Chapter 3). However, very little is known of the transfer systems of most of them. Since many of these plasmids have no common DNA sequences with F, it will be interesting to know how different their transfer systems turn out to be functionally. Those

Table 5.2
Relationships of different transfer systems of F-related plasmids (after Gasson and Willetts 1975; Willetts and Maule 1974; Willetts 1977a and personal communication). Labelling as groups 1–5 is on a separate arbitrary basis for each column.

Plasmid	Incompatibility group	oriT	Surface exclusion	Pili	finP
F	1	1	1	1	1
V2	1	1	2	1	1
R1	2	3	3	3	3
R100	2	4	4	4	4
R136	2	4	4	4	4
R538–1	2	3	2	1	5
ColB2	2	1	2	2	2
ColB4	2 or 3	3	2	5	5
ColVBtrp	4	1	3	1	2
R124	4	1	2	1	2

that can exist in *E. coli*, that have been investigated, include members of the I, N, P and S groups (see Willetts 1977a, for review). All except R6K are plasmids present in a small number of copies. Some phages can absorb to both N and P group donor strains (which may be correlated with some homology between the DNAs of these plasmids, see Chapter 2). Further cases of interactions between the transfer systems of plasmids belonging to different incompatibility groups have been reported, for instance by Pinney and Smith (1974) and Gasson and Willetts (1975; 1976; 1977), but these are probably exceptions rather than the rule. Thus, when an F-like and an I-like plasmid are present in the same cell, each specifies its own type of pilus (Lawn *et al*. 1971); there is no transfer inhibition between plasmids (Lawn *et al*. 1967; Romero *et al*. 1969); and no complementation occurs between transfer-defective mutants (Willetts 1970; Cooke *et al*. 1970). Therefore, the existence of pili, of single-stranded transfer by R64-11 as by F (Vapnek *et al*. 1971), and of surface exclusion (e.g., Fenwick and Curtiss 1973) and transfer inhibition systems in more than one plasmid-type may well be examples of convergent evolution. It is noteworthy that neither pili nor transfer inhibition are apparently essential components of transfer systems (Brodt *et al*. 1974).

Conjugation in some other groups of bacteria. The transmissible plasmids from *Pseudomonas aeruginosa* are of two types from the point of view of transfer (see Chandler and Krishnapillai 1974a, b). Some (e.g., RP1) can transfer widely among Gram-negative bacteria, whereas others (e.g.,

R91) are apparently confined to *Ps. aeruginosa*. But it is not yet known whether the difference in host range between the two classes of plasmid depends upon the transfer or the replication systems. Mutant plasmids de-repressed for transfer have now been isolated in *Ps. aeruginosa* (Chandler and Krishnapillai 1977). Plasmid-specified pili and phage receptors, and the corresponding phages, have been described for a number of classes of R factors in *Ps. aeruginosa* (Bradley 1977; Olsen *et al*. 1977). There have also been a number of reports of inhibition of transfer of one plasmid by another (Sagai *et al*. 1977). Plasmid RP1 and its relations and their derivatives are proving valuable for generating sexual systems for genetic analysis in a wide range of Gram-negative bacteria (see, for instance, Sistrom 1977; Mylroie *et al*. 1977; Beringer *et al*. 1978; Haas and Holloway 1978; Holloway 1978, 1979; Barth 1979). Genetic analysis of RP4 using the transposon Tn7 shows that its transfer system is composed of at least five genes (Barth *et al*. 1978).

Recently there have been the first reports of conjugational systems in Gram-positive bacteria (*Streptococcus faecalis*: Jacob and Hobbs 1974; Jacob *et al*. 1975; Dunny and Clewell 1975; oral streptococci: LeBlanc *et al*. 1978; and group B streptococci: Hershfield 1979). Recipient cells of *Strep. faecalis* produce a sex hormone, probably a protein, that causes certain donor strains to aggregate with them (Dunny *et al*. 1978). Also a conjugation system has been studied in *Streptomyces* (Hopwood *et al*. 1973, and Chapter 6).

Barriers to conjugation. There are a number of barriers to successful transfer between bacteria. In some cases the strains may be unable to make contact, as often, presumably, between unrelated strains. Surface exclusion has already been discussed. It is also not clear that the conditions used for study correspond to natural or optimum conditions. Thus, Burman (1977) observed that anaerobiosis (such as obtains in the intestine) had greatly differing effects on the fertility of different plasmids, relative to those observed under aerobic conditions. In one case (R1) this was depressed ten-thousandfold, while in others it was unaffected.

Once inside the recipient cell, DNA may be subject to restriction enzymes. Also, it must either be able to replicate as a plasmid or be integrated into the host chromosome. In the former case it must be able to make use of the replication machinery of the cell or provide its own, and not disrupt the host cell unduly, for instance by over-replicating. It must also be compatible with any plasmids that are already present, or else be able to displace them.

While it is clear that plasmids have been a major agent of gene exchange and therefore evolution in bacteria, it also seems that mechanisms making for genetic isolation between bacterial populations have also been important and successful.

Summary
All known conjugation systems in bacteria are plasmid-determined. The related plasmids F and R100 in *E. coli* provide the models for transfer. It here depends upon at least 20 genes, which specify the pilus, enzymes that effect DNA transfer proper, and control at two levels. This complexity allows metabolism connected with transfer to be repressed unless recipients are available, when transfer through the recipient population can occur free of these constraints. Other plasmids have transfer systems unrelated to that of F. It is unknown to what extent unrelated systems share common mechanisms.

6
Plasmids in Human and Veterinary Medicine

Bacterial infection has always been a major cause of disease in humans and animals. Some of the classic disease-causing bacteria (see Table 6.1) have become less important through improved hygiene and the use of antibacterial drugs. Others remain important, and still other organisms have recently become more important. An increasing proportion of infections are caused by Gram-negative rather than Gram-positive bacteria (Finland 1960). Among the newer pathogens are the 'opportunists' such as *Pseudomonas aeruginosa* and strains of *Serratia* and *Proteus*, which infect people who are particularly 'at risk' (see p. 113).

When antibiotics were first introduced they were extremely effective in killing bacteria of sensitive species. However, many thousands of drug-resistant strains have been isolated in many groups of bacteria. For most pathogens, effective antibiotics are still available, but the situation is continually changing (Finland 1970). For example, the strains of *Staph. aureus* causing hospital wound infections in the 1940s were initially sensitive to penicillin, but after a year or two penicillin-resistant strains emerged and became common. Drug resistance emerged fairly rapidly to each new antibiotic that was introduced thereafter, e.g., streptomycin, tetracycline, chloramphenicol, erythromycin. Multiply-resistant strains of *Staph. aureus* were a major cause for concern during the 1950s. Plasmids were later shown to be responsible for at least part of this resistance. Fortunately, resistance did not emerge as rapidly to the cloxacillins, and staphylococcal infections were brought under control again in the 1960s. Cloxacillin resistance is now causing problems in some areas, but several other effective antistaphylococcal agents are now available.

A similar picture was seen with *E. coli* and other Gram-negative bacilli, with the progressive selection of strains resistant to sulphonamides, ampicillin, streptomycin, tetracycline, etc. This trend still continues and many problems today are caused by strains of Gram-negative bacilli that have now

Table 6.1
Some pathogenic bacteria of humans, referred to in the text. Cruick-shank *et al.* (1974) and Davis *et al.* (1973) are examples of standard textbooks of medical microbiology in which the full range of clinically important bacteria are described.

Organism	Common pathogenic role
Gram-negative bacilli	
Enterobacteriaceae	
Escherichia coli	Gut commensal;
	Urinary tract infections; infantile enteritis; neonatal meningitis; septicaemia
Shigella spp.	Bacillary dysentery
Salmonella typhimurium and other food-poisoning salmonellae	Food poisoning
Salmonella typhi	Typhoid fever
Proteus spp.	Gut commensals;
	Urinary tract infections
Klebsiella spp.	Gut commensals;
	Urinary tract infections; pneumonia
Serratia spp.	Opportunist pathogens
Pseudomonas aeruginosa	Occasional gut commensal;
	Infection of burns, urinary tract infections, opportunist pathogen
Vibrio cholerae	Cholera
Haemophilus influenzae	Chronic bronchitis, bronchopneumonia, meningitis.
Bacteroides fragilis	Anaerobic gut commensal;
	Post-operative wound infection
Gram-negative cocci	
Neisseria gonorrhoeae	Gonorrhoea
Neisseria meningitidis	Meningitis
Gram-positive cocci	
Staphylococcus aureus	Boils, post operative wound infections, infection of burns
Streptococcus pyogenes	Tonsillitis, wound infections, skin infections glomerulo-nephritis, rheumatic fever
Streptococcus faecalis	Gut commensal; urinary tract infection, sub-acute bacterial endocarditis
Streptococcus viridans	Throat commensal
	Dental abscess; sub-acute bacterial endocarditis
Streptococcus pneumoniae	Pneumonia, meningitis

acquired resistance to such important antibiotics as gentamicin and carbenicillin; this is a particular problem with *Pseudomonas aeruginosa*, which
is naturally resistant to most of the older antibiotics. At present such resistance is relatively uncommon, but if it became more frequent it would create
serious problems in the treatment of hospital infections.

Enterobacteria and the gut
The intestine contains many species of commensal bacteria (for a review, see
Savage 1977). Most individuals are members of the anaerobic groups *Bacteroides* and bifidobacteria. *E. coli*, the predominant aerobe, constitutes
only about 1 per cent of the total bacterial population in faeces (Table 6.2).
The control of the numbers of intestinal *E. coli* appears to be predominantly
due to such anaerobes.

Table 6.2
**The bacterial flora of faeces of healthy English subjects (after Hill
et al. 1971). +,−: Gram-positive, Gram-negative.**

Bacterial group	Gram reaction and shape	Mean number of cells per gm of faeces
Anaerobes		
Bacteroides spp.	− bacilli	6.3×10^9
Bifidobacteria	+ bacilli	6.3×10^9
Lactobacillus spp.	+ bacilli	3.2×10^6
Clostridium spp.	+ bacilli	1×10^5
Veillonella spp.	− cocci	1.6×10^4
Aerobes		
Enterobacteria	− bacilli	8×10^7
Bacillus spp.	+ bacilli	5×10^3
Streptococcus spp.	+ cocci	1.3×10^7
Enterococci	+ cocci	6.3×10^5
Total anaerobes		1.3×10^{10}
Total aerobes		1×10^8

A variety of enterobacteria may be pathogenic in the human gut.
(1) Most strains of *E. coli* are harmless commensals in the gut of man and
    animals, but a few are now recognized to be enteropathogenic (see later),
    causing traveller's diarrhoea or acute diarrhoeal illness in infants. Other
    strains are implicated in similar diseases of young animals, e.g., piglets and
    calves.
(2) Shigellae cause dysentery by invading the mucosa of the large gut.
    Sh. sonnei dysentery is the commonest form in Britain; it is often not
    very serious and usually does not need treatment with antibiotics.

Shigella infections are confined to humans and associated with poor hygiene.

(3) Food poisoning salmonellae, e.g., *Salm. typhimurium* invade the mucosa of the small gut of animals and man. Infections of man are often due to inadequate cooking of contaminated food.

(4) *Salm. typhi* is the causative agent of typhoid fever in man. The organism may contaminate water supplies in areas with poor sanitation. It passes from the gut into the blood and causes severe generalized illness.

(5) Although strains of *Proteus* and *Klebsiella* are harmless in the gut, they can cause urinary tract infections. They can also be opportunist pathogens causing, for instance, infections in individuals with impaired defence mechanisms.

The classification of enterobacteria and their plasmids. To understand the work on enteric bacteria, we must first consider how the strains and the R plasmids they carry have been analysed. Such work has been vital for the tracing of the original sources and spread of outbreaks of infection and resistance.

The identification in the diagnostic laboratory of different genera of the *Enterobacteriaceae* is done on the basis of biochemical tests such as the ability to ferment lactose, glucose and sucrose, and of other characteristics such as motility. *E. coli* (much the commonest *Escherichia* species) are lactose-fermenting organisms that grow on bile-containing media such as MacConkey's agar. Subdivision into 'strains' for *E. coli* (see Ørskov *et al.* 1977, for a review) is done by serology. The serotypes are based on somatic (O), flagellar (H) and capsular (K) antigens. About 150 O-serotypes of *E. coli* are known.

Shigellae are non-motile, non-lactose-fermenting organisms that do not produce gas when fermenting glucose. They are classified into four species on the basis of their O antigens. For epidemiological purposes they may be further subdivided on the basis of their sensitivity to a series of colicins.

Salmonellae are motile non-lactose-fermenting organisms that may be subdivided serologically into species on the basis of O and H antigens. More than one antigen of each class may be present in salmonellae and the pattern of these antigens allows classification into about 1,000 species generally named after the place of first isolation, e.g., *Salm. dublin*; *Salm. panama*. Some species are very common. For instance, *Salm. typhimurium* causes about half of all *Salmonella* food poisoning in Britain. Therefore further classification of this species is necessary for epidemiological purposes; this classification is based on the pattern of sensitivity to a range of virulent bacteriophages. This pattern depends primarily on the different receptors for the phages themselves, but in some cases also reflects host-controlled restriction systems (see Chapter 3). Strains of *Salm. typhi* are also characterized by phage typing.

Such detailed classification of a given organism is generally done in a few reference laboratories only. At some of these a large number of R factors from all over the world are also studied. A list of the properties that have been used to characterize R factors in one leading laboratory (the Enteric Reference Laboratory in London) is given in Table 6.3. Of these, incompatibility is one of the most important because, as discussed in Chapters 3 and 4, classification of R factors in Gram-negative bacteria is based primarily upon this criterion. We may note in passing that at present there is some correlation between the incompatibility group of a given R factor and the species of its host strain. It may therefore be that, although plasmids are often transmissible, many are best adapted to a particular host.

Table 6.3
Possible tests in the characterization of plasmids of newly isolated, drug-resistant strains (after Anderson and Threlfall 1974).

1. Resistances of wild host strain.
2. Resistances conferred upon a standard recipient strain.
3. Degrees of drug resistance conferred.
4. Number of plasmids that together carry these resistances.
5. Whether the transfer factor and the resistance determinant are on the same plasmid.
6. Kinetics of transfer to a recipient strain.
7. Whether non-autotransmissible plasmids are mobilized by a standard transfer factor.
8. Whether the host strain can now support the growth of donor-specific phages ($\mu2$ for F-like pili and If1 for I-like pili).
9. Whether Fi$^+$; that is, whether it inhibits the fertility of F.
10. Incompatibility group.
11. Presence and identity of colicinogeny, using *E.coli* K-12 as the indicator strain.
12. Whether it restricts phage previously able to lyse the cell.
13. Molecular characterization: size, homology with other plasmids.

The rise and fall of Salmonella typhimurium *type 29.* *Salm. typhimurium* and the other food-poisoning salmonellae can infect cattle and other farm animals as well as man. Epidemics may therefore have both human and veterinary aspects that must be considered together. An excellent example is that of *Salm. typhimurium* type 29 (Anderson 1968; 1969).

Until about 1960, type 29 was an uncommon strain. At that time, no isolates were drug-resistant, but in the following years there was an increase in the proportion of *Salmonella* infections in calves in Britain that were due to strains of this type, and also in the number of drug resistances that were carried by these strains. Resistances to streptomycin and sulphonamide (which are due to different mechanisms, but are generally found together) appeared in type 29 in 1963 (Fig. 6.1), tetracycline resistance first appeared

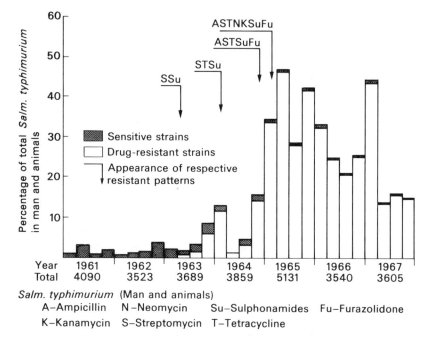

Fig. 6.1. Type 29 as a percentage of total isolations of *Salmonella typhimurium* from man and animals, from 1961 to 1967. (From Anderson 1969, with permission of author and publisher.)

in January, 1964, to be followed successively by resistance to ampicillin, furazolidone and kanamycin–neomycin over the next 18 months. This succession correlates with the sequence in which these drugs started to be used in the affected calves. A few type 29 strains finally appeared that were resistant to all these drugs. Furazolidone resistance was chromosomally borne, but the other resistances were carried on plasmids. Although there were many cases of human infection with these organisms, they could generally be traced to bovine sources. One piece of evidence for this was the resistance to furazolidone, a drug used only in veterinary practice.

The cause of this outbreak was the adoption of intensive rearing practices with calves, which started in about 1962 and had become very important by 1965. The animals were handled with little respect for their physical condition or for hygiene. Antibiotics are widely prescribed for the treatment of infections in farm animals. One of the main differences between veterinary and medical practice is a tendency for treatment of a population of animals rather than an individual human patient. Sometimes such a population is treated in the hope that the infected animals will be cured and infection of the others will be prevented. In other circumstances, farmers are accustomed to administer low doses of antibiotics to a whole population of animals that are judged to be under stress and therefore particularly liable to develop infection.

It was in this context that when type 29 infection gained access to intensive breeding units it spread rapidly. Infected animals were distributed widely through markets and dealers, and type 29 strains spread to farms throughout Britain. There is evidence that there was a single primary source of this infection. Shortly after its removal, the incidence of type 29 strains declined rapidly, and it has not subsequently been a major problem.

A number of conclusions could be drawn from these studies. With time, and the continued use of antibiotics, resistant bacteria appear, become more widespread, and carry more resistances. Under challenge, those cells that are already R^+ or to which R factors can be transferred can survive and drug-sensitive members of the intestinal flora will be reduced. If the pathogen is already resistant, this makes a bad situation worse. Commensal organisms such as *E. coli* that already carry R factors can form a reservoir from which an incoming pathogen which may not be R^+ can acquire drug-resistances (see later). Thus in the epidemic due to *Salm. typhimurium* type 29, *E. coli* strains carrying the same R factors were also isolated from the affected animals. It was evident in this case that the reservoirs of infectious and resistant *Salm. typhimurium* type 29 bacteria were common to animals and humans.

It might be noted here that it was once thought possible that the R factors carried might determine the phage typing pattern, and that the type 29 strains might be of mixed origin. Although such a case has since been documented (van Embden *et al.* 1976), the type 29 outbreak was one of a classic epidemic in which members of a single clone progressively acquired a series of resistance determinants.

Chloramphenicol-resistant typhoid bacilli. Chloramphenicol has for long been the fastest acting and most effective drug for the treatment of typhoid fever and is widely used in this serious infection, even though toxic and occasionally lethal side effects may occur. Although *Salm. typhi* is often sensitive to ampicillin *in vitro*, it is much less effective clinically. In the absence of antibiotic therapy the mortality rate from typhoid fever is usually about 10 per cent whereas chloramphenicol can reduce this rate to less than 1 per cent. There are few satisfactory substitutes, although cotrimoxazole (sulphonamide and trimethoprim) has proved effective and recent penicillin derivatives may be considerably better than ampicillin. In 1972 and 1973 there was an outbreak of typhoid fever in Mexico, involving over 10,000 cases. All isolates of the *Salm. typhi* strain responsible that were investigated carried R factors of a new incompatibility group (H) and conferred resistance to chloramphenicol and also to streptomycin, sulphonamide and tetracycline. At about the same time other outbreaks involving chloramphenicol-resistant strains occurred in South India, South Vietnam and Thailand. In Mexico and India single (but different) clones seemed to be involved, but in the other countries several independent clones were implicated (Table 6.4). However, in all cases, the R factors belonged to the H incompatibility group and had similar resistances (see also Table 3.4). Anderson (1975a) proposed that each pathogenic strain acquired its R factor as a unique event, probably from a non-pathogenic intestinal organism like *E. coli* in which such R factors, specifying chloramphenicol resistance, might have been already present in the areas concerned. He points out that in the affected countries there are no restrictions in the sale of antibiotics, so that they can be purchased by the general public directly from pharmacists. This presumably led to gross overuse of antibiotics. It seems clear that such catastrophes can only be avoided by a more rational and conservative use of antibiotics, applied on a world-wide scale, so as to reduce the overall incidence of R factors.

Table 6.4
Analysis of chloramphenicol-resistant *Salm. typhi* strains (after Anderson 1975a). Strains were classified by phage typing. All R plasmids belonged to the H1 incompatibility group.[1]

Country of origin	Year of isolation	Number of isolates tested	Minimum number of different strains	Drug resistances
Mexico	1972	8	1	CmSmSuTc
India	1972	26	1	..
S. Vietnam	1972–4	71	at least 5	.. , CmSmSu (1 isolate)
Thailand	1973–4	18	3	.. , ApCmSmSuTc (5 isolates)

[1] Further studies on the extent of variation among H1 plasmids are reported in H. W. Smith *et al*. 1978.

The ecology of *E. coli* and its R factors

Normally, in healthy humans, one or a few *E. coli* serotypes will predominate at one time. Some serotypes will persist for a number of months or even years before giving way to others. Others occur more transiently (Hartley *et al*. 1977). The ability of particular strains to colonize the intestine may depend in part upon the details of their surface structure. Studies such as those of Richmond, Linton and their associates (summarized in Linton 1977) have also shown that particular *E. coli* strains move within and between human and animal populations. Some of the principal conclusions from such studies are the following.

(1) In adult cattle *E. coli* are not regularly present in faeces (Howe *et al*. 1976a). However, in veal calves, other animals and man large numbers of *E. coli* occur regularly. In calves this is due at least in part to rearing on a diet that encourages a high proportion of coliforms in the gut flora.

(2) *E. coli* from humans fall into a similar range of O-types as do those from pigs, poultry and calves. It is therefore likely that these form a common pool, with exchange (Hartley *et al*. 1975; Howe and Linton 1976).

(3) Beef, veal and pork often show substantial contamination with *E. coli* from the animal's intestine, and those of others slaughtered at the same time. This is a possible route for the transfer to man (Howe *et al*. 1976b; Linton *et al*. 1976).

(4) Significant numbers of *E. coli* reach the kitchen from chicken carcasses, especially those that are frozen. Because the thawed fluid contains bacteria and is handled, some bacteria can be ingested and subsequently established in the human gut (Linton *et al*. 1977a, b). Inadequate thawing and cooking may also result in some live bacteria being ingested.

The ecology of R factors in *E. coli* strains has also been documented. Among cattle and sheep maintained outdoors no R^+ coliforms are found. They are also only present as a very small proportion of the total *E. coli* population in most healthy humans who have not received antibiotics. However, it seems clear that antibiotic usage in man and in animals (usually by the addition of drugs to feed) has selected for bacteria carrying R plasmids. Thus:

(1) With calves, pigs and poultry in particular, most *E. coli* cells are resistant at least to sulphonamides, and many are also resistant to ampicillin, streptomycin and tetracycline (Linton *et al*. 1976; Linton *et al*. 1977b). Individual animals generally carry a variety of R^+ O-serotypes. Even those pigs and calves reared by intensive methods that do not receive medicated diets have antibiotic-resistant organisms in surprisingly high numbers (Table 6.5).

Table 6.5
Reservoirs of resistant *E.coli* in faeces from farm animals and man in Britain. The antibiotics tested were sulphonamides, streptomycin, tetracycline, ampicillin, chloramphenicol, neomycin and furazolidone. Adapted from Linton 1977.

Host	Source	%resistant E. coli	Mean number of resistances[1]
Sheep	abattoir	0	–
Cattle	farm	0	–
Calves	farm	38	2.8
Pigs	farm	49	2.0
Poultry	farm	83	1.9
Man	non-hospital	9	2.1

[1] Among those clones isolated as being resistant to at least one drug.

(2) There is a common pool of R factors in the commensal *E. coli* of man and animals (Anderson *et al*. 1975). This is also implied in the work of Levy *et al*. (1976a, b) on chickens and chicken farmers, and of Linton *et al*. (1977a, b) on the handling of chicken carcasses.
(3) Certain O-serotypes in human faeces are more likely to carry R factors than others (Hartley and Richmond 1975; Hartley *et al*. 1975; Petrocheilou and Richmond 1976). Many people carry large populations of R⁺ *E. coli* in their gut for long periods without apparent ill effects. Their persistence in the absence of obvious selection pressure seems to depend more on the nature of the strain (that is, its O-type) than on the plasmid carried. At present R plasmids are relatively rare among those coliforms that colonize the human gut most successfully.

Antibiotic therapy must increase the opportunities not only for person-to-person and animal-to-person spread of infection by resistant organisms, but also the dissemination of R plasmids. At present, resistant bacteria tend to disappear from man when a course of antibiotic treatment ends (see for instance Aserkoff and Bennett 1969; Price and Sleigh 1970). However, this situation could change dramatically if R plasmids became more prevalent among the most effective colonizers of the human gut (Hartley and Richmond 1975). This may already have happened in pigs (Smith 1975b). In the four years (1971–1975) after the practice of feeding tetracycline to pigs to promote growth was prohibited in Britain the total proportion of tetracycline-resistant *E. coli* in the pig population might have decreased slightly, but in the same period the proportion of pigs excreting resistant organisms rose from about 93 per cent to 100 per cent. Smith suggests that resistant strains have emerged that are now able to compete on equal terms with sensitive strains. It should however be noted that the total amounts of tetracycline and other antibiotics administered to livestock may not have changed very much in this period since their prophylactic and therapeutic use is permitted and widespread.

In another study, the effect upon humans of adding tetracycline to chicken feed was studied. Within a week virtually all the faecal enterobacteria of the chickens were resistant to this antibiotic (see also Howe *et al*. 1976c), and by five months about 30 per cent of the faecal samples from the farm dwellers contained over 80 per cent tetracycline-resistant bacteria; many of these were multiply resistant. Here rather indirect selection has resulted in resistance in man as well as chickens (Levy *et al*.1976a, b). It therefore appears likely that the levels of R^+ *E. coli* in man have several causes (see Fig. 6.2). The most important is probably contamination from other people (perhaps particularly those who have received antibiotics) but there is also contamination from animal populations.

By now it may be impossible to avoid being colonized by R^+ bacteria. This is one interpretation of the results of Guinée *et al*. (1970). Their study with babies and vegetarians (including those avoiding milk, cheese and eggs as well as meat) indicated that such individuals carried just as many, if not more, resistant bacteria as the population at large.

R plasmid transfer between bacterial strains in vivo.   Transfer of R plasmids between strains is not difficult to demonstrate in the laboratory. But to what extent do R plasmids from a reservoir of commensal strains, such as *E. coli*, transfer to incoming strains, including antibiotic-sensitive pathogens? Although R factors tend to persist in clones (Hartley and Richmond 1975), the epidemiological evidence shows that transfer between organisms must also occur, at least occasionally, *in vivo*. But it may be that conditions in the normal gut (for instance alkaline pH, bile salts and fatty acids) are not very suitable for conjugation. Also, enterobacteria constitute less than 1 per cent of the total flora in the gut so that their numbers are considerably lower than the numbers of *E. coli* commonly used in the laboratory. Most R plasmids isolated from nature transfer with low efficiency. In some cases at least this is due to repression mechanisms (see Chapter 5). In addition, J. D. Anderson (1975) has suggested that *Bacteroides* cells in the gut produce substances that inhibit mating of *E. coli*. Nevertheless, pairing is very efficient once collisions occur with competent donors, at least for Hfr × F⁻ crosses in *E. coli in vitro* (Collins and Broda 1975). Also, although it was previously thought that conjugation is inefficient under anaerobic conditions, it now

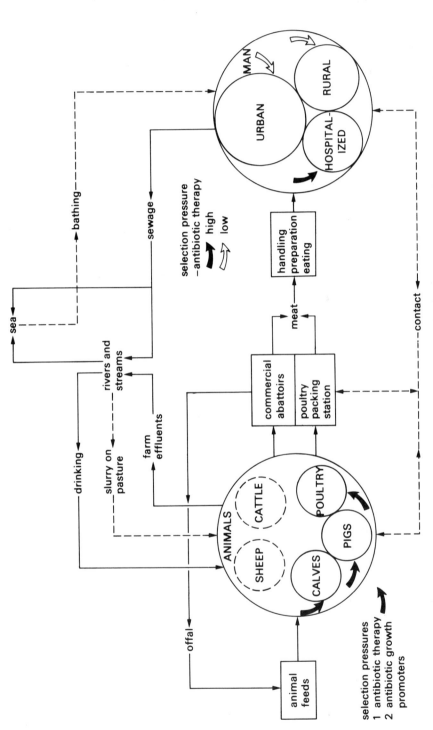

Fig. 6.2. Routes of exchange of *E. coli* between animals and man. (After Linton 1977, with permission of author and publisher.)

seems that for some plasmids it is about as efficient as in aerobic conditions (Stallions and Curtiss 1972; Burman 1977).

It has been difficult to show spread of R factors between strains in normal hosts in the absence of antibiotic (by direct methods as distinct from by inference from epidemiological data). It is a technical problem to be sure in a given case that transfer has actually occurred *in vivo*, rather than that the novel type merely results from the selection of a minor part of the population that was not previously detected. J. D. Anderson *et al*. (1973a, b) could detect transfer between strains in a person's gut only in the presence of an antibiotic, which allowed an increase in the number of R^+ cells, including those of other strains that have received the R plasmid. They used molecular criteria to show that the R factors acquired by the recipient strain were indeed those originally present only in the donors. Subsequently Ingram *et al*. (1974) presented molecular evidence for recombination between two R factors in the gut of a person receiving antibiotics.

More recently Petrocheilou *et al*. (1976) have reported an instance of transfer between strains of *E. coli* in the gut of a healthy human volunteer in the absence of selection. However, the fact that, although the donor strain became the dominant one within ten days, 202 days elapsed before the R factor was first detected in another strain emphasizes that such transfer may not occur at all commonly. On the other hand, transfer between strains in the rumen of the sheep occurs efficiently after 24 hours starvation (M. G. Smith 1977). Transfer also occurs efficiently in mice otherwise free of bacteria (Reed *et al*. 1969; Jones and Curtiss 1970).

It must therefore be borne in mind that when an antibiotic is given to cure an infection, it may also select pre-existing clones of resistant commensal or pathogenic organisms, and is liable to increase the number of other strains acquiring R factors, and possibly also select for recombinant R factors. Some antibiotics select more strongly than others for these effects. Thus tetracycline and ampicillin are poorly absorbed in the small gut, so that much of what is ingested is carried into the lower intestine and faeces, where selection and transfer presumably occur. Other new penicillins (e.g., amoxycillin) are more efficiently absorbed, so that selection for resistance is likely to be less strong.

Pseudomonas aeruginosa and other opportunist pathogens

Where the normal microbial flora is inhibited by the use of antibiotics other, drug-resistant organisms which would normally be excluded can come to occupy the vacant niche. In this way one indirect effect of the widespread use of antibiotics has been the emergence as pathogens of organisms that are normally harmless. Infections by such 'opportunist' strains are a hazard among patients with lowered resistance. Examples are patients suffering from leukaemia or tumours, those being treated with radiotherapy or immunosuppressive drugs, or recovering from burns or major surgery (von Graevenitz 1977). Septicaemia due to Gram-negative bacilli results in a very high mortality, and drug-resistance makes such infections even more difficult to treat.

Pseudomonas aeruginosa is naturally resistant to all generally used antibiotics except carbenicillin and gentamicin. It grows in the hospital environment, colonizing sinks and medical apparatus, and is a cause of local infections, especially on burns, but can also cause general septicaemia (Lowbury 1975). *Pseudomonas* respiratory tract infection is also a principal cause of death among children suffering from cystic fibrosis (Raeburn 1976).

In March 1969 two unrelated *Ps. aeruginosa* strains, which were isolated within 24 hours of each other at a burns unit in Birmingham, were found to carry resistance to very high levels of carbenicillin. By May 1969, resistant strains had replaced all others in the wards and the use of carbenicillin was discontinued (Lowbury *et al.* 1969). The suspicion that a transmissible R factor (RP1) was involved was confirmed by Sykes and Richmond (1970), Fullbrook *et al.* (1970) and Grinsted *et al.* (1972). Roe *et al.* (1971) showed that the R factor was freely transferable in mixed infections on burned mice, not only between strains of *Ps. aeruginosa*, but also to bacteria of distinct genera: *Pr. mirabilis*, *E. coli* and *K. aerogenes*. As well as being of great clinical importance, this remarkable promiscuity is of great interest from the point of view of molecular genetics (see Chapters 5, 7 and 8). In *E. coli* RP1 confers resistance to kanamycin, tetracycline and ampicillin (to all of which *Ps. aeruginosa* is naturally resistant) as well as to carbenicillin. As discussed in Chapter 3, the β-lactamase that confers resistance to ampicillin and carbenicillin is carried on transposon A.[1]

Although gentamicin resistance has not been a problem until recently, there have now been a number of cases of R factors conferring such resistance in hospital infections by *Ps. aeruginosa* and *K. aerogenes* (Bryan *et al.* 1974; Jacoby 1974a; Bryan and van den Elzen 1977; A. Richmond *et al.* 1975; Kontomichalou *et al.* 1976). This is a very serious development as we have few effective drugs for treating these very resistant strains.

R plasmids in *Haemophilus* and gonococci.

Haemophilus influenzae is a common cause of lower respiratory tract infection, e.g. bronchopneumonia or acute exacerbations of chronic bronchitis. It

---

[1] However, at the last count at least seven types of β-lactamases are known to be specified by plasmids from different *Pseudomonas* isolates (Jacoby and Matthew 1979).

may also be responsible for bacterial meningitis in children and this is a serious clinical emergency. The organism is naturally sensitive to ampicillin, which has been widely used in treatment. In the past few years strains that produce a β-lactamase and are highly resistant to ampicillin have appeared. This produces serious problems in choosing an effective antibiotic. The resistance has proved to be plasmid-borne (Elwell *et al*. 1975; van Klingeren *et al*. 1977). Otherwise unrelated plasmids carried by two strains had in one case all, and in the other case one-third, of the TnA sequence (DeGraaff *et al*. 1976). It is suggested that these R factors may have arisen through the aquisition of the TnA transposon by indigenous cryptic plasmids (Laufs and Kaulfers 1977; Kaulfers *et al*. 1978; Elwell *et al*. 1977b). Chloramphenicol is one of the few alternatives to ampicillin in the treatment of *Haemophilus* meningitis, but plasmid-borne chloramphenicol resistance is also beginning to appear. It is perhaps remarkable that such resistance determinants have been so long in appearing in *Haemophilus*.

Treatment of gonococcal infections was for long very successful with penicillin or ampicillin. Over the years the gonococci became rather more resistant, by mutation, although still treatable with these drugs. More recently, highly resistant strains have emerged. Here too, all or part of TnA in plasmids is the cause of the resistance. At least two of these plasmids show extensive homology with an R factor from *H. influenzae* (Elwell *et al*. 1977a; Roberts *et al*. 1977). Conjugative plasmids apparently existed in gonococci before the appearance of penicillinase-producing strains (Roberts and Falkow 1977 and 1978; Sox *et al*. 1978). Resistance to other antimicrobial agents has also occurred in gonococci. In one case these, and also penicillin resistance, are due to chromosomal mutations (Biswas *et al*. 1976).

R plasmids in Gram-positive bacteria

Most of the drugs used against infections by Gram-negative bacteria are also used against Gram-positive bacteria. These include penicillins, amino-glycosides, tetracycline and chloramphenicol. In addition, erythromycin and lincomycin are important in the treatment of staphylococcal infections. Among Gram-positive species drug resistance in *Staphylococcus aureus* has been the most studied from the clinical as well as the molecular point of view. As with the enterobacteria, much of this resistance is plasmid-determined, and the only clinically useful antibiotic to which little resistance has yet been reported is gentamicin (see Lacey 1975, for a review; Porthouse *et al*. 1976). Penicillin resistance in *Staph. aureus* is due to the production of a β-lactamase that is specified by a plasmid. Since about 1960 *Staph. aureus* infections have been controlled with the cloxacillins, which are not suscept-ible to the staphylococcal penicillinase. Some strains of *Staph. aureus* are already resistant to low levels of cloxacillin; but such resistance is chromosomally specified, and is not due to β-lactamases ('cloxacillinases'). Since cloxacillinases do exist in Gram-negative bacteria, it is possible that such enzymes will eventually appear in *Staph. aureus*.

A major difference from the situation in the enterobacteria is that, with *Staph. aureus*, transduction is the only mechanism known so far for the transfer of plasmids between strains. The phage vectors are rather specific and animal and human strains of *Staph. aureus* tend to remain confined to respective hosts. The situation may therefore be clinically less menacing (and easier to analyse) than that in the enterobacteria.

On the other hand, strains of *Streptococcus* have now been described that can undergo conjugation (see previous chapter and van Embden *et al*. 1977). *Strep. pyogenes* infections were very serious before the introduction of penicillin but the organism remains penicillin-sensitive and the principal anxiety is that by one means or another it will aquire resistance, for instance from a β-lactamase-specifying plasmid from staphylococci. Yagi *et al*. (1975) have already described a strain of *Strep. pyogenes* with an R plasmid that confers resistance to erythromycin and two other antibiotics. This may have come from *Strep. faecalis*, since 95 per cent of its DNA is homologous to that of a *Strep. faecalis* plasmid.

Mechanisms of drug resistance

Most known antibiotics are produced by actinomycetes (a group of mycelial bacteria) though some are synthesized by other bacteria or by true fungi (see Table 6.6 and Hopwood and Merrick 1977). Their natural function is unknown, though it may well be to inhibit the growth of competing organisms, e.g., in the soil. Some antibiotics fall into families; thus the aminoglycosides streptomycin, kanamycin and gentamicin, for instance, share structural features. In addition, many semi-synthetic derivatives are now available (see Table 6.6). Such compounds may be more useful for any of a number of reasons. They might act against a different spectrum of strains, have increased activity, be easier to administer (e.g., orally instead of by injection) or might avoid host-specified resistance.

Plasmid-mediated resistance is usually due to enzymes that modify the antibiotic. Such modification of antibiotics of the penicillin family is generally by cleavage of the β-lactam ring, whereas aminoglycosides can be inactivated by addition of various groups (Table 6.6; Fig. 6.3). Semisynthetic drugs may be designed so as to be unaffected by each type of modifying enzyme, which may be a difficult objective to achieve. For example, the reason why amikacin is not attacked by the common R-factor enzymes is that it lacks the appropriate groupings that might be modified

Table 6.6

Some antimicrobial drugs, their origins and the mechanisms of plasmid-borne drug resistance. See Garrod, Lambert and O'Grady (1973) for a standard account of current usage of antibacterial drugs in medicine. Davies and Smith (1978) provide a detailed account of plasmid-determined resistance to antimicrobial agents.

Antimicrobial agent	Mechanism of plasmid-borne acquired resistance
1. Antibiotics formed by fungi (*Penicillium* and *Cephalosporium*) β Lactams	
Penicillins	cleavage of lactam ring
Benzyl penicillin	(=β-lactamase)
Methicillin[1]; cloxacillins[1]	
Ampicillin[1]; amoxycillin[1]	
Carbenicillin[1]	
Mecillinam[1]	
Cephalosporins[2]	
2. Antibiotics formed by bacteria (i) *Bacillus* species	
Bacitracin	none
(ii) Actinomycetes (*Streptomyces*) Aminoglycosides	
Streptomycin; neomycin	Modifying enzymes: N-acetylation,
Kanamycin; amikacin[1]	O-nucleotidylation, and O-phosphorylation
Gentamicin; tobramycin	
Chloramphenicol	O-acetylation
Tetracyclines	altered transport system
Erythromycin	ribosome binding site
Lincomycin; clindamycin[1]	modification (in staphylococci)
3. Synthetic antimicrobial drugs	
Sulphonamides	alternative drug-resistant target enzyme in a vitamin
Trimethoprim	pathway

[1] Semi-synthetic derivatives. [2] The cephalosporins are produced by true fungi, but the related cephamycins are produced by *Streptomyces* species.

(see Fig. 6.3). Cefoxitin is a semi-synthetic cephamycin resistant to most *E. coli* β-lactamases.

Resistance to the sulphonamides and trimethoprim, which are not of microbial origin, is due to additional R-plasmid-specified drug-insensitive enzymes in vitamin-synthesis pathways (Wise and Abou-Donia 1975; Amyes and Smith 1974). Resistance to each of these agents can be carried on transposons (Table 3.7).

Generally the mechanisms of resistance specified by plasmids are differ-

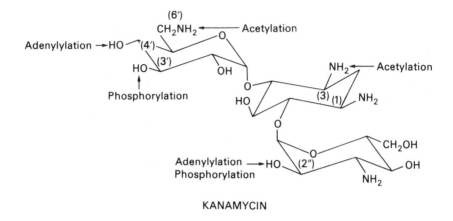

KANAMYCIN

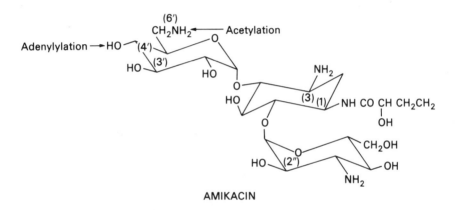

AMIKACIN

Fig. 6.3. Structures of kanamycin A and amikacin. The hydroxyaminobutyric acid side chain of amikacin protects it from 3'-O-phosphorylation and 2"-O-adenylylation, and also increases its anti-*Pseudomonas* activity.

ent from those of host-specified resistance (see for instance Sykes and Matthew 1976). However, in a few cases (Richmond 1972; Korfhagen *et al.* 1976) they may have a common origin. Transposition is an obvious mechanism in such instances. It is likely that 'fixing' of resistances in the chromosomes of cells of newly resistant strains will emerge as an important consequence of selection.

Resistance to other agents. Many R factors (and other plasmids) confer resistance to metal ions and/or organometallic compounds (Novick and Roth 1968; Jacoby 1974b; Schottel *et al.* 1974; Nakahara *et al.* 1977; Summers and Jacoby 1977; Clark *et al.* 1977; Weiss *et al.* 1977; Wang *et al.*

1978). Dean *et al*. (1977) observed that more of a series of *Ps. aeruginosa* clinical isolates were resistant to Hg^{2+} than to any one of a range of antibiotics. The biological rationale for metal ion resistance is unclear, although such resistances might suggest a soil origin for the determinants.

R plasmids can also determine altered sensitivity to radiation and mutagens (Howarth 1965; Krishnapillai 1975; Tweats *et al*. 1976; Lehrbach *et al*. 1977) or can specify restriction and modification systems (Bannister and Glover 1968; Bannister 1970; Smith *et al*. 1976; Jacoby and Sutton 1977).

Presence of R plasmids in the absence of drugs. It appears that R plasmids were present in small numbers of organisms before the introduction of antibiotics into clinical practice. D. H. Smith (1967) reported that a strain of *E. coli* isolated before 1937 and lyophilized in 1946 contained an R factor specifying resistance to streptomycin and tetracycline. Maré (1968) examined the incidence of drug-resistant Gram-negative gut bacteria among a group of 47 Kalahari bushmen who had not been in contact with other humans for about 10 years. He found no streptomycin, tetracycline or chloramphenicol-resistant bacteria, but nine of the group carried bacteria that were resistant to high levels of ampicillin. A similar proportion of various mammals from two southern African game reserves carried bacteria resistant to ampicillin, chloramphenicol or streptomycin. In no case was this property auto-transmissible, and no segregants were found, so that it was not certain that these resistances were plasmid-borne. Gardner *et al*. (1969) reported that one among 21 Solomon Islanders tested carried an *E. coli* strain with an R plasmid specifying resistance to streptomycin and tetracycline, and also that a soil sample from that area contained a Gram-negative bacillus carrying an R plasmid specifying the same two resistances. These results and similar studies in Borneo (Davis and Anandan 1970) suggest that even where drugs are not used clinically, R factors do exist.

Origin of drug resistance and R plasmids. R factors have apparently evolved by an accretion of separate functions, perhaps by classic recombination or, as in the case of ampicillin resistance, the insertion of transposons (see previous chapter: Hedges and Jacob 1974; Heffron *et al*. 1975b). Therefore separate 'modules' may have come from entirely independent sources. The molecular evidence suggests that plasmids related in their incompatibility functions (that is, in replication) have an overall relatedness. However, such a correlation between compatibility groups and hosts, for instance in the case of group H plasmids and different *Salm. typhi* strains (see earlier), may merely reflect constraints on transfer and/or replication and a grafting of determinants on to already-resident cryptic plasmids.

One suggestion (Walker and Walker 1970; Benveniste and Davies 1973) is that the resistance determinants may have originated in the very organisms that produce the antibiotics. This is because many such strains contain enzymes that resemble the R enzymes in the way that they inactivate the antibiotics. At least four of the eight known ways of modifying the aminoglycosides are also found in antibiotic-producing organisms (Dowding and Davies 1975). Since such organisms are themselves vulnerable to their own products, the enzymes might serves as detoxifiers, or play a role in their biosynthesis, or in their transport out of the cell. On this theory, one might be able to predict what mechanisms of inactivation of new antibiotics are likely to arise from R factors that are still to be encountered.

R factor chloramphenicol resistance is generally due to the production of chloramphenicol-acetylating enzymes (see, for instance, Gaffney *et al.* 1978). Many streptomycetes are able to acetylate chloramphenicol but Shaw and Hopwood (1976) could not detect chloramphenical acetylation in *Streptomyces venezuelae*, which is the organism that produces chloramphenicol and which is highly resistant to it. It is likely that the drug is inactivated here by another mechanism. But *Streptomyces acrimycini* (a non-producer of chloramphenicol) appears to owe some of its rather low level of resistance to the presence of an acetylating enzyme, since a point mutation which leads to loss of the enzyme resulted in a considerable increase in sensitivity (Wright and Hopwood 1977).

Another approach was to ask whether DNA from a producing strain could confer resistance upon a sensitive strain. Courvalin *et al.* (1977) used DNA from a strain of *Bacillus circulans* that is used industrially for producing an aminoglycoside antibiotic (butirosin). After formation of chimaeras between such DNA and a ColE1-Ap^r plasmid, and their introduction by transformation into *E. coli*, clones were isolated that were resistant to neomycin (a related aminoglycoside) as well as to ampicillin. Neomycin resistance was due to an enzyme similar to those present in clinical isolates of aminoglycoside-resistant bacteria, suggesting that resistance genes might indeed have come ultimately from antibiotic-producing organisms.

Plasmids conferring pathogenicity
The effect of R factors is merely to confer drug resistance on bacteria that may be pathogenic. There are other plasmids that contribute directly to virulence. Enteropathogenic bacteria are an important cause of gastroenteritis, although viruses and other microorganisms are also responsible in many cases. In developing countries diarrhoeal disease is one of the princi-

pal causes of death among those under five. In recent years it has been increasingly appreciated that some strains of *E. coli* as well as species of *Salmonella, Shigella* and *Vibrio* can cause such illness (Nalin *et al*. 1975; Ryder *et al*. 1976). Milder conditions, such as 'travellers diarrhoea' in adults, may also be due to meeting enteropathogenic strains of *E. coli*. In more affluent countries infantile enteritis caused by strains of *E. coli* has been a serious problem, particularly in hospitals. Certain strains of *E. coli* can also cause serious diarrhoeal infections in piglets and calves.

In some cases the ability to cause disease depends upon the presence of enterotoxin-producing (Ent) plasmids in the strain of *E. coli* (see Sack 1975; So *et al*. 1975a for reviews). Normally *E. coli* is found largely in the lower part of the human small intestine and in the large intestine. Disease occurs when enterotoxigenic *E. coli* colonize the small intestine. The symptoms are similar to those of cholera and can be almost as acute (Finkelstein *et al*. 1976). There is a massive outpouring of fluid and electrolytes by the secretory cells of the small intestine. The classic assay system involves observing the accumulation of fluid and therefore the swelling of the ileum of suckling mice or infant rabbits. However, sometimes little or no enterotoxin is detected, and enteritis, caused by strains belonging to only a small number of serotypes, may depend upon a completely different mechanism (Anon. 1975; Rowe *et al*. 1975).

Carriage by an *E. coli* strain of an Ent plasmid is not in itself sufficient to cause diarrhoea in piglets. Smith and Linggood (1971) observed that another plasmid, specifying the (capsular) K88 antigen, which is a fimbrial protein (Ørskov *et al*. 1977), is also required. The strain carrying either Ent or the K88 plasmid alone was non-pathogenic but when carrying both it was pathogenic. The reason is that the K88 antigen allows adhesion and proliferation high up in the small intestine. The Ent plasmid by itself does not produce this colonization of the upper small intestine and the organisms therefore do not produce the disease. An analogous plasmid-specified antigen (K99) is found in *E. coli* strains that infect calves. Evans *et al*. (1975) have shown that in at least one strain of human origin, too, the entertoxin and a heat labile 'colonization factor' are determined by separate plasmids.

Enterotoxins from *E. coli* are of two types. At least one component of LT toxin is a heat-labile protein which is immunologically related to the cholera toxin. Cholera toxin (produced by *Vibrio cholerae*) activates the adenylate cyclase enzyme of the gut epithelial host cells, thereby greatly increasing levels of cyclic AMP; this leads to the secretion of fluid and electrolytes into the gut lumen (see van Heyningen 1977; Finkelstein and Boesman-Finkelstein 1978). This suggests an evolutionary relationship, even though the cholera toxin is chromosomally specified. ST toxin is heat-stable and is probably smaller than the LT toxin (see below). It stimulates guanylate cyclase in host cells (Field *et al*. 1978). At present tissue culture methods of assay will only detect LT toxin.

Some Ent plasmids produce both ST and LT toxins (Smith and Gyles 1970). Other plasmids only specify the ST toxin. The Ent (ST + LT) plasmids form a homogeneous group with molecular sizes of about 60 megadaltons and G·C ratios of 0.50. Annealing experiments showed that their DNA sequences were closely related and that they also had substantial homology with F and R1. The type Ent plasmid in this study, P307, is also incompatible with F (So *et al*. 1975a, b). Heteroduplex analysis revealed that the homology of P307 with F lay in four regions, three containing genes for transfer and the other genes for replication and incompatibility (Santos *et al*. 1975). In contrast the Ent (ST) group plasmids varied in size from 21 megadaltons to 80 megadaltons, and their DNA was unrelated to that of F (So *et al*. 1975a, b). At least one clinical isolate carried both an R plasmid and an Ent plasmid (Wachsmuth *et al*. 1976) and plasmids carrying both resistance and enterotoxin determinants have now been described (So *et al*. 1976; Gyles *et al*. 1977).

Techniques of molecular genetics have yielded further information on both types of toxin. An Ent(ST + LT)TcSmSu plasmid has been used to isolate mutants producing altered LT molecules. This made use of 'co-mutagenesis' of a tetracycline-sensitive mutant and screening of the tetracycline-resistant revertants (Silva *et al*. 1978). Other workers have cloned the same LT determinant on a multicopy plasmid (So *et al*. 1978a).[1] The amplification of ST production afforded by the cloning by So *et al*. (1976) of the ST determinants with pSC101 should allow studies on this toxin also to proceed more readily. Indeed, the base sequence of the ST determinant is now known, and shown to be bounded by a pair of IS1 sequences; the whole structure constitutes a transposon (So *et al*. 1979).

Another class of transmissible plasmids, found in *E. coli* infecting pigs, produce haemolysins (Smith and Halls 1967). Hly⁺ clones are recognized by the zones of clearing that they produce on blood agar plates. Such plasmids have been found in association with Ent and K88 plasmids, but have no demonstrated pathogenic role (Smith and Linggood 1971). It is not known what selective advantage they confer on their host strain. Some but not others are partially homologous in their DNA to F (Royer-Pokora and Goebel 1976). A haemolysin-specifying self-transmissible plasmid has also been described in *Streptococcus faecalis* (Oliver *et al*. 1976).

---

[1] Using such hybrid plasmids in an *E. coli* minicell-producing strain it has now been shown that LT is composed of at least an 11,500 and a 25,000 molecular weight protein (Dallas and Falkow 1979).

The need for restraint in drug usage

Within a few years of an antimicrobial agent being introduced its value may diminish as resistant bacteria arise. R plasmids, previously uncommon, became widespread in commensals and pathogens during the 1960s. Even though transfer between strains is not very frequent, it does occur *in vivo*, and, because of the very strong selective pressures, organisms that are or can become resistant prosper at the expense of their drug-sensitive competitors. This situation is seen most dramatically in intensive care units of hospitals, and under conditions of intensive animal production.

No doubt many resistances have arisen in man, but human medicine cannot afford to ignore the use of antibiotics in agriculture. It is clear that there is a common pool of R plasmids in the commensal *E. coli* and pathogenic salmonellae that occur in both man and domestic animals.

At present, approximately equal amounts of antimicrobial agents are used in man and in animals in developed countries. In Britain the recommendation of the Swann report (1969) that those antibiotics used against infections in man should not be used for growth promotion in animals has been implemented. However, antibiotic usage in agriculture has probably not decreased overall since antibiotics may still be used prophylactically and therapeutically. In the U.S.A. at least, there is strong opposition from agricultural interests and drug companies to restrictions on the use of drugs. It has been argued that they are essential in large-scale production units, especially for poultry, and that there are no harmful consequences for man.

In general, medicine is still coping. This has led some to believe that the dangers to man are purely hypothetical. However, in a few cases R plasmid resistance has undoubtedly already created serious consequences. Two examples are the emergence of chloramphenicol-resistant *Salm. typhi* and of carbenicillin and gentamicin strains of *Ps. aeruginosa* in intensive care units. Others are the appearance of TnA on plasmids of *N. gonorrhoeae* and of *H. influenzae*. However, at present the average family doctor is unlikely to be greatly inconvenienced.

Thus far, an increasing incidence of resistance among bacteria has been countered by the introduction of further antibiotics. It is optimistic to assume that the flow of new antibiotics can be expected to continue indefinitely. There has been some success in designing drugs that evade the known mechanisms of resistance. Most new antibiotics produced recently have been semi-synthetic derivatives of established antibiotics. Resistance to some synthetic drugs may prove to arise less readily than resistance to semi-synthetic antibiotics. One alternative remedy (which at present seems implausible) is that drugs against R plasmids themselves ('curing agents') will be developed. The real response must be restraint in the use of anti-microbial agents exercised consistently, both in the long term and on a world-wide scale.

This can take several forms. Where drugs need to be used at all, those that can be used most sparingly should be used. Thus, amoxycillin seems preferable to ampicillin or tetracycline, since it is fully absorbed from the gut. This minimizes the chances of transfer and of selection. Then, use of drugs may often be unnecessary for the individual and merely lead to trouble later for the community. It seems more than a coincidence that in the countries where chloramphenicol-resistant *Salm. typhi* eventually appeared, chloramphenicol had been freely available, even without prescription, and was used in far too indiscriminate a manner.

On a small scale, withdrawal of drugs has sometimes been the most effective means of dealing with a persistent infection (e.g., Aserkoff and Bennett 1969; Lowbury *et al.* 1969; Price and Sleigh 1970). In such cases the normal flora has competed successfully with the R-plasmid-carrying pathogen. On a larger scale, as with poultry, if drugs must be used so extensively, which is questionable, they should be different from those used in infections of people, as recommended by Swann. But even such drugs can change the balance of organisms in the gut in favour of salmonellae (Smith and Tucker 1978).

Finally, where possible cross-infection should be prevented by the well-established methods of hygiene. Here again, the problems raised by large-scale poultry farming seem the most intractable.

Summary

The effect of antibiotic usage has been to select for strains that are resistant. Among the coliforms and other groups this has been due to the accretion of resistances on R plasmids. Both commensal bacteria and transmissible R plasmids from man and domestic animals form common pools. Overuse of drugs in the past has led to resistance becoming a serious clinical problem in some instances, such as with typhoid fever and also infections in intensive care units. Transposition and the wide host range of some plasmids have both had medical repercussions. A possible source of the determinants of plasmid-borne antibiotic resistance may be the producer organisms. While R plasmids merely make pathogenic strains resistant, Ent and K88 plasmids together cause pathogenicity. We do not know whether other plasmids also play a part in determining virulence. Avoiding cross-infection, together with restraint in drug usage, is essential if the damage caused by resistant pathogens is to be minimized.

7
Other Plasmids

Many other plasmid-specified functions have been described (see Table 1.1). A number of the best-studied types will be discussed in this chapter.

Bacteriocins

In 1925 Gratia demonstrated that some bacteria released agents (bacteriocins) into the surrounding medium that killed other bacteria, but to which other individuals of the producing strain were resistant. This killing is observed on agar plates as clear zones on lawns of sensitive bacteria, each zone originating from a single bacteriocinogenic bacterium. Normally only a small proportion of the cells of such a population are actively producing such bacteriocin. However, agents that include ultraviolet light 'induce' the synthesis of some bacteriocins. Bacteriocins have been described from a wide range of Gram-positive and Gram-negative bacteria (see Reeves 1972). Thus Gratia and Frédéricq (1946) found that about 20 per cent of *E. coli* strains that they tested could produce substances that acted on a particular indicator strain. Bacteriocins are given names that indicate their origins: examples are megacins from *Bacillus megaterium*, subtilicins from *Bacillus subtilis* and colicins from *E. coli*. They may have evolutionary relations with other structures, such as pili, toxins and phage proteins. Indeed, there are a number of strains, for instance of *Pseudomonas aeruginosa*, which produce complex defective phage-like structures that affect other cells at least superficially in the same way as bacteriocins, and are so classed by some authors (Bradley 1967; Holloway and Krishnapillai 1975) but not by others (Reeves 1972; Hardy 1975). The biological role of bacteriocins seems to be to give the carrier strain (and the population of plasmids that these cells carry) a selective advantage over other closely related strains, by killing them. Although the minority of cells that actually produce the bacteriocin are killed themselves, the clone as a whole can then prosper. There are, perhaps, analogies with lysogeny and most transfer systems, in that in each case only a minority of the members of the population become released from control.

Colicins are the best studied both because of the efforts over many years of Frédéricq and others, and because it has been possible to relate these studies to the wider corpus of knowledge of the molecular biology of *E. coli* (see Hardy 1975, for a review). All colicins studied so far are proteins specified by plasmids. These plasmids (e.g., ColE1 and ColI) have been discussed in Chapters 2–5 as objects for the study of structure, replication and transfer; and the proteins they produce have been studied for the ways in which they exert their lethal effects on other cells. As has been noted earlier, the distinction between temperate phage and plasmids (e.g., P1 and λ and its λdv derivatives) can be rather fine.

Colicins are classified on the basis of their activity spectra against other strains. Such analysis is sometimes complicated by the presence of more than one Col factor in a cell. Frédéricq (1948) found that 88 Col⁺ strains fell into 17 classes on testing against 316 indicator strains. An alternative method of classification has been by determining the activity of colicins against a set of derivatives of an originally sensitive strain, each derivative being resistant to one of a series of colicins. This approach constitutes the basis of current colicin classification.

Col factors (i.e., the plasmids) fall into the same two classes as do R factors. Some are large (60 megadaltons and more), conjugative, and present in only a few copies, while others are of about 5 megadaltons, non-conjugative and present in many copies. As discussed in previous chapters, some are very closely related to plasmids specifying other functions. One example is ColV-K94, which shares substantial homology with F and R1 (Sharp *et al*. 1973). Since the principles of structure, replication and transfer have already been discussed, we shall concentrate here on the modes of action of some Col plasmid products.

Attachment of colicin to sensitive cells.   Several colicin receptors have been identified as proteins in the outer membrane. In many but not all instances resistance is due to alteration or loss of these receptors. In some cases colicins and phages absorb to the same outer membrane; these receptors may also be involved in transporting metabolites such as vitamin B12 and Fe^{3+} into the cell (see Hardy 1975). Davies and Reeves (1975a, b) used all 19 available colicin types to isolate resistant *E. coli* mutants, and then tested these mutants for their cross-resistances to other colicins. The colicins fell unambiguously into two groups. Mutants selected as resistant to group A colicins (see Table 7.1) might or might not show cross-resistance to other group A colicins, but were never resistant to group B colicins. Similarly mutants resistant to group B colicins were never resistant to group A

Table 7.1
Properties of some colicinogenic factors.

Name of plasmid	Size of col factor DNA (megadaltons)	Incompatibility group	Sex pili	Site of of action of colicin
Group I (Group A colicins)				
E1-K30	4.2	–	–	membrane
E2-P9	4.6	–	–	DNA
E3-CA38	4.6	–	–	rRNA
K-235	4.6	–	–	membrane
Group II (Group B colicins)				
B-K77	70	F III	F-like	membrane
Ib-P9	61.5	I a	I-like	membrane
V-K94	85	?	F-like	?

colicins. Mutants isolated as resistant to colicins of groups A and B fell into 21 and 9 phenotypic classes respectively on the basis of their resistance spectra. Some mutants corresponded to mutants selected in other ways; these included mutants that were resistant to bacteriophages, and strains of one class were defective as F⁻ strains in conjugation. Such mutants should prove very valuable as tools for the study of cell envelope functions. In an earlier study Hardy *et al.* (1973) divided the smaller number of colicins that they studied also into two groups which correspond to groups A and B. They used several criteria, including the size of the plasmid molecule (i.e., about 5 megadaltons and about 60 megadaltons respectively), and suggested that each group may have descended from a single ancestral plasmid. Further data supporting this division are presented by Hughes *et al.* 1978.

Mechanism of colicin action.   There are three ways in which colicins are known to kill cells.

(1) Some, such as colicins E1 and K, appear to act on the cytoplasmic membrane, and to uncouple energy-dependent processes. The loss of potassium ions from colicin-treated cells has been noted.

(2) Colicin E2 brings about the degradation of DNA and the inhibition of cell division (Nomura 1963), presumably after entering the cell. Purified colicin E2 is inactive against DNA until a tightly bound 'immunity protein' is removed (Schaller and Nomura 1976).

(3) Colicin E3 prevents protein synthesis by cleaving the 16-S ribosomal RNA (Bowman *et al.* 1971; Senior and Holland 1971). Thus it is a nuclease acting on RNA rather than DNA. Cleavage *in vitro* is inhibited by a colicin-E3-associated immunity protein, which is analogous to that of

colicin E2, and which is specified by ColE3 itself (Sadikaro and Nomura 1975).

The plasmids ColE2 and ColE3 are very closely related. They are incompatible (Inselburg 1974) and 80 per cent of their DNA is homologous by the heteroduplex criterion (Inselburg 1973). The colicins themselves have similar but not identical patterns of specificity on tester strains (Davies and Reeves 1975b) and their amino acid sequences are partially similar (Herschman and Helinski 1967). ColE1, on the other hand, is not closely related to these plasmids but is related to the mini-plasmid from *E. coli* 15 (Goebel and Schrempf 1972b).

Ozeki *et al.* (1959) observed that the colicin-producing cells in populations of ColI, ColE1 and ColE2 cells are killed. The reason for this killing is unclear. The mechanism of induction is also unknown, but the analogy with the induction of phage λ lysogens referred to earlier can be taken further, in that ultraviolet irradiation, mitomycin C treatment and thymine starvation can cause both. Since maintenance of the λ prophage state depends upon a repressor molecule specified by the λ C_I gene, a protein with an analogous function is postulated for colicins. In the case of λ, entry of the prophage into a prophage-free recipient results in release of this repression and killing of the recipient ('zygotic induction'). However, neither zygotic induction by Col factors on transfer nor derepressed mutants have been observed. The extent of spontaneous induction of a given Col factor may vary. In exponential growth at low densities only about 0.01 per cent of the cells of a ColE2 culture are in the induced state, but at higher cell densities this proportion increases about one-hundredfold (Hardy and Meynell 1972).

Gene expression in CloDF13.　　Whereas ColE1 has contributed most to studies of plasmid replication, a related and similarly sized plasmid, CloDF13, has so far given most information on the expression of other gene functions. CloDF13 originated in *Enterobacter cloacae*, but is now studied in *E. coli*. Nijkamp and his colleagues had demonstrated that ColDF13 segregates efficiently into *E. coli* minicells. They then showed that such minicells synthesize CloDF13-determined messenger RNA and protein. While in the repressed state one mRNA species and three polypeptides were made, and on induction a total of four mRNA species and eight polypeptides could be demonstrated. The mRNA corresponded to 85 per cent of the DNA and the polypeptides to 85 per cent of the coding capacity of the mRNA (Kool *et al.* 1974). Subsequently (Konings *et al.* 1976), they found that in a cell-free system CloDF13 directs the synthesis of at least ten polypeptides. Two of these were identified respectively as the cloacin itself and as the CloDF13 immunity protein (Kool *et al.* 1975a, b). This was important as a demonstration that the plasmid and not the host cell specifies the immunity protein.

Cloacin DF13 has an extraordinary range of specific interactions.

(1) It binds selectively to receptor sites of sensitive cells.

(2) It inhibits protein synthesis *in vivo* and *in vitro* in the same way as colicin E3, by cleaving 16-S ribosomal RNA.

(3) It forms a tight complex with its immunity protein, when they are synthesized both *in vivo* and *in vitro*. Such a complex can inhibit protein synthesis in sensitive cells but not in a cell-free system.

(4) Most surprisingly, it binds tightly to a unique site on CloDF13 *in vivo* and *in vitro*, but does not bind to other species of DNA.

(5) The cloacin also apparently makes two staggered single-strand endo-nucleolytic cuts in duplex CloDF13 DNA (Veltkamp *et al.* 1976). This activity is inhibited by the immunity protein. It is tempting to suppose that such cleavage has a role in replication. This could either be in its initiation, or, if replication proceeds by a rolling circle mechanism, by then cleaving it into monomers that are able to circularize because of cohesive ends.

Degradative plasmids in pseudomonads

It has long been known that pseudomonads are able to utilize a wide range of organic compounds as carbon and energy sources. In 1966 Stanier *et al.* presented a classification of aerobic pseudomonads that was largely based upon which of a collection of 167 such compounds the different strains were able to use. Many of the strains could utilize about half the compounds, and one strain could utilize 108. The question arose whether the genome of *Pseudomonas* species (which is probably about the same size as that of *E. coli*) is adequate in size to code for so many catabolic functions. Some have now been mapped at chromosomal loci (see Wheelis 1975 for a review) but it emerges that some are catabolised by plasmid-specified enzymes (see Table 7.2 and Gunsalus *et al.* 1975, and Wheelis 1975, for reviews). At least in the case of TOL (see below) the plasmid carries a whole array of function-ally related genes.

SAL (salicylate utilization) was the first such plasmid to be discovered (Chakrabarty 1972). The criteria used were transmissibility (at a frequency of about 10^{-5} per donor, compared with less than 10^{-9} for a chromosomal marker), and segregation and its enhancement by mitomycin C. Curing and transmissibility were also the bases for the proposals that CAM (camphor) OCT (octane), NAH (naphthalene) and TOL (benzoate and toluate) were plasmid-borne determinants. The degradative pathway specified by TOL was subsequently found to extend back as far as toluene and *m*- and *p*-xylene (Worsey and Williams 1975). It will be noted that NAH, SAL and TOL all specify pathways that converge on catechol (Fig. 7.1). Whereas in the cured derivatives of these strains catechol is further metabolized by cleavage in the *ortho* position, in the plasmid-carrying strains this cleavage occurs in the *meta* position, and it is therefore likely that the plasmid-specified enzymes include those of this latter pathway. In addition, there may be some redundancy in enzymes prior to catechol conversion. Thus benzoate is oxidized to catechol mainly by a plasmid-specified enzyme in Tol^+ strains and by a chromosomally specified enzyme in Tol^- segregants (Williams and Murray 1974). In the NAH, SAL and TOL-containing strains, the plasmid-specified pathway is induced by the substrate of the first enzyme of the pathway. In contrast, with toluate degradation at least, the chromosomal pathway is induced by a product. It is too early to make a general comment on the functions of such partially redundant pathways. However, it is worth noting that the plasmid-specified pathway has a wider specificity, being able to utilize not only the hydrocarbon toluene, but also the xylenes, whereas the chromosomal pathway only starts with benzoate (which it utilizes more efficiently) and is unable to degrade the methylated analogues, the toluates.

A certain amount is now known about the relationship of these plasmids to each other or to other plasmids. CAM and OCT fall into the P-2 incompatibility group, together with a number of R factors (Chakrabarty 1973; Chou *et al*. 1974; Korfhagen *et al*. 1978) and TOL and NAH are in the P-9 group, which also contains R factors. However, studies on relationships must depend primarily on molecular methods (see below).

Only recently (Palchaudhuri and Chakrabarty 1976) has it been possible to isolate plasmid DNA from such strains. For unknown reasons, methods that are effective in the isolation of plasmids from *E. coli*, in particular the use of clearing spins, resulted in the loss of the plasmid DNA. However, the sizes of the plasmid molecules have now been determined (Table 7.2), and some of the plasmids have been introduced into new host strains by transformation (Duggleby *et al*. 1977). With one group of Tol^+ strains loss of the ability to utilize toluene can be due to loss of either the whole plasmid or only a specific region (Bayley *et al*. 1977). The toluene-degrading genes of TOL constitute a transposon (see Table 3.7; Jacoby *et al*. 1978). They can be transferred to *E. coli* either on a hybrid RP4–Tol molecule (Jacoby *et al*. 1978; Nakazawa *et al*. 1978) or on TOL labelled with the carbenicillin transposon Tn401 (Benson and Shapiro 1978). The fact that the Tol genes are poorly expressed in *E. coli* obscured the fact that TOL is a wide-host-range plasmid (Benson and Shapiro 1978).

How ubiquitous are such plasmids in nature? Williams and Worsey (1976) made independent isolates from soil of bacteria that were able to utilize *m*-toluate as their sole carbon source. They found that they all could

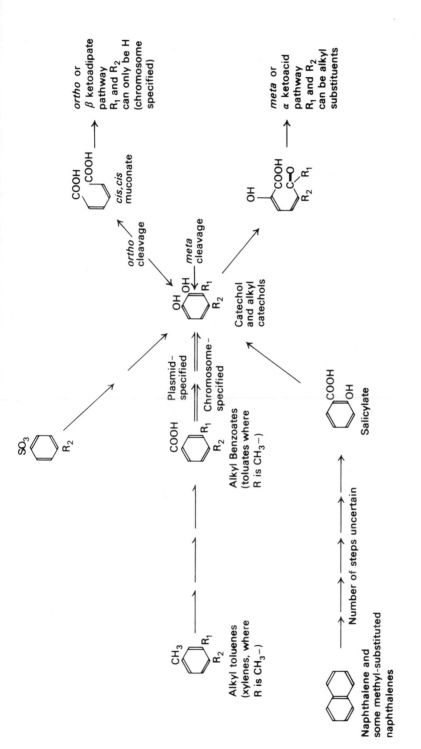

Fig. 7.1. *Ps. putida*-borne plasmid-mediated degradative pathways that converge upon catechol.

Table 7.2
Some degradative plasmids in strains of *Pseudomonas putida*.

Plasmid	Apparent primary substrate	*Ps. putida* strain	Number of enzyme steps	Tra[+]	Size (mega-daltons)	Refer-ences
CAM	camphor	PpG1	15–20	+	165	[1,2]
NAH	naphthalene	PpG7	>11	+	49	[3]
OCT	*n*-octane	PpG6	3	−[a]	?	[4,5]
SAL	salicylate	R1	8	+	51	[6]
TOL	toluene and xylenes	mt-2	>11	+	77	[7–9]
XYL	xylene	Pxy	>11	−	?	[10]

[a] Transfer of OCT from strain PpG6 is mediated by a sex factor, K (Chakrabarty 1974).
[1] Rheinwald *et al.* 1973; [2] Shaham *et al.* 1973; [3] Dunn and Gunsalus 1973; [4] Chakrabarty *et al.* 1973; [5] Fennewald and Shapiro 1977; [6] Chakrabarty 1972; [7] Williams and Murray 1974; [8] Wong and Dunn 1974; [9] Duggleby *et al.* 1977; [10] Friello *et al.* 1976.

utilize the same substrates, including toluene and the xylenes, as the original TOL-carrying strain. All the strains were pseudomonads, although not all were *Ps. putida*. However, this result may have reflected selection of particular strains during the enrichment procedure that was employed rather than the fact that this function is unique to pseudomonads. With some, the property was transmissible, and from all, non-utilizing segregants were obtained. The strains could be divided into groups on physiological criteria. The plasmid DNA of some was indistinguishable from that of the TOL strain, in terms of their sizes and the sizes of the fragments they gave after digestion with restriction endonucleases (Duggleby *et al.* 1977). Others were, on this criterion, unrelated to each other. However, more sensitive methods involving molecular hybridization of endonuclease fragments revealed relationships between most of the plasmids, and between the TOL, SAL, NAH and, to a lesser extent, OCT plasmids (Heinaru *et al.* 1978; Morris and Broda unpublished results). It may therefore be that some plasmid types are very widely distributed in nature, but there are nevertheless a number of ways of solving a given degradative problem. It is therefore of great interest to determine the details of the enzymology and regulation of the pathways. It has also been found that TOL and NAH have significant homology with R plasmids of the P-9 group (Bayley and Broda unpublished results).

The degradative plasmids provide an excellent model to illustrate the evolutionary potential of bacteria, once thought by many to be the organisms with the least opportunities for change because of their supposed confinement to asexual propagation. In the soil many groups each of a few cells carrying a particular type of plasmid that might be transmissible would allow the exploitation of a wide range of nutritional possibilities. No single bacterial chromosome could carry a comparable amount of information. It is likely that very many other degradative plasmids await discovery. It has been suggested that transfer of plasmids between strains plays a role in the response of the soil microflora to herbicides (Waid 1973; Fisher *et al*. 1978). The possibilities for developing such strains and plasmids for re-cycling of waste and natural products, and their economic use, are evident.

Tumorogenic plasmids of *Agrobacterium tumefaciens*
For many years the similarities between temperate phages and plasmids in bacteria have been recognized. Since some viruses of eukaryotes are tumorogenic (see Tooze 1973) it was possible that viruses and/or plasmids carried by bacteria could also cause tumours. 'Ti' plasmids of *A. tumefaciens* have this property. When some strains of this bacterial species infect wounds in dicotyledonous plants, bulbous growths can occur within weeks. The continued presence of bacteria is not essential. Such 'crown galls' are genuine tumours that can grow in culture medium that lacks growth hormones required for growth of normal tissue. They can be maintained for many years, and will cause tumours in healthy plants.

One possibility was that part or all of the bacterial genome was present in some form in such neoplastic cells. However, DNA hybridization experiments did not reveal such sequences. A correlation was then found between those strains that carried large plasmids (about 95–156 megadaltons) and virulence (Zaenen *et al*. 1974). Genetic manipulations (transfer by conjugation, testing of plasmid-deficient segregant strains and transforming of plasmid DNA into avirulent strains) show that these plasmids are indeed at least partly responsible (van Larebeke *et al*. 1974; Watson *et al*. 1975; Kerr *et al*. 1977; Genetello *et al*. 1977; Holsters *et al*. 1978b). The plasmids in different strains are only partially homologous. Currier and Nester (1976b) observed that the homology between the large plasmids of 15 virulent pathogenic strains of *A. tumefaciens* varied from 3 per cent to 100 per cent, although the plasmids tended to fall into two groups on this criterion. Heteroduplex analysis of avirulent deleted plasmids and between different plasmids suggest that the virulence gene(s) tend(s) to map in the small region that is homologous (see also Sciaky *et al*. 1978; Drummond and Chilton 1978; Hepburn and Hindley 1979).

Not even the whole plasmid has been demonstrated in tumour cells. Instead, it has recently been shown by molecular hybridization of crown gall cell DNA with separated endonuclease-generated fragments of plasmid

DNA that a specific segment of the plasmid, about 5 per cent of its total size, is present in crown gall tissue (Chilton *et al*. 1977) and transcribed there (Drummond *et al*.1977). This segment is one shared by the different types of Ti plasmid (Chilton *et al*. 1978a; Depicker *et al*. 1978). Such integration is analogous to the transformation of animal cells by adenovirus and is the first instance of bacterial DNA being integrated and/or transcribed in eukaryotic cells. However, agrobacteria are close relatives of the rhizobia, which are the symbionts involved in nitrogen fixation by legumes, and analogies between tumorogenesis and nodulation may emerge. It will be of great interest to establish the precise role of the plasmids that have recently been implicated in nodulation (Johnston *et al*. 1978).

It has been observed that the property of virulence is closely linked genetically but not necessarily functionally with the ability on the part of the plasmid-carrying strain of *A. tumefaciens* to induce the synthesis by the host tumour tissue of either one or the other of two analogues of arginine, octopine and nopaline (Bomhoff *et al*. 1976). These are apparently not synthesized in normal plant cells. The plasmid also generally confers upon its bacterial host the specific ability to utilize the particular amino acid as its sole carbon and nitrogen source. This nutritional capacity is used as a biochemical marker to detect Ti plasmids in host bacteria. However, in some cases, both compounds could be utilized, but only nopaline was produced by the tumours that were induced by the strain. Another class gave tumours in which neither compound was produced. Non-utilizing bacterial mutants could still induce tumours. Such results indicate that the plasmid genes evoking their synthesis by the tumour tissue are distinct from those determining their catabolism in the bacteria (Montoya *et al*. 1977). Octopine-Ti plasmids are closely related to each other, but nopaline-Ti plasmids are more heterogeneous (Sciaky *et al*. 1978). However, the observation that at least some plasmids from one group are probably incompatible with plasmids of the other suggests some underlying relationship (Montoya *et al*. 1978).

Another finding was that if the R factor RP4 is used to enhance the transfer efficiency of the Ti plasmids (Chilton *et al*. 1976; van Larebeke *et al*. 1977) a proportion of the RP4 plasmids form tandem structures with the Ti plasmids. RP4 can mobilize Ti plasmids to a strain of *Rhizobium* as well as to other strains of *Agrobacterium*, rendering such strains tumorogenic (Hooykaas *et al*. 1977).

Tumorogenesis by Ti plasmids can be viewed in population terms, as an individual plasmid evoking from a plant the synthesis of octopine or nopaline, which can then be used by other individuals in that bacterial population. Another point that may prove of very general significance is that these substances themselves act as inducers for the transfer of the Ti plasmid between bacteria (Petit *et al*. 1978).[1] In this way an increase in the plasmid population within the bacterial population is selected for.

Streptomyces coelicolor A3(2)

The streptomycetes are bacteria that are of particular interst as the organisms that produce more than two-thirds of the world's known antibiotics (see review by Hopwood and Merrick 1977). Genetically the best-studied organism is *Streptomyces coelicolor* A3(2), which has a conjugational system determined by the efficient sex factor SCP1 (Hopwood *et al*. 1973). F'-like elements (SCP1') carrying chromosomal segments have also been described (Hopwood and Wright 1976); one of these could integrate into the chromosome and give polarized transfer. Unlike normal Hfr strains in *E. coli*, however, this transfer resulted in the inheritance of fragments of donor chromosome extending in both directions from the point of integration of the plasmid. Since very little is known of the nature of conjugation in this organism, it is hard to know how far analogies from F are useful.

SCP1 is also implicated in the synthesis of and resistance to an antibiotic (Kirby *et al*. 1975), methylenomycin A (Wright and Hopwood 1976; Kirby and Hopwood 1977). Although it is perhaps unlikely to become important clinically, the mechanism of its synthesis and of its producer's resistance to it are of great interest. Plasmids may have a role in the synthesis of antibiotics in other cases too, as suggested by Akagawa *et al*. (1975) and Freeman and Hopwood (1978) for chloramphenicol. This role may generally be in the regulation of their synthesis rather than in specifying the biosynthetic enzymes themselves (Hopwood 1978).

It has not yet been possible to characterize SCP1 physically, although another plasmid with a size of about 20 megadaltons has been identified in *S. coelicolor* A3(2) (Schrempf and Goebel 1977). Recently it has been shown that this plasmid corresponds to a second sex factor, SCP2, which is responsible for (most of) the gene transfer that occurs in the absence of SCP1 (Bibb *et al*. 1977).

Summary

Bacteriocins are widespread. Those of *E. coli* are plasmid-specified; such plasmids fall into two groups. The modes of action of different colicins are of great interest. Another group of widely distributed plasmid-borne functions are those for degradation by soil pseudomonads of semi-exotic organic

---

[1] Mutants have now been described in which the regulation of both the utilisation of these compounds and transfer are affected (Klapwijk *et al*. 1978; Petit and Tempé 1978).

compounds. Within this group of plasmids too there are extensive relationships. Also related to each other are the tumorogenic plasmids of *A. tumefaciens*. Here a segment of the plasmid is integrated into the genome of a plant cell, and causes it to synthesize compounds that other individuals of the bacterial strain, and they alone, can utilize. *Streptomyces* spp. carry plasmids that may be implicated in the synthesis or processing of antibiotics.

8
Prospects and Conclusions

The emphasis of plasmid research (and therefore of this book) has been on plasmids of *E. coli* and its relatives, in particular F, ColE1 and some R factors. Although this is a narrow base from which to draw general conclusions, there are inherent constraints on the properties of plasmids, in particular their replication and its control, that define them as a class. But it is not, for instance, obvious that all plasmids must be covalently closed circular molecules, or even be composed of DNA rather than RNA; the methods currently used to isolate them generally depend upon this covalently closed circular property (see Chapter 2), and therefore assume that plasmids will be of this type. Nor is it evident that conjugational systems need to be as complex as those of F-like plasmids.

The ubiquity of plasmids
Only now is it being recognized how common plasmids are in bacteria (see for instance the appendices in Bukhari *et al*. 1977). This realization comes from the development and application of methods for isolating plasmid DNA. Relating phenotypes to such plasmids will often depend upon developing transformation methods for the particular systems. The current view is that the role of plasmids in nature is to carry 'optional' functions. This view is partly held because many plasmids are indeed dispensable (these are, of course, the ones with the functions that are easiest to demonstrate) and partly because of the intuitive feeling that essential functions are best carried by the chromosome. This view may have to be revised.

Genetical methods (Meynell and Datta 1966; Meynell *et al*. 1968; Datta 1975) showed that many plasmids appeared to be related in their transfer properties (the various Fi$^+$ plasmids) and replication (since they fall into incompatibility groups). Experiments employing the annealing and heteroduplex methods have confirmed these suggestions. Thus F is related to R1, R6, R100 and ColV (Sharp *et al*. 1973) and also to a typical Ent plasmid (Santos *et al*. 1975). Different types of plasmids therefore form an interconnected population.

There are a number of examples of independently isolated plasmids (e.g., R factors, Col factors, Ent plasmids) showing indistinguishable properties of part or the whole plasmid, suggesting a common origin. The following are examples:

(1) Similar TOL plasmids were found in independently isolated organisms (Chapter 7).

(2) At least some of the known transposons are widely distributed (Chapters 2 and 6). Laboratory-constructed plasmids acquiring such transposons can be apparently identical to clinical isolates (Heffron *et al*. 1977b). When ampicillin-resistant *Haemophilus influenzae* type b and gonococcal strains appeared, the resistance function was homologous with that of one in *E. coli* (Chapter 6).

(3) After a number of years of use (and abuse) of chloramphenicol, a set of (related) R factors appeared in strains of *Salm. typhi* (Chapter 6). Analogous cases have also been reported among the SmSu plasmids (Grinter and Barth 1976; Chapter 3) and R plasmids of strains of *Shigella* (Crosa *et al*.1977) and *Vibrio* (Hedges and Jacob 1975).

(4) Some of the Ent plasmids form an homogeneous group (Chapter 6).

(5) Plasmids conferring the ability to utilize lactose have been described from a wide range of enterobacterial species. The galactosidases and permeases seem to be closely related to those of *E. coli* (Guiso and Ullmann 1976). In one case, the *lac* region is homologous with that of *E. coli* and carried on a transposon (Cornelis *et al*. 1978; Table 3.7).

We may conclude that, in spite of the very widespread occurrence of drug-resistance and other functions on plasmids, a large proportion of the reported cases are probably due to a few originating events. This being the case, it is not surprising that some novel strains that one might have expected to arise have not yet been encountered. For instance, *Streptococcus pyogenes* remains penicillin-sensitive, and certain pollutants are still non-biodegradable. Therefore, although many opportunities exist for new combinations of genes to be selected for, the appearance of the plasmid required for exploitation of a particular opportunity may be quite long-delayed, depending on rare chance events.

Under laboratory conditions plasmids characterized in a particular host can often be established in very different strains. Examples are the staphylococcal plasmids introduced into *Bacillus subtilis* (Ehrlich 1977) and transfer of the following into *E. coli*: TOL from *Ps. putida* (Benson and Shapiro 1978); Ti from *A. tumefaciens* (Holsters *et al*. 1978b); R plasmids from *Bacteroides ochraceus*, an obligate anaerobe of the mouth (Guiney and

Davis 1978; Saunders 1978), and *Neisseria* (Sox *et al*. 1978); the P-1 group plasmids of *Pseudomonas*. With accumulation of such data on the one hand, and molecular hybridization studies on the other, it will become clearer to what extent plasmids in natural populations are related.

Origin and role in evolution of bacterial populations

The genesis of plasmids in natural populations has not been observed. However, plasmids of *E. coli* have recently been formed using both *in vivo* and *in vitro* methods. Some at least of these depend upon the chromosomal replication origin region (Masters 1975; Hiraga 1976; Yasuda and Hirota 1977; von Mayenburg *et al*. 1978; Messer *et al*. 1978).

The survival of plasmids can be considered in terms of the individual bacteria, of the bacterial populations and of the plasmids themselves. The existence of self-transmissible, mobilizable and non-transmissible plasmids have all to be explained (see Stewart and Levin 1977, for conjugationally transmitted plasmids). The real question is what selective advantage there is for the host bacteria and the plasmids in the maintenance of the autonomous state. Clearly individual bacteria under given selective conditions can benefit from possessing plasmids specifying particular phenotypes. Also, plasmids provide selective advantages to the population as a whole (Anderson 1966). These are likely to be of at least two kinds: (1) the increase in the variability within in the whole population, and (2) the opportunity the plasmid may sometimes provide for transfer and recombination of chromosomal genes. A recent discussion of this problem is by Reanney (1977). From the point of view of the evolutionary constraints, the plasmid and the bacterium are symbionts.

If bacteria with similar chromosomes carry a range of different plasmids, which are dispensable and transmissible by some means, the total number of functions that will be present in the population as a whole can be greatly increased. We can take as a highly simplistic example the type of situation that may be occurring in the soil, although we have no notion how many compounds are in fact available for soil bacteria to degrade. If in a gram of soil each of 10^8 bacteria of a particular taxonomic group were to carry a plasmid capable of specifying one or other of 10^5 pathways, there would on average be 10^3 cells carrying each plasmid type. Also, the real function of R factors in nature might be to defend their hosts against other, antibiotic-producing organisms in the soil. It would be interesting to know whether in soil there exist R factors that confer resistance on any of the 2,000-odd actinomycete-elaborated antibiotics that have been described but are not in clinical use.

The evolutionary potential of organisms depends not just on the amount of variation in the population but also on the amount of recombination. The possibility of recombining genes on plasmids, both self-transmissible and non-self-transmissible, and the alternative modes of genetic exchange, transduction and transformation, must greatly increase the variation upon which natural selection can act. Transposons also add to the means by which genetic material can be formed into novel combinations (see Chapter 3; Kopecko *et al*. 1976; Shapiro *et al*. 1977). Since the range of possible hosts in nature at least for transforming DNA and for plasmids such as RP4 is so large, one feels that at least in Gram-negative bacteria all populations may indeed be connected. It is known that bacterial DNA can be expressed in widely different host species (Timmis *et al*. 1975; Ehrlich 1977). It may indeed be impossible to view bacterial evolution in terms of simple family trees; rather, a network, with converging as well as diverging junctions, may be a more appropriate metaphor.

One problem is that the course of bacterial evolution is ill-defined because, for instance, of the absence of much fossil evidence. There are suggestions from the comparison of sequences of amino acids in proteins that some analogous proteins from apparently related bacteria are quite different, whereas other apparently unrelated bacteria share a common type of protein (Ambler 1978). However, the overall importance of such exchange, and the relative importance of the different mechanisms in such a process, will be difficult to assess.

Plasmids in eukaryotes?
Plasmid-like systems are known in some simple eukaryotes (see Beale and Knowles 1978). An example is the 2-μm species of the yeast *Saccharomyces cerevisiae* (see, for instance, Sanders *et al*. 1977; Livingston and Klein 1977). Another is the double-stranded RNA 'killer particle' also found in *Sacch. cerevisiae* (for a review, see Wickner 1976). Here at least ten chromosomal genes are essential for replication or maintenance of the plasmid, and others are needed for the expression of the killer function. The sizes of these particles are in the range 1.4.–1.7 megadaltons (Leibowitz and Wickner 1976).

Circular DNA species have also been demonstrated in a variety of animal cells, usually in culture (see for instance DeLap *et al*. 1978). However, as well as being perhaps technically more difficult to study in multicellular organisms, plasmids may also turn out to be less common in them. This might be because higher eukaryotes, with their formalized sexual systems, have no special opportunities for the exchange of autonomously replicating DNA. If plasmids are important to them, it will rather be because they modify the genetic constitution of cells within the individual, i.e., be part of the mechanism of differentiation.

As is well known, both chloroplasts and mitochondria contain DNA. In *Saccharomyces*, where the respiratory functions are dispensable, the analogy with plasmids is close (see Linnane and Nagley 1978).

The impact of man

Hitherto, the role of man is most likely to have been in accelerating evolution in bacteria and their plasmids, rather than changing its nature. For instance, although R factors have certainly increased in number, and evolved rapidly, they preceded man's use of antibiotics (see Chapter 6). Now in addition to accelerating bacterial evolution by making numerous changes in the environment, man is taking a direct hand in the manipulation of genetic material. As well as 'genetic engineering' (see below) there are novel techniques, first developed in eukaryotic systems, for fusing protoplasts with the aid of polyethylene glycol. Such fusion has been studied in *Bacillus megaterium* (Fodor *et al*. 1978) and *Streptomyces* (Hopwood and Wright 1978). The latter study showed that the process acts independently of known sex factors and can involve the mixing of two or more complete genomes.

Genetic engineering

This topic inevitably dominates any discussion on the prospects in future work with plasmids. Here man is making recombinants *in vitro* that may not arise frequently in nature. We shall first discuss what seems feasible, and then what may be desirable from different points of view.

As outlined in Chapter 3 (Table 3.9), the essential steps in the technique are the joining *in vitro* of DNA from different sources, and the introduction of the chimaeric molecule into a host, which in principle can be a bacterial or eukaryotic cell, in which it can replicate. It is generally useful to have some selection that allows the recombinant molecules to be detected (see below). A clone carrying a chimaera is an agent for the synthesis in pure form of the chimaeric DNA, and if it is properly transcribed and translated, of its gene products.

There is also what has come to be called '*in vivo* genetic engineering' (for a review see Kleckner *et al*. 1977). This involves the construction of hybrids (so far only of prokaryotic DNA) using genetic rather than biochemical methods, and plasmids with more or less extended host ranges. Examples are hybrids of F (from *E. coli*) carrying nitrogenase genes (involved in nitrogen fixation) from *Klebsiella* (Cannon *et al*. 1976). Another example is the use of RP4 (originally from *Ps. aeruginosa*, but able to replicate in *E. coli*, for instance) to mobilize the transfer of a Ti plasmid between strains of *A. tumefaciens*. Here tandem plasmids arise at a rather high frequency

(Chapter 7). In addition methods have been developed by which RP4, in conjunction with the mutator phage Mu, can pick up any gene (in principle) from any organism in which RP4 can replicate (Faelen and Toussaint 1976; Boucher *et al*.1977). It may often be easier to make recombinants *in vivo* than *in vitro*.

Types of chimaera.   Two rather different objectives exist. One is to make new combinations of prokaryotic DNA. An example is the joining of replication functions from plasmids R6-5 and F*lac* from *E. coli* to genes specifying ampicillin resistance from *Staph. aureus* (Chapter 4; Timmis *et al*. 1975). This resistance function, although coming from a Gram-positive host, is expressed in the *E. coli* background. The second object is to use bacterial hosts and vectors for the study and exploitation of eukaryotic DNA. Morrow *et al*. (1974) showed that DNA from the African clawed toad, *Xenopus laevis*, that coded for ribosomal RNA, could be recombined *in vitro* with a plasmid vector, and that this DNA could be transcribed. Subsequent work (Chang *et al*. 1975; Kedes *et al*. 1975b) has shown that although the pickup of eukaryotic DNA of known function can be demonstrated, and can even be translated, this translation is not faithful. In one case (Chang *et al*. 1975) the complete mitochondrial DNA genome from mouse was placed on an *E. coli* plasmid. There was some protein synthesis directed by this mitochondrial DNA, but this did not correspond to the normal products. Also replication of the chimaera was only from the pSC101 origin. Whether such unfaithful translation will be a basic problem in the exploitation of chimaeras to make eukaryotic gene products is not yet clear. Struhl *et al*. (1976) and Struhl and Davis (1977) and Ratzkin and Carbon (1977) have reported complementation of histidine mutations of *E. coli* by functions carried by λ-yeast and ColE1-yeast chimaeras respectively, implying that, in these cases at least, functional eukaryotic gene products can be formed in prokayotes. Complementation of an arginine mutation and a tryptophan mutation have also been reported (Clarke and Carbon 1978; Walz *et al*. 1978). In the latter case a variant that grew faster was found to contain an IS2 sequence (which carries a promoter) close to the *trp* genes.

Vectors.   The vectors most commonly used thus far fall into five groups. pSC101 was the original vector, and RK2 and RP4 are especially valuable for manipulations involving hosts other than *E. coli*. Of the other three types, those based on ColE1 and phage λ have most advantages. Hybrid λ-ColE1 vectors, themselves made *in vitro*, are also available. These can be grown either as phage particles or as plasmids, depending upon conditions

(Donoghue and Sharp 1978). λdv has also been used. Some of the criteria for a good vector are the following (see also Tables 8.1; 8.2).

(1) Ease of isolation of DNA. Chimaeras based on plaque-forming phage λ can be isolated as phage particles. Those based on ColE1 can also be easily isolated, because they are small and can be present in many copies, especially after chloramphenicol treatment.

(2) The number of endonucleases that can be used to insert foreign DNA. Some of the ColE1 derivatives, particularly, have been 'constructed' so as to contain a single cleavage site for each of a number of endonucleases (Bolivar *et al*. 1977b, c).

(3) Amount of DNA that can be incorporated into it. For plasmids there may not be a clear upper limit, but with phage vectors the problem of packaging into a phage coat determines this quantity.

(4) Whether a means exists for recognizing and/or selecting those vectors that have acquired the desired foreign DNA. The λ derivatives used can only give plaques if DNA has been inserted, because the λ DNA alone is insufficiently large to allow phage particle maturation (Murray *et al*. 1977). Cleavage of plasmid pBR322 (an example of the ColE1 family of vectors) within the genes conferring tetracycline resistance or ampicillin resistance, using any of a number of endonucleases, allows the insertion of alien DNA to be recognized by loss of resistance (Bolivar *et al*. 1977c).

(5) Any vector-borne aids for the expression of inserted DNA. Both λ and ColE1 derivatives exist in which expression of inserted genes is controlled

Table 8.1
Some representative cloning vectors for use in prokaryotes.

Vector	Recognition	Reference
For *E.coli*		
pSC101[1]	Tc^r	Cohen and Chang, 1977
ColE1	immunity to colicin E1	Hershfield *et al*. 1974
pBR322[2]	Ap^r or Tc^r	Bolivar *et al*. 1977b
Plasmid λdv	λ immunity	Mukai *et al*. 1976
Phage λ	λ plaques	Murray *et al*. 1977
For Gram-negative bacteria		
RP4	Ap^r, Km^r, Tc^r	Jacob *et al*. 1976
		Hedges *et al*. 1976
RK2	Ap^r, Km^r, Tc^r	Meyer *et al*. 1975

[1] The original cloning vehicle.
[2] Representative of a family of ColE1 derivatives; all these are obtainable in many copies on chloramphenicol treatment.

Table 8.2
Some examples of the use of cloning vectors in *E.coli*.

Vector	DNA carried	Reference
Prokaryotic-prokaryotic chimaeras		
Replication region of R6–5	Ap[r] ex pl258 from *Staph. aureus*	Timmis *et al.* 1975
pSC101	enterotoxin	So *et al.* 1976
ColE1	*E.coli* genome (in a bank of many chimaeras)	Clarke and Carbon, 1976
pMB9	nitrogen-fixation genes from *Klebsiella*	Cannon *et al.* 1977
Prokaryotic-eukaryotic chimaeras		
λ	*Drosophila*	Thomas *et al.* 1974
pSC101	*Xenopus* rDNA	Morrow *et al.* 1974
	Drosophila	Wensink *et al.* 1974
	Sea urchin histone	Kedes *et al.* 1975a
	mouse mitochondria	Chang *et al.* 1975
		Brown *et al.* 1976
mini-ColE1	rabbit globin	Rabbitts 1976
λgt	Yeast DNA	Struhl *et al.* 1976
ColE1–RSF1010	*Drosophila*	Tanaka *et al.* 1975
	human chorionic somatomammotropin	Shine *et al.* 1977
	somatostatin	Itakura *et al.* 1977

at a high level from vector-borne promoters (Hopkins *et al*. 1976; Backman and Ptashne 1978).

Accounts of the construction of valuable plasmid vectors for *E. coli* are given by Bolivar *et al*. (1977b, c) Chang and Cohen (1978) and Collins and Brüning (1978). Vectors have also been developed for use in the Gram-positive species *Bacillus subtilis* (Ehrlich 1978; Gryczan and Dubnau 1978; Keggins *et al*. 1978), and *Staph. aureus* (Wilson and Baldwin 1978). Hydroxyurea can be used to increase the copy-number of some such plasmids in *B. subtilis* (Shivakumar and Dubnau 1978).

The host cell. Virtually all experiments performed thus far have used *E. coli* strains. There has been discussion on whether, on safety grounds, these are the ideal host strains (see later), but there are great practical advantages in using strains as well-characterized as these. A number of experiments have involved the use of minicell-producing strains; Frazer and Curtiss (1973) showed that plasmid DNA present in minicells produces biologically active enzymes, and therefore minicells offer a considerable purification from chromosomally specified products.

Benefits and risks. 'Genetic engineering' offers clear benefits for both academic research and the development of medical, industrial and agricultural technology. A frequently given example is for the synthesis of insulin and other hormones. Another is the extension of the range of free-living and symbiotic nitrogen-fixing organisms. Some applications would involve the intentional release of organisms into the wider biosphere. Moreover, in any industrial process there is a high risk that the organisms used will escape. The question therefore is: are there any risks that can reasonably be foreseen that make regulations governing safety at work and operation of simple common sense insufficient? The problem lies in the paucity of evidence on which to base an answer. There are those (Chargaff 1976; see Wade 1976) who argue that in the face of conceivable hazard and little knowledge, the risks that would be taken in pursuing recombinant DNA research are too high. Others maintain that there are no obvious hazards (Pritchard 1978); that precautions that are standard in medical microbiology are sufficient; and that it is not justified to restrict or hamper research or to create public anxiety (Davis 1976; Watson 1976). It is of course possible here, as in other branches of science, to devise experiments that no reasonable person would be likely to sanction.

The anxieties (Berg *et al.* 1974) have centred around three types of experiment.

(1) 'Construction of new, autonomously replicating bacterial plasmids that might result in the introduction of genetic determinants for antibiotic resistance or bacterial toxin formation into bacterial strains that do not at present carry such determinants, or construction of new bacterial plasmids containing combinations of resistances to clinically useful antibiotics, unless plasmids containing such combinations of antibiotic resistance determinants already exist in nature.'

(2) 'Linkage of all or segments of the DNAs from oncogenic or other animal viruses to autonomously replicating DNA elements such as bacterial plasmids or other viral DNAs. Such recombinant DNA molecules might be more easily disseminated to bacterial populations in humans and other species, and thus possibly increase the incidence of cancer or other diseases.'

(3) Linkage of 'fragments of animal DNAs to bacterial plasmid DNA or bacteriophage DNA', because 'many types of animal cell DNAs contain sequences common to RNA tumour viruses.'

The arguments for considering that the risks are small, in this type of research, are: that recombinant DNA will not be truly novel, in that substantial opportunities exist in nature for the uptake by cells of foreign DNA; that such recombinant DNA is unlikely to be hazardous; and that one can effectively contain organisms and molecules by physical and biological means.

Clear scientific and economic benefits must be weighed against the possibility of irreversible hazards. It is therefore a political as well as a scientific question. Perhaps it is a social question too; many people must have felt from the experience of the development of nuclear weapons that there are few if any opportunities for a group of interested people (such as scientists) to call a halt to further developments in a given area. It appeared that the advent of genetic engineering involved one such moment (see Berg *et al.* 1974). Other areas of cell biology may involve comparable dangers (see for instance the discussion by Weiss 1975, on the hazards of placing tumour virus genomes into novel backgrounds), but such areas have developed more gradually. Subsequent discussions (Berg *et al.* 1975) resulted in official bodies drawing up guidelines for the conduct of future research with recombinant DNA *in vitro*. Those issued by the National Institutes of Health (NIH), Washington, DC, in July 1978 (National Institutes of Health 1978) will provide the framework for the following discussion.

The basic principle adopted was that, since there might be an element of risk, containment should be an essential consideration in experimental design, and that the level of containment should match the scale of the estimated risk. Also, scientific rewards should be weighed against conceivable hazards. For this reason some types of experiment have been deemed impermissible. These include the formation of recombinants with pathogens and cancer-causing viruses; some experiments with plant pathogens, and those with genes for potent toxins. Also in this category is the transfer of resistance to novel hosts not known to acquire such resistance in nature, if this were to compromise the use of the corresponding drug. However, since the nature of any hazards is unclear, such judgements are inevitably intuitive. It was recognized too that the scale of an experiment (e.g., academic vs. industrial) would affect the extent of any risks, and that containment would create problems of methodology for industry, in medical areas and in agriculture.

With vectors such as RP4 and its transfer-deficient derivatives, that might be used in more exotic hosts, the additional problem exists that they can persist in a wide range of hosts.

The case of 'in vivo genetic engineering' experiments (see earlier) deserves very serious consideration. Plasmids such as RP4, which can pick up fragments of DNA in many hosts and are transmissible between these hosts, seem to be the agents of nature's own 'shotgun' experiments. Therefore in nature 'anything goes' already, at least in a large group of bacteria. We then have to ask whether *in vitro* manipulations by man add significantly to what is already occurring largely through man's other activities, and, if so, whether that is a bad thing. The true and unsatisfactory answer is that we do not know.

Containment. There are two types of containment, physical and biological. The NIH guidelines propose four categories of physical containment, from P1 (minimum risk) to P4, which involves high capital expenditure, and will only be feasible in a few institutions and for rather small-scale experiments. Biological containment involves the use of fastidious hosts, unable to survive in natural environments, and non-transmissible and fastidious vectors, unable to survive outside such hosts. One argument has been about whether *E. coli* is a suitable host organism. Its advantages are that much is known about it; that its properties can be modified conveniently, and that it has been demonstrated that at least some foreign DNA can be expressed within it. On the other hand, it is a normal inhabitant of the human gut; some strains (although not apparently *E. coli* K-12) are or can become pathogenic (see Chapter 6); and genetic exchange is known to occur directly or through intermediate strains between *E. coli* and members of at least 40 other bacterial genera.

For the latter reasons some regard the use of *E. coli* as a 'cardinal folly' (Chargaff 1976) and insist that the only adequate hosts are organisms that cannot colonize man or animals. *Bacillus subtilis* and *Pseudomonas putida*, both soil organisms, have been suggested for this role. It has been pointed out for *Ps. putida* (Chakrabarty 1976) that it is a strict aerobe, non-pathogenic and unable to grow at human body temperatures (but see Gilardi 1972). *E. coli* K-12 is unable to compete effectively with the normal intestinal flora of humans. Further, neither an *E. coli* strain nor a transmissible R factor that were used routinely in a laboratory without special precautions could be detected in the stools of those working with them (Petrocheilou and Richmond 1977). Derivatives of *E. coli* K-12 are therefore considered by NIH and other bodies to be acceptable hosts (National Institutes of Health 1978 p.33123). A number of attenuated strains of *E. coli* K-12, unable to survive outside defined laboratory conditions, are being developed and improved. Although more robust *E. coli* K-12 strains do not flourish in the human gut, they can survive sufficiently for plasmid transfer from them to have been demonstrated there (Anderson 1975b; Smith 1975a). For this reason *E. coli* K-12 strains harbouring transmissible plasmids are not sanctioned for use in DNA cloning experiments. Exchange of plasmid DNA by transformation does not depend upon efficient survival of the donor strain but bacterial and plasmid DNA are rapidly degraded by low dilutions of rat intestinal contents (Maturin and Curtiss 1977).

The different combinations of DNA to be cloned and of vectors and hosts have been categorized by NIH in the U.S.A. and under the auspices of comparable bodies in the U.K. (the Medical Research Council) and other countries. Since these regulations are continually under review the interested reader will refer to the appropriate body for the most recent details. Experiments with DNA from mammals and their viruses are considered to warrant the highest degrees of containment. That from non-pathogenic bacteria can be cloned under conditions similar to those used for handling routine clinical isolates. A recent move in the U.S.A. has been to exempt recombinant molecules derived entirely from large groups of species that are known to exchange genetic material (National Institutes of Health 1978).

Summary

Plasmids are ubiquitous. There are extensive relationships between many plasmids both within and between species. They have probably always played a major role in providing variability upon which natural selection has acted. This is both by increasing the number of functions a population as a whole can carry, and by providing a vehicle for genetic exchange. The microbial world is dramatically affected by mankind's industrial, agricultural and medical activities. The amount that genetic engineering *in vivo* and *in vitro* could add to this process may be small.

References

The following abbreviations have been used: *AAC*: Antimicrobial Agents and Chemotherapy; *Ann. Rev. Micro.*: Annual Reviews of Microbiology; *Bact. Rev.*: Bacteriological Reviews; *BBA*: Biochimica Biophysica Acta; *BBRC*: Biochemical and Biophysical Research Communications; *Biochem.*: Biochemistry; *C.R. Acad. Sci.*: Comptes rendus hebdomadaires des Séances de l'Academie des Sciences, France; *CSH*: Cold Spring Harbor Symposia in Quantitative Biology; *Gen.*: Genetics; *Gen. Res.*: Genetical Research (Cambridge); *J. App. Bact.*: Journal of Applied Bacteriology; *JB*: Journal of Bacteriology; *JBC*: Journal of Biological Chemistry; *JGM*: Journal of General Microbiology; *J. Hyg.*: Journal of Hygiene (Cambridge); *JMB*: Journal of Molecular Biology; *J. Med. Micro.*: Journal of Medical Microbiology; *MGG*: Molecular and General Genetics; *Microbiology 1974–*: A series edited by D. Schlessinger for the American Society for Microbiology. *PNAS*: Proceedings of the National Academy of Sciences, Washington; *Microbiol. Rev.*: Microbiological Reviews; *Nat.*: Nature (Lond); *NNB*: Nature New Biology; *Virol.*: Virology.

ABE, M. (1974). The replication of prophage P1 DNA. *MGG* **132**, 63–72.

ACHTMAN, M. (1971). A semi-automatic technique for conducting many bacterial matings concurrently. *Gen. Res.* **17**, 261–6.

—— (1973a). Transfer-positive J-independent revertants of the F factor in *E. coli* K12. *Gen. Res.* **21**, 67–77.

—— (1973b). Genetics of the sex factor F in Enterobacteriaceae. *Current Topics in Microbiology and Immunology* **60**, 79–123.

—— (1975). Mating aggregates in *Escherichia coli* conjugation. *JB* **123**, 505–15.

—— KENNEDY, N. and SKURRAY, R. (1977). Cell–cell interactions in conjugating *Escherichia coli*: role of *traT* protein in surface exclusion. *PNAS* **74**, 5104–8.

—— KUSECEK, B. and TIMMIS, K. (1978a). *tra* cistrons and proteins encoded by the *Escherichia coli* antibiotic resistance plasmid R6-5. *MGG* **163**, 169–79.

—— MORELLI, G. and SCHWUCHOW, S. (1978b). Cell–cell interactions in conjugating *Escherichia coli*: role of F pili and fate of mating aggregates. *JB* **135**, 1053–61.

—— SCHWUCHOW, S., HELMUTH, R., MORELLI, G. and MANNING, P. A. (1978c). Cell–cell interactions in conjugating *Escherichia coli*: Con⁻ mutants and stabilization of mating aggregates. *MGG* **164**, 171–83.

—— SKURRAY, R. A., THOMPSON, R., HELMUTH, R., HALL, S., BEUTIN, L. and CLARK, A. J. (1978d). Assignment of *tra* cistrons to *Eco*RI fragments of F sex factor DNA. *JB* **133**, 1383–92.

—— WILLETTS, N. and CLARK, A. J. (1972). Conjugational complementation analysis of transfer-deficient mutants of F*lac* in *Escherichia coli*. *JB* **110**, 831–42.

AKAGAWA, H., OKANISHI, M. *and* UMEZAWA, H. (1975). A plasmid involved in chloramphenicol production in *Streptomyces venezuelae*: evidence from genetic mapping. *JGM* **90**, 336–46.

AKIBA, T., KOYAME, K., ISHIKI, Y. *and* KUMIRA, S. (1960). On the mechanism of the development of multiple drug-resistance clones of *Shigella*. *Japan. J. Microbiol.* **4**, 219.

ALBERTS, B. *and* STERNGLANZ, R. (1977). Recent excitement in the DNA replication problem. *Nat.* **269**, 655–61.

AMBLER, R. P. (1978). Aminoacid sequences and bacterial phylogeny. In: *Evolution of Protein Molecules*, H. Matsubara *and* T. Yamanaka, eds. Univ. of Tokyo Press.

AMYES, S. G. B. *and* SMITH, J. T. (1974). R-factor trimethoprim resistance mechanism on insusceptible target site. *BBRC* **58**, 412–18.

ANDERSON, E. S. (1966). Possible importance of transfer factors in bacterial evolution. *Nat.* **209**, 637.

—— (1968). The ecology of transferable drug resistance in the enterobacteria. *Ann. Rev. Micro.* **22**, 131–80.

—— (1969). Ecology and epidemiology of transferable drug resistance. In *Bacterial Episomes and Plasmids*, G. E. W. Wolstenholme *and* M. O'Connor, eds. J. and A. Churchill Ltd.

—— (1975a). The problem and implications of chloramphenicol resistance in the typhoid bacillus. *J. Hyg.* **74**, 289–99.

—— (1975b). Viability of, and transfer of a plasmid from *E. coli* K12 in the human intestine. *Nat.* **255**, 502–4.

—— HUMPHREYS, G. O. *and* WILLSHAW, G. A. (1975). The molecular relatedness of R factors in enterobacteria of human and animal origin. *JGM* **91**, 376–382.

—— *and* THRELFALL, E. J. (1974). The characterization of plasmids in the enterobacteria. *J. Hyg.* **72**, 471–87.

ANDERSON, J. D. (1975). Factors that may prevent transfer of antibiotic resistance between Gram-negative bacteria in the gut. *J. Med. Micro.* **8**, 83–8.

—— GILLESPIE W. A. *and* RICHMOND, M. H. (1973a). Chemotherapy and antibiotic-resistance transfer between enterobacteria in the human gastro-intestinal tract. *J. Med. Micro.* **6**, 461–73.

—— INGRAM, L. C., RICHMOND, M. H. *and* WIEDEMANN, B. (1973b). Studies on the nature of plasmids arising from conjugation in the human gastro-intestinal tract. *J. Med. Micro.* **6**, 475–86.

ANDREOLI, P. M., OVERBEEKE, N., VELTKAMP, E., VAN EMBDEN, J. D. A. *and* NIJKAMP, H. J. J. (1978) Genetic map of the bacteriocinogenic plasmid Clo DF13 derived by insertion of the transposon Tn901. *MGG* **160**, 1–11.

ANDRÉS, I., SLOCOMBE, P. M., CABELLO, F., TIMMIS, J. K., LURZ, R., BURKARDT, H. J. *and* TIMMIS, K. N. (1979). Plasmid replication functions. II. Cloning analysis. *MGG* **168**, 1–15.

ANDRESDOTTIR, V. *and* MASTERS, M. (1978). Evidence that F'*lac* replicates asynchronously during the cell cycle of *Escherichia coli* B/r. *MGG* **163**, 205–12.

ANON. (1975). *E. coli* enteritis. *Lancet* **II**, 1131–2.

ANTHONY, W. M., DEONIER, R. C., LEE, H. J., HU, S., OHTSUBO, E., DAVIDSON, N. *and* BRODA, P. (1974). Electron microscope heteroduplex studies of sequence relations among plasmids of *Escherichia coli*. IX. Note on the deletion mutant of F, FΔ(33–43). *JMB* **89**, 647–50.

ASERKOFF, B. *and* BENNETT, J. V. (1969). Effect of antibiotic therapy in acute salmonellosis in the faecal excretion of salmonellae. *New England Journal of Medicine* **281**, 636–40.

AUSTIN, S., STERNBERG N. *and* YARMOLINSKY, M. (1978). Miniplasmids of bacteriophage P1. I. Stringent plasmid replication does not require elements that regulate the lytic cycle. *JMB* **120**, 297–309.

BACHMANN, B. J., LOW, K. B. *and* TAYLOR, A. L. (1976). Recalibrated linkage map of *Escherichia coli* K-12. *Bact. Rev.* **40**, 116–67.

BACKMAN, K. *and* PTASHNE, M. (1978). Maximizing gene expression on a plasmid using recombination *in vitro*. *Cell* **13**, 65–71.

BANNISTER, D. (1970). Explanation of the apparent association of host specificity determinants with fi⁺ R factors. *JGM* **61**, 283–87.

—— *and* GLOVER, S. W. (1968). Restriction and modification of bacteriophages by R⁺ strains of *Escherichia coli* K12. *BBRC* **30**, 735–38.

BARNES, W. M. (1977). Plasmid detection and sizing in single colony lysates. *Science* **195**, 393–4.

BARTH, P. T. (1979). Plasmid RP4, with *Escherichia coli* DNA inserted *in vitro*, mediates chromosome transfer. *Plasmid* **2**, 130–6.

—— DATTA, N., HEDGES, R. W. *and* GRINTER, N. J. (1976). Transposition of a deoxyribonucleic acid sequence encoding trimethoprim and streptomycin resistance from R483 to other replicons. *JB* **125**, 800–10.

—— *and* GRINTER, N. J. (1974). Comparison of the deoxyribonucleic acid molecular weights and homologies of plasmids conferring linked resistance to streptomycin and sulphonamides. *JB* **120**, 618–30.

—— —— (1975). Assay of deoxyribonucleic acid homology using a single-strand-specific nuclease at 75° C. *JB* **121**, 434–41.

—— —— *and* BRADLEY, D. E. (1978a). Conjugal transfer system of plasmid RP4: analysis by transposon 7 insertion. *JB* **133**, 43–52.

—— RICHARDS, H. *and* DATTA, N. (1978b). Copy numbers of co-existing plasmids in *Escherichia coli* K-12 *JB* **135**, 760–65.

BASTIA, D. (1978). Determination of restriction sites and the nucleotide sequence surrounding the relaxation site of ColE1. *JMB* **124**, 601–34.

BAYLEY, S. A., DUGGLEBY, C. J., WORSEY, M. J., WILLIAMS, P. A., HARDY, K. G. *and* BRODA, P. (1977). Two modes of loss of the Tol function from *Pseudomonas putida* mt-2. *MGG* **154**, 203–4.

BAZARAL, M. *and* HELINSKI, D. R. (1970). Replication of a bacterial plasmid and an episome in *Escherichia coli*. *Biochem.* **9**, 399–406.

BAZZICALUPO, P. *and* TOCCHINI-VALENTINI, G. P. (1972). Curing of an *Escherichia coli* episome by rifampicin. *PNAS* **69**, 298–300.

BEALE, G. *and* KNOWLES J. (1978). *Extranuclear Genetics*. Edward Arnold, London.

BEARD, J. P. *and* BISHOP, S. F. (1975). Role of the cell surface in bacterial mating: requirement for intact mucopeptide in donors for the expression of surface exclusion in R⁺ strains of *Escherichia coli*. *JB* **123**, 916–20.

—— *and* CONNOLLY, J. C. (1975). Detection of a protein, similar to the sex pilus subunit, in the outer membrane of *Escherichia coli* cells carrying a de-repressed F-like R factor. *JB* **122**, 59–65.

BENNETT, P. M., GRINSTED, J., CHOI, C. L. *and* RICHMOND, M. H. (1978). Characterisation of Tn501, a transposon determining resistance to mercuric ions. *MGG* **159**, 101–6.

—— —— *and* RICHMOND, M. H. (1977). Transposition of TnA does not generate deletions. *MGG* **154**, 205–11.

—— *and* RICHMOND, M. H. (1976). Translocation of a discrete piece of deoxyribonucleic acid carrying an *amp* gene between replicons in *Escherichia coli*. *JB* **126**, 1–6.

BENSON, S. *and* SHAPIRO, J. (1978). TOL is a broad-host-range plasmid. *JB* **135**, 278–80.

BENVENISTE, R. *and* DAVIES, J. (1973). Aminoglycoside antibiotic-inactivating enzymes in actinomycetes similar to those present in clinical isolates of antibiotic-resistant bacteria. *PNAS* **70**, 2276–80.

BENZINGER, R. (1978). Transfection of Enterobacteriaceae and its applications. *Microbiol. Rev*. **42**, 194–236.

BERG, D. (1974). Genes of phage λ essential for λ*dv* plasmids. *Virol*. **62**, 224–233.

—— (1977). Insertion and excision of the transposable kanamycin resistance determinant TnK(1). In: *DNA Insertion Elements, Episomes and Plasmids*. J. Shapiro, S. Adhya and A. I. Bukhari, eds., Cold Spring Harbor.

—— DAVIES, J. E., ALLET, B. *and* ROCHAIX, J-D. (1975). Transposition of R factor genes to bacteriophage lambda. *PNAS* **72**, 3628–32.

BERG, P., BALTIMORE, D., BOYER, H. W., COHEN, S. N., DAVIS, R. W., HOGNESS, D. S., NATHANS, D., ROBLIN, R. O., WATSON, J. D., WEISSMAN, S. *and* ZINDER, N. (1974). Potential biohazards of recombinant DNA molecules. *Science* **185**, 303; *PNAS* **71**, 2593–4; *Nat*. **250**, 175.

—— —— BRENNER, S., ROBLIN, R. O. III, *and* SINGER, M. F. (1975). Summary statement of the Asilomar conference on recombinant DNA molecules. *PNAS* **72**, 1981–4; *Nat*. **255**, 442–4.

BERINGER, J. E., HOGGAN, S. A. *and* JOHNSTON, A. W. B. (1978). Linkage mapping in *Rhizobium leguminosarum* by means of R plasmid-mediated recombination. *JGM* **104**, 201–7.

BEZANSON, G. S. *and* GOEBEL, W. (1979). *In vitro* system for the replication of the mini R1 factor Rsc11. *MGG* **170**, 49–56.

BIBB, M. J., FREEMAN, R. F. *and* HOPWOOD, D. A. (1977). Physical and genetical characterisation of a second sex factor, SCP2, for *Streptomyces coelicolor* A3(2). *MGG* **154**, 155–66.

—— WARD, J. M. *and* HOPWOOD, D. A. (1978). Transformation of plasmid DNA into *Streptomyces* at high frequency. *Nat*. **274**, 398–400.

BIRD, R. E., CHANDLER, M. *and* CARO, L. (1976). Suppression of an *Escherichia coli dnaA* mutation by the integrated R factor R100.1: change of chromosome replication origin in synchronized cultures. *JB* **126**, 1215–23.

—— *and* TOMIZAWA, J. (1978). Ribonucleotide-deoxyribonucleotide linkages at the origin of DNA replication of colicin E1 plasmid. *JMB* **120**, 137–143.

BISWAS, G., COMER, S. *and* SPARLING, P. F. (1976). Chromosomal location of antibiotic resistance genes in *Neisseria gonorrhoea*. *JB* **125**, 1207–10.

BLAIR, D. G. *and* HELINSKI, D. R. (1975). Relaxation complexes of plasmid DNA and protein. I. strand specific association of protein and DNA in the relaxed complexes of plasmids ColE1 and ColE2. *JBC* **250**, 8785–9.

—— SHERRATT, D. G., CLEWELL, D. B. *and* HELINSKI, D. R. (1972). Isolation of supercoiled colicinogenic factor E1 DNA sensitive to ribonuclease and alkali. *PNAS* **69**, 2518–22.

BOLIVAR, F., BETLACH, M. C., HEYNECKER, H. L., SHINE, J., RODRIGUEZ, R. L. *and* BOYER, H. W. (1977a). Origin of replication of pBR345 plasmid DNA. *PNAS* **74**, 5265–9.

—— RODRIGUEZ, R. L., BETLACH, M. C. *and* BOYER, H. W. (1977b). Construction and characterization of new cloning vehicles. I. Ampicillin resistant derivatives of the plasmid pMB9. *Gene* **2**, 75–93.

—— —— GREENE, P. J., BETLACH, M. C., HEYNECKER, H. L., BOYER, H. W., CROSA, J. H. *and* FALKOW, S. (1977c). Construction and characterization of new cloning vehicles. II. A multiple cloning system. *Gene* **2**, 95–113.

BOMHOFF, G., KLAPWIJK, P. M., KESTER, H. C. M., SCHILPEROORT, R. A.,

HERNALSTEENS, J. P. *and* SCHELL, J. (1976). Octopine and nopaline synthesis and breakdown genetically controlled by a plasmid of *Agrobacterium tumefaciens*. *MGG* **145**, 177–81.

BONHOEFFER, F., HOESSELBARTH, R. *and* LEHMAN, K. (1967). Dependence of the conjugal DNA transfer on DNA synthesis. *JMB*. **29**, 539–41.

BOUCHÉ, J-P., ZECHEL, K. *and* KORNBERG, A. (1975). *dnaG* gene product, a rifampicin-resistant RNA polymerase, initiates the conversion of a single-stranded coliphage DNA to its duplex replicative form. *JBC* **250**, 5995–6001.

BOUCHER, C., BERGERON, B., BARATE DE BERTALMIO, M. *and* DÉNARIÉ, J. (1977). Introduction of bacteriophage Mu into *Pseudomonas solanacearum* and *Rhizobium meliloti* using R factor RP4. *JGM* **98**, 253–63.

BOULNOIS, G. J. *and* WILKINS, B. M. (1978). A ColI-specified product, synthesised in newly infected recipients, limits the amount of DNA transferred during conjugation in *Escherichia coli* K-12. *JB* **133**, 1–9.

BOWMAN, C. M., DAHLBERG, J. E., IKEMURA, T., KONISKY, J. *and* NOMURA, M. (1971). Specific inactivation of 16S ribosomal RNA induced by colicin E3 *in vitro*. *PNAS* **68**, 964–8.

BRADLEY, D. E. (1967). Ultrastructure of bacteriophages and bacteriocins. *Bact. Rev*. **31**, 230–314.

—— (1977). Pili and associated bacteriophages in *Pseudomonas aeruginosa*. In: *Microbiology 1977*.

BRENNER, D. J., FANNING, G. R., JOHNSON, K. E., CITARELLA, R. V. *and* FALKOW, S. (1969). Polynucleotide sequence relationships among members of Enterobacteriaceae. *JB* **98**, 637–50.

BRINTON, C. C. (1971). The properties of sex pili, the viral nature of conjugal genetic transfer systems, and some possible approaches to the control of bacterial drug resistance. *Critical Reviews in Microbiology*. **1**, 105–60.

—— GEMSKI, P. *and* CARNAHAN, J. (1964). A new type of bacterial pilus genetically controlled by the fertility factor of *E. coli* K-12 and its role in chromosome transfer. *PNAS* **52**, 776–83.

BRODA, P. (1967). The formation of Hfr strains in *Escherichia coli* K12. *Gen. Res*. **9**, 35–47.

—— (1975). Transience of the donor state in an *Escherichia coli* K12 strain carrying a repressed R factor. *MGG* **138**, 65–9.

—— BAYLEY, S. A., DUGGLEBY, C. J., HEINARU, A., WORSEY, M. J. *and* WILLIAMS, P. A. (1978). TOL plasmids in *Pseudomonas* species. In: *Microbiology 1978*.

—— BECKWITH, J. R. *and* SCAIFE, J. (1964). The characterisation of a new type of F-prime factor in *Escherichia coli* K12. *Gen. Res*. **5**, 489–94.

—— *and* COLLINS, J. F. (1978). Role of simple and complex aggregates in Hfr × F⁻ matings. *Gen. Res*. **31**, 167–75.

—— *and* MEACOCK, P. (1971). Isolation and characterization of Hfr strains from a recombination-deficient strain of *Escherichia coli*. *MGG* **113**, 166–73.

BRODT, P., LEGGATT, F. *and* IYER, R. (1974). Absence of a pilus receptor for filamentous phage Ike. *Nat*. **249**, 856–58.

BROWN, W. M., WATSON, R. M., VINOGRAD, J., TAIT, K. M., BOYER, H. W. *and* GOODMAN, H. M. (1976). The structures and fidelity of replication of mouse mitochondrial DNA-pSC101 *Eco*RI recombinant plasmids grown in *E. coli* K12. *Cell* **7**, 517–30.

BRYAN, L. E., SEMAKA, S. D., VAN DEN ELZEN, H. M., KINNEAR, J. E. *and* WHITEHOUSE, R. L. S. (1973). Characteristics of R931 and other *Pseudomonas aeruginosa* R-factors. *AAC* **3**, 625–37.

—— SHAHRABADI, M. S. *and* VAN DEN ELZEN, H. M. (1974). Gentamicin resistance in *Pseudomonas aeruginosa*: R-factor-mediated resistance. *AAC* **6**, 191–9.

—— *and* VAN DEN ELZEN, H. M. (1977). Spectrum of antibiotic resistance in clinical isolates of *Pseudomonas aeruginosa*. In: *Microbiology, 1977*.

BUKHARI, A. I. *and* ZIPSER, D. (1972). Random insertion of Mu-1 DNA within a single gene. *NNB* **236**, 240–3.

—— SHAPIRO, J. A. *and* ADHYA, S. (1977). *DNA Insertion Elements, Episomes and Plasmids*. Cold Spring Harbor.

BURMAN, L. (1977). Expression of R-plasmid functions during anaerobic growth of an *Escherichia coli* K-12 host. *JB* **131**, 69–75.

—— *and* OSTENSSON, R. (1978). Efficient transfer of conjugative plasmids by multipoint inoculation and some observations on host range and prevalence of R plasmids. *Plasmid* **1**, 346–56.

CABELLO, F., TIMMIS, K. *and* COHEN, S. N. (1976). Replication control in a composite plasmid constructed by *in vitro* linkage of two distinct replicons. *Nat.* **259**, 285–90.

CAIRNS, J. (1963). The bacterial chromosome and its manner of replicating as seen by autoradiography. *JMB* **6**, 208–13.

CALOS, M. P., JOHNSRUD, L. *and* MILLER, J. H. (1978). DNA sequences at the integration sites of the insertion element IS1. *Cell* **13**, 411–18.

CAMPBELL, A. (1962). Episomes. *Advances in Genetics* **11**, 101–45.

CANNON, F. C., DIXON, R. A. *and* POSTGATE, J. R. (1976). Derivation and properties of F-prime factors in *Escherichia coli* carrying nitrogen fixation genes from *Klebsiella pneumoniae*. *JGM* **93**, 111–25.

—— *and* POSTGATE, J. R. (1976). Expression of *Klebsiella* nitrogen fixation genes (*nif*) in *Azotobacter*. *Nat.* **260**, 271–2.

—— REIDEL, G. E. *and* AUSUBEL, F. M. (1977). Recombinant plasmid that carries part of the nitrogen fixation (*nif*) gene cluster of *Klebsiella pneumoniae*. *PNAS* **74**, 2963–7.

CANOSI, U., MORELLI, G. *and* TRAUTNER, T. A. (1978). The relationship between molecular structure and transformation efficiency in some *S. aureus* plasmids isolated from *B. subtilis*. *MGG* **166**, 259–67.

CHABBERT, Y. A., SCAVIZZI, M. R., WITCHITZ, J. L., GERBAUD, G. R. *and* BOUANCHAUD, D. H. (1972). Incompatibility groups and the classification of fi^- resistance factors. *JB* **112**, 666–75.

CHAKRABARTY, A. M. (1972). Genetic basis of the biodegradation of salicylate in *Pseudomonas*. *JB* **112**, 815–23.

—— (1973). Genetic fusion of incompatible plasmids in *Pseudomonas*. *PNAS* **70**, 1641–4.

—— (1974). Dissociation of a degradative plasmid aggregate in *Pseudomonas*. *JB* **118**, 815–20.

—— (1976). Molecular cloning in *Pseudomonas*. In: *Microbiology, 1976*.

—— CHOU, G. *and* GUNSALUS, I. C. (1973). Genetic regulation of octane dissimilation plasmid in *Pseudomonas*. *PNAS* **70**, 1137–40.

—— FRIELLO, D. A. *and* BOPP, L. H. (1978). Transposition of plasmid DNA segments specifying hydrocarbon degradation and their expression in various microorganisms. *PNAS* **75**, 3109–12.

CHAMPOUX, J. J. (1977). Renaturation of complementary single-stranded DNA circles: complete rewinding facilitated by the DNA untwisting enzyme. *PNAS* **74**, 5328–32.

CHANDLER, M., ALLET, B., GALLAY, E., BOY DE LA TOUR, E. *and* CARO, L. (1977a). Involvement of IS1 in the dissociation of the r-determinant and RTF components of the plasmid R100.1. *MGG* **153**, 289–95.

—— SILVER, L. *and* CARO, L. (1977b). Suppression of an *Escherichia coli dnaA* mutation by the integrated R factor R100.1. III. Origin of chromosome replication during exponential growth. *JB* **131**, 421–30.

—— —— FREY, J. *and* CARO, L. (1977c). Suppression of an *E. coli dnaA* mutation by the integrated R factor R100.1: generation of small plasmids following integration. *JB* **130**, 303–11.

—— —— ROTH, Y. *and* CARO, L. (1976). Chromosome replication in an Hfr strain of *Escherichia coli*. *JMB* **104**, 517–23.

CHANDLER, P. M. *and* KRISHNAPILLAI, V. (1974a). Phenotypic properties of R factors of *Pseudomonas aeruginosa*: R factors readily transferable between *Pseudomonas* and the Enterobacteriaceae. *Gen. Res.* **23**, 239–50.

—— —— (1974b). Phenotypic properties of R factors of *Pseudomonas aeruginosa*: R factors transferable only in *Pseudomonas aeruginosa*. *Gen. Res.* **23**, 251–7.

—— —— (1977). Characterization of *Pseudomonas aeruginosa* de-repressed R plasmids. *JB* **130**, 596–603.

CHANG, A. C. Y. *and* COHEN, S. N. (1978). Construction and characterization of amplifiable multicopy DNA cloning vehicles derived from the P15A cryptic miniplasmid. *JB* **134**, 1141–56.

—— LANSMAN, R. A., CLAYTON, D. A. *and* COHEN, S. N. (1975). Studies of mouse mitochondrial DNA in *Escherichia coli*: structure and function of the eucaryotic-procaryotic chimeric plasmids. *Cell* **6**, 231–44.

CHANG, B. J. *and* HOLLOWAY, B. W. (1977). Bacterial mutation affecting plasmid maintenance in *Pseudomonas aeruginosa*. *JB* **130**, 943–5.

CHANG, S. *and* COHEN, S. N. (1977). *In vivo* site-specific genetic recombination promoted by the *Eco*RI restriction endonuclease. *PNAS* **74**, 4811–15.

—— —— (1979). High frequency transformation of *Bacillus subtilis* protoplasts by plasmid DNA. *MGG* **168**, 111–15.

CHARGAFF, E. (1976). On the dangers of genetic meddling. *Science* **192**, 938–40.

CHESNEY, R. H. *and* SCOTT, J. R. (1978). Suppression of a thermosensitive *dnaA* mutation of *Escherichia coli* by bacteriophage P1 and P7. *Plasmid* **1**, 145–63.

CHILTON, M-D., DRUMMOND, M. H., MERLO, D. J. *and* SCIAKY, D. (1978a). Highly conserved DNA of Ti plasmids overlaps T-DNA maintained in plant tumours. *Nat.* **275**, 147–9.

—— —— —— MONTOYA, A. L., GORDON, M. P. *and* NESTER, E. W. (1977). Stable incorporation of plasmid DNA into higher plant cells: the molecular basis of crown gall tumorigenesis. *Cell* **11**, 263–71.

—— FARRAND, S. K., LEVIN, R. *and* NESTER, E. W. (1976). RP4 promotion of transfer of a large *Agrobacterium* plasmid which confers virulence. *Genetics* **83**, 609–18.

—— MONTOYA, A. L., MERLO, D. J., DRUMMOND, M. H., NUTTER, R., GORDON, M. P. *and* NESTER, E. W. (1978b). Restriction endonuclease mapping of plasmid that confers oncogenicity upon *Agrobacterium tumefaciens* strain B6-806. *Plasmid* **1**, 254–69.

CHOU, G. I. N., KATZ, D. *and* GUNSALUS, I. C. (1974). Fusion and incompatibility of camphor and octane plasmids in *Pseudomonas*. *PNAS* **71**, 2675–78.

CLARK, A. J. (1963). Genetic analysis of a 'double male' strain of *Escherichia coli* K-12. *Gen.* **48**, 105–20.

—— MAAS, W. K. *and* LOW, B. (1969). Production of a merodiploid strain from a double male strain of *E. coli* K12. *MGG* **105**, 1–15.

—— *and* MARGULIES, A. D. (1965). Isolation and characterization of recombination deficient mutants of *E. coli* K12. *PNAS* **53**, 451–9.

CLARK, D., WEISS, A. A. *and* SILVER, S. (1977). Mercury and organomercurial resistances determined by plasmids in *Pseudomonas*. *JB* **132**, 186–96.

CLARKE, L. and CARBON, J. (1976). A colony bank containing synthetic ColE1 hybrid plasmids representative of the entire *E. coli* genome. *Cell* **9**, 91–9.

—— —— (1978). Functional expression of cloned yeast DNA in *Escherichia coli*: specific complementation of arginosuccinate lyase (*argH*) mutations. *JMB* **120**, 517–32.

CLEWELL, D. B. (1972). Nature of ColE1 plasmid replication in *Escherichia coli* in the presence of chloramphenicol. *JB* **110**, 667–76.

—— EVENCHICK, B. and CRANSTON, J. W. (1972). Direct inhibition of ColE1 plasmid DNA replication in *Escherichia coli* by rifampicin. *NNB* **237**, 29–31.

—— and HELINSKI, D. R. (1969). Supercoiled circular DNA protein complex in *Escherichia coli*: purification and induced conversion to an open circular DNA form. *PNAS* **62**, 1159–66.

—— —— (1970). Properties of a supercoiled DNA-protein relaxation complex and strand specificity of the relaxation event. *Biochem.* **9**, 4428–40.

CLOWES, R. C. (1972). Molecular structure of bacterial plasmids. *Bact. Rev.* **36**, 361–404.

COHEN, S. N. (1975). The manipulation of genes. *Scientific American* July, 24–33.

—— (1976). Transposable genetic elements and plasmid evolution. *Nat.* **263**, 731–8.

—— and CHANG, A. C. Y. (1977). Revised interpretation of the origin of the pSC101 plasmid. *JB* **132**, 734–7.

—— —— and HSU, L. (1972). Non-chromosomal antibiotic resistance in bacteria: genetic transformation of *Escherichia coli* by R factor DNA. *PNAS* **69**, 2110–14.

—— and MILLER, C. A. (1969). Multiple molecular species of circular R-factor DNA isolated from *Escherichia coli*. *Nat.* **224**, 1273–7.

—— —— (1970a). Non-chromosomal antibiotic resistance in bacteria. II. Molecular nature of R-factors isolated from *Proteus mirabilis* and *Escherichia coli*. *JMB* **50**, 671–87.

—— —— (1970b). Non-chromosomal antibiotic resistance in bacteria. III. Isolation of the discrete transfer unit of the R-factor R1. *PNAS* **67**, 510–16.

COLLINS, J. and BRÜNING, H. J. (1978). Plasmids useable as gene-cloning vectors in an *in vitro* packaging by coliphage λ: "cosmids". *Gene* **4**, 85–107.

—— and PRITCHARD, R. H. (1973). Relationship between chromosome replication and F'*lac* episome replication in *Escherichia coli*. *JMB* **78**, 143–55.

—— WILLIAMS, P. and HELINSKI, D. R. (1975). Plasmid ColE1 DNA replication in *Escherichia coli* strains temperature sensitive for DNA replication. *MGG* **136**, 273–89.

COLLINS, J. F. and BRODA, P. (1975). Motility, diffusion and cell concentration affect pair formation in *Escherichia coli*. *Nat.* **258**, 722–3.

CONTENTE, S. and DUBNAU, D. (1979). Characterization of plasmid transformation in *Bacillus subtilis*: kinetic properties and the effect of DNA conformation *MGG* **167**, 251–8.

COOKE, M., MEYNELL, E. and LAWN, A. M. (1970). Mutant Hfr strains defective in transfer: restoration by F-like and I-like de-repressed R factors. *Gen. Res.* **16**, 101–12.

COOPER, S. (1972). Relationship of F*lac* replication and chromosome replication. *PNAS* **69**, 2706–10.

CORNELIS, G., GHOSAL, D. and SAEDLER, H. (1978). Tn951: a new transposon carrying a lactose operon. *MGG* **160**, 215–24.

COSLOY, S. D. and OISHI, M. (1973). Genetic transformation in *Escherichia coli* K12. *PNAS* **70**, 84–7.

COURVALIN, P., WEISBLUM, B. and DAVIES, J. (1977). Aminoglycoside modifying enzyme of an antibiotic-producing bacterium acts as a determinant of antibiotic resistance in *Escherichia coli*. *PNAS* **74**, 999–1003.

COUTURIER, M., JANSSENS, J., BEX, F., DESMYTER, A. *and* BONNEVALLE, I. (1979). Construction *in vitro* of "Phage-plasmid" chimerae; a new tool to analyse the mechanism of plasmid maintenance. *MGG* **169**, 113–16.

COZZARELLI, N. R., KELLY, R. B. *and* KORNBERG A. (1968). A minute circular DNA from *Escherichia coli* 15. *PNAS* **60**, 992–9.

CRESS, D. E. *and* KLINE, B. L. (1976). Isolation and characterization of *Escherichia coli* chromosomal mutations affecting plasmid copy number. *JB* **125**, 635–42.

CROSA, J. H., BRENNER, D. J. *and* FALKOW, S. (1973). Use of a single-strand specific nuclease for analysis of bacterial and plasmid deoxyribonucleic acid homo- and heteroduplexes. *JB* **115**, 904–11.

—— LUTTROPP, L. K. *and* FALKOW, S. (1976a). Covalently closed circular DNA molecules deficient in superhelical density as intermediate forms in plasmid life cycle. *Nat.* **261**, 516–19.

—— —— —— (1976b). Mode of replication of the conjugative R plasmid RSF1040 in *Escherichia coli*. *JB* **126**, 454–66.

—— —— HEFFRON, F. *and* FALKOW, S. (1975). Two replication initiation sites on R-plasmid DNA. *MGG* **140**, 39–50.

—— OLARTE, J., MATA, L. T., LUTTROPP, L. K. *and* PEÑARANDA, M. E. (1977). Characterization of an R plasmid associated with ampicillin resistance in *Shigella dysenteriae* type 1 isolated from epidemics. *AAC* **11**, 553–8.

CRUICKSHANK, R., DUGUID, J. P., MARMION, B. P. *and* SWAIN, R. H. A. (1974). *Medical Microbiology*, vol. I. 12th edition. Churchill Livingstone.

CULLUM, J. *and* BRODA, P. (1979a). Hfr formation and chromosome transfer by F in *rec*+ and *recA* strains of *Escherichia coli* K12. *Plasmid* **2**, in the press.

—— —— (1979b). Recipient competence in F'*lac* matings in *Escherichia coli* K12. *JB* **137**, 281–4.

—— —— (1979c). Rate of segregation due to plasmid incompatibility. *Gen. Res.* **33**, 61–79.

—— COLLINS, J. F. *and* BRODA, P. (1978a). Factors affecting the kinetics of progeny formation with F'*lac* in *Escherichia coli* K12. *Plasmid* **1**, 536–44.

—— —— —— (1978b). The spread of plasmids in model populations of *Escherichia coli* K12. *Plasmid* **1**, 545–56.

CURRIER, T. C. *and* NESTER, E. W. (1976a). Isolation of covalently closed circular DNA of high molecular weight from bacteria. *Analytical Biochemistry* **76**, 431–41.

—— —— (1976b). Evidence for diverse types of large plasmids in tumour-inducing strains of *Agrobacterium*. *JB* **126**, 157–65.

CURTISS, R. (1969). Bacterial conjugation. *Ann. Rev. Micro.* **23**, 69–136.

—— CARO, L. G., ALLISON, D. P. *and* STALLIONS, D. R. (1969). Early stages in conjugation in *Escherichia coli*. *JB* **100**, 1091–104.

—— *and* RENSHAW, J. (1969a). F+ strains of *Escherichia coli* K12 defective in Hfr formation. *Gen.* **63**, 7–26.

—— —— (1969b). Kinetics of F transfer and recombinant production in F+ × F⁻ matings in *Escherichia coli* K12. *Gen.* **63**, 39–52.

—— *and* STALLIONS, D. R. (1967). Energy requirements for specific pair formation during conjugation in *Escherichia coli* K-12. *JB* **94**, 490–2.

—— —— (1969). Probability of F integration and frequency of stable Hfr donors in F+ populations of *Escherichia coli* K12. *Gen.* **63**, 27–38.

CUZIN, F. (1962). Multiplication autonome de l'épisome sexuel d' *Escherichia coli* K-12 dans une souche Hfr. *C.R. Acad. Sci.*, Paris **254**, 4511.

—— and JACOB, F. (1967a). Association stable de deux épisomes F differents dans une clone d'*Escherichia coli*. *Annales de Institut Pasteur* **113**, 145–55.

—— —— (1967b). Bacterial episomes as a model of replicon. In: *Regulation of Nucleic Acid and Protein Synthesis*. V. Koningsberger and L. Bosch, eds., Elsevier, London.

DALLAS, W. S. and FALKOW, S. (1979). The molecular nature of heat-labile enterotoxin (LT) of *Escherichia coli*. *Nature* **277**, 406–7.

DANNA, K. J., SACK, G. H. and NATHANS, D. (1973). Studies on simian virus 40 DNA. VII. A cleavage map of the SV40 genome. *JMB* **78**, 363–76.

DATTA, N. (1962). Transmissible drug resistance in an epidemic strain of *Salmonella typhimurium*. *J. Hyg.* **60**, 301–10.

—— (1975). Epidemiology and classification of plasmids. In: *Microbiology 1974*.

—— and BARTH, P. T. (1976). Hfr formation by I pilus determining plasmids in *Escherichia coli* K-12. *JB* **125**, 811–17.

—— HEDGES, R. W., SHAW, E. J., SYKES, R. and RICHMOND, M. H. (1971). Properties of an R factor from *Pseudomonas aeruginosa*. *JB* **108**, 1244–9.

DAVIDSON, N., DEONIER, R. C., HU, S. and OHTSUBO, E. (1975). Electron microscope heteroduplex studies of sequence relations among plasmids of *Escherichia coli*. X. Deoxyribonucleic acid sequence organisation of F and F-primes, and the sequences involved in Hfr formation. In: *Microbiology 1974*.

—— and SZYBALSKI, W. (1971). Physical and chemical characteristics of lambda DNA. In: *The Bacteriophage Lambda*. A. D. Hershey, Ed. Cold Spring Harbor.

DAVIES, J. and SMITH, D. I. (1978). Plasmid-determined resistance to antimicrobial agents. *Ann. Rev. Micro.* **32**, 469–518.

DAVIES, J. K. and REEVES, P. (1975a). Genetics of resistance to colicins in *Escherichia coli*: cross-resistance among colicins of group B. *JB* **123**, 96–101.

—— —— (1975b). Genetics of resistance to colicins in *Escherichia coli*: cross-resistance among colicins of group A. *JB* **123**, 102–17.

DAVIS, B. D. (1950). Non-filtrability of the agents of genetic recombination in *E. coli*. *JB* **60**, 507–8.

—— (1976). Evolution, epidemiology and recombinant DNA. *Science* **193**, 442.

—— DULBECCO, R., EISEN, H. M., GINSBERG, M. S. and WOOD, W. B. (1973). *Microbiology*, 2nd edition. Harper and Row.

DAVIS, C. E. and ANANDAN, J. (1970). The evolution of an R factor: a study of a 'preantibiotic' community in Borneo. *New England Journal of Medicine* **282**, 117–22.

DAVIS, D. B. and HELMSTETTER, C. E. (1973). Control of F'*lac* replication in *Escherichia coli* B/r *JB* **114**, 294–9.

DAVIS, R. W., SIMON, M. and DAVIDSON, N. (1971). Electron microscope heteroduplex methods for mapping regions of base sequence homology in nucleic acids. 413–28. In: *Methods in Enzymology*, vol. 21. L. Grossman and K. Moldave, eds. Academic Press Inc., New York.

DEAN, H. F., MORGAN, A. F., ASCHE, L. V. and HOLLOWAY, B. W. (1977). Isolates of *Pseudomonas aeruginosa* from Australian hospitals having R-plasmid determined antibiotic resistance. *Medical Journal of Australia* **2**, 116–19.

DEGRAAFF, J., ELWELL L. P. and FALKOW, S. (1976). Molecular nature of two beta-lactamase-specifying plasmids isolated from *Haemophilus influenzae* type B. *JB* **126**, 439–46.

DELAP, R. J., RUSH, M. G., ZOUZIAS, D. and KHAN, S. (1978). Isolation and preliminary characterization of the small circular DNA present in African Green Monkey kidney (BSC-1) cells. *Plasmid* **1**, 508–21.

DELLA LATTA, P., BOUANCHAUD, D. and NOVICK, R. P. (1978). Partition kinetics and thermosensitive replication of pT169, a naturally occurring multicopy tetracycline resistance plasmid of *Staphylococcus aureus*. *Plasmid* **1**, 366–75.

DENNISTON-THOMPSON, K., MOORE, D. D., KRUGER, K. E., FURTH, M. E. *and* BLATTNER, F. R. (1977). Physical structure of the replication origin of bacteriophage lambda. *Science* **198**, 1051–6.

DEONIER, R. C. *and* DAVIDSON, N. (1976). The sequence organisation of the integrated F plasmid in two Hfr strains of *Escherichia coli*. *JMB* **107**, 207–22.

—— *and* HADLEY, R. G. (1976). Distribution of inverted IS-length sequences in the *E. coli* K12 genome. *Nat.* **264**, 191–3.

—— *and* MIRELS, L. (1977). Excision of F plasmid sequences by recombination of directly repeated insertion sequence 2 elements: involvement of *recA*. *PNAS* **74**, 3965–9.

—— OH, G. R. *and* HU, MING. (1977). Further mapping of IS2 and IS3 in the *lac-purE* region of the *Escherichia coli* K-12 genome: structure of the F-prime ORF203. *JB* **129**, 1129–40.

DEPICKER, A., VAN MONTAGU, M. *and* SCHELL, J. (1978). Homologous DNA sequences in different Ti-plasmids are essential for oncogenicity. *Nat.* **275**, 150–3.

DEVRIES, J. K. *and* MAAS, W. K. (1971). Chromosomal integration of F' factors in recombination-deficient strains of *E. coli*. *JB* **106**, 150–6.

—— —— (1973). Description of an incompatibility mutant of *Escherichia coli*. *JB* **115**, 213–20.

—— PFISTER, A., HAENNI, C., PALCHAUDHURI, S. *and* MAAS, W. (1975). F incompatibility. In: *Microbiology, 1974*.

DONACHIE, W. D. (1968). Relationships between cell size and time of initiation of DNA replication. *Nat.* **219**, 1077–9.

DONOGHUE, D. J. *and* SHARP, P. A. (1978a). Replication of colicin E1 plasmid DNA *in vivo* requires no plasmid-encoded proteins. *JB* **133**, 1287–94.

—— —— (1978b). Construction of a hybrid bacteriophage-plasmid recombinant DNA vector. *JB* **136**, 1192–6.

DOUGAN, G., SAUL, M., WARREN, G. *and* SHERRATT, D. (1978). A functional map of plasmid ColE1. *MGG* **158**, 325–7.

DOWDING, J. *and* DAVIES, J. (1975). Mechanisms and origins of plasmid-determined antibiotic resistance. In: *Microbiology, 1974*.

DRUMMOND, M. H. *and* CHILTON, M-D. (1978). Tumor-inducing (Ti) plasmids of *Agrobacterium* share extensive regions of DNA homology. *JB* **136**, 1178–83.

—— GORDON, M. P., NESTER, E. W. *and* CHILTON, M-D. (1977). Foreign DNA of bacterial plasmid origin is transcribed in crown gall tumours. *Nat.* **269**, 535–6.

DUBNAU, E. *and* MAAS, W. K. (1968). Inhibition of replication of an F'*lac* episome in Hfr cells of *Escherichia coli*. *JB* **95**, 531–9.

DUGGLEBY, C. J., BAYLEY, S. A., WORSEY, M. J., WILLIAMS, P. A. *and* BRODA, P. (1977). Molecular sizes and relationships of TOL plasmids in *Pseudomonas*. *JB* **130**, 1274–80.

DUNN, N. W. *and* GUNSALUS, I. C. (1973). Transmissible plasmid coding early enzymes of naphthalene oxidation in *Pseudomonas putida*. *JB* **114**, 974–9.

DUNNY, G. M., BROWN, B. L. *and* CLEWELL, D. B. (1978). Induced cell aggregation and mating in *Streptococcus faecalis*: evidence for a bacterial sex pheromone. *PNAS* **75**, 3479–83.

—— *and* CLEWELL, D. B. (1975). Transmissible toxin (hemolysin) plasmid in *Streptococcus faecalis* and its mobilization of a non-infectious drug resistance plasmid. *JB* **124**, 784–90.

DURKACZ, B. W. *and* SHERRATT, D. J. (1973). Segregation kinetics of colicinogenic factor ColE1 from a bacterial population temperature sensitive for DNA polymerase I. *MGG* **121**, 71–5.

ECHOLS, H. (1963). Properties of F′ strains of *Escherichia coli* superinfected with F-lactose and F-galactose episomes. *JB* **85**, 262–8.

ECKHARDT, T. (1978). A rapid method for the identification of plasmid des-oxyribonucleic acid in bacteria. *Plasmid* **1**, 584–8.

EHRLICH, S. D. (1977). Replication and expression of plasmids from *Staphylococcus aureus* in *Bacillus subtilis*. *PNAS* **74**, 1680–2.

—— (1978). DNA cloning in *Bacillus subtilis*. *PNAS* **75**, 1433–6.

EICHENLAUB, R., FIGURSKI, D. and HELINSKI, D. R. (1977). Bidirectional replication from a unique origin in a mini-F plasmid. *PNAS* **74**, 1138–41.

ELWELL, L. P., DE GRAAFF, J., SEIBERT, D. and FALKOW, S. (1975). Plasmid-linked ampicillin resistance in *Haemophilus influenzae* type B. *Infection and Immunity* **12**, 404–10.

—— ROBERTS, M., MAYER, L. W. and FALKOW, S. (1977a). Plasmid-mediated beta-lactamase production in *Neisseria gonorrhoea*. *AAC* **11**, 528–33.

—— SAUNDERS, J. R., RICHMOND, M. H. and FALKOW, S. (1977b). Relationships among some R plasmids found in *Haemophilus influenzae*. *JB* **131**, 356–362.

ENGBERG, B. and NORDSTRÖM, K. (1975). Replication of R-factor DNA in *Escherichia coli* at different growth rates. *JB* **123**, 179–86.

EVANS, D. G., SILVER, R. P., EVANS, D. J., CHASE, D. G. and GORBACH, S. C. (1975). Plasmid-controlled colonisation factor associated with virulence in *Escherichia coli* enterotoxigenic for humans. *Infection and Immunity* **12**, 656–67.

EVENCHIK, Z., STACEY, K. A. and HAYES, W. (1969). Ultraviolet induction of chromosome transfer by autonomous sex factors in *Escherichia coli*. *JGM* **56**, 1–14.

FAELEN, M. and TOUSSAINT, A. (1976). Bacteriophage mu-1: a tool to transpose and to localise bacterial genes. *JMB* **104**, 525–39.

FALKINHAM, J. O., III, and CLARK, A. J. (1974). Genetic analysis of a double male strain of *Escherichia coli* K12. *Gen.* **78**, 633–44.

—— and CURTISS, R. III. (1976). Isolation and characterization of conjugation-deficient mutants of *Escherichia coli* K-12. *JB* **126**, 1194–206.

FALKOW, S., GUERRY, P., HEDGES, R. W. and DATTA, N. (1974). Polynucleotide sequence relationships among plasmids of the I compatibility complex. *JGM* **85**, 65–76.

—— TOMPKINS, L. S., SILVER, R. P., GUERRY, P. and LEBLANC, D. J. (1971). The replication of R-factor DNA in *Escherichia coli* K-12 following conjugation. *Annals of the New York Academy of Sciences* **182**, 153–71.

—— WOHLHIETER, J. A., CITARELLA, R. V. and BARON, L. S. (1964). Transfer of episomic elements to *Proteus*. I. transfer of F-linked chromosomal determinants. *JB* **87**, 209–19.

FENNEWALD, M., PREVATT, W., MEYER, R. and SHAPIRO, J. (1978). Isolation of Inc P-2 plasmid DNA from *Pseudomonas aeruginosa*. *Plasmid* **1**, 164–73.

—— and SHAPIRO, J. (1977). Regulatory mutations of the *Pseudomonas* plasmid *alk* regulon. *JB* **132**, 622–7.

FENWICK, R. G. and CURTISS, R. (1973). Conjugal DNA replication by *Escherichia coli* K-12: stimulation in *dnaB*(ts) donors by minicells. *JB* **116**, 1212–23.

FIANDT, M., SZYBALSKI, W. and MALAMY, M. H. (1972). Polar mutations in *lac*, *gal* and phage λ consist of a few IS-DNA sequences inserted with either orientation. *MGG* **119**, 223–31.

FIELD, M., GRAF, L. H., LAIRD, W. J. *and* SMITH, P. L. (1978). Heat-stable enterotoxin of *Escherichia coli*: *in vitro* effects on guanylate cyclase activity, cyclic GMP concentration, and ion transport in small intestine. *PNAS* **75**, 2800–4.

FINKELSTEIN, M. *and* HELMSTETTER, C. E. (1977). Cell cycle analysis of F*lac* replication in *Escherichia coli* B/r. *JB* **132**, 884–95.

FINKELSTEIN, R. A. *and* BOESMAN-FINKELSTEIN, M. (1978). Cholera and related diarrhoeas ('turista'). *Nat*. **275**, 173–174.

—— VASIL, M. L., JONES, J. R., ANDERSON, R. A. *and* BARNARD, T. (1976). Clinical cholera caused by enterotoxigenic *Escherichia coli*. *J. Clinical Microbiology* **3**, 382–4.

FINLAND, M. (1960). Treatment of pneumonia and other serious infections. *New England Journal of Medicine* **263**, 207–21.

—— (1970). Changing ecology of bacterial infections as related to antibacterial therapy. *Journal of Infectious Diseases* **122**, 419–31.

FINNEGAN, D. J. *and* WILLETTS, N. S. (1973). The site of action of the F transfer inhibitor. *MGG* **127**, 307–16.

FISHER, P. R., APPLETON, J. *and* PEMBERTON, J. M. (1978). Isolation and characterization of the pesticide-degrading plasmid pJP1 from *Alcaligenes paradoxus*. *JB* **135**, 798–804.

FODOR, K., DEMIRI, E. *and* ALFÖLDI, L. (1978). Polyethylene glycol-induced fusion of heat-inactivated and living protoplasts of *Bacillus megaterium*. *JB* **135**, 68–70.

FOSTER, T. J., HOWE, T. G. B. *and* RICHMOND, K. M. V. (1975). Translocation of the tetracycline resistance determinant from R100-1 to the *Escherichia coli* K-12 chromosome. *JB* **114**, 1153–8.

—— *and* WILLETTS, N. S. (1977). Characterization of transfer-deficient mutants of the R100-1 Tc^S plasmid pDU202, caused by insertion of Tn10. *MGG* **156**, 107–14.

FRAME, R. *and* BISHOP, J. O. (1971). The number of sex-factors per chromosome in *Escherichia coli*. *Biochemical Journal* **121**, 93–103.

FRANKLIN, N. C., DOVE, W. F. *and* YANOFSKY, C. (1965). The linear insertion of a prophage into the chromosome of *E. coli* shown by deletion mapping. *BBRC* **18**, 910–23.

FRAZER, A. C. *and* CURTISS, R. III. (1973). Derepression of anthranilate synthase in purified minicells of *Escherichia coli* containing the Col-*trp* plasmid. *JB* **115**, 615–22.

—— —— (1975). Production, properties and utility of bacterial minicells. *Current Topics in Microbiology and Immunology*. **69**, 1–84.

FRÉDÉRICQ, P. (1948). Actions antibiotiques réciproques chez les Entérobactériacées. *Revue Belge de Pathologie et de Médecine Expérimentale*. **19**, Supp. 4, 1–107.

FREEMAN, R. F. *and* HOPWOOD, D. A. (1978). Unstable naturally occurring resistance to antibiotics in *Streptomyces*. *JGM* **106**, 377–81.

FREIFELDER, D. (1968). Studies on *Escherichia coli* sex factors. III. Covalently closed F*lac* DNA molecules. *JMB* **34**, 31–8.

FRIELLO, D. A., MYLROIE, J. R., GIBSON, D. T., ROGERS, J. E. *and* CHAKRABARTY, A. M. (1976). XYL, a non-conjugative xylene-degrading plasmid in *Pseudomonas* Pxy. *JB* **127**, 1217–24.

FUKE, M. *and* INSELBURG, J. (1972). Electron microscope studies of replicating and catenated colicin factor E1 DNA isolated from minicells. *PNAS* **69**, 89–92.

FULLBROOK, P. D., ELSOM, S. W. *and* SLOCOMBE, B. (1970). R-factor mediated β-lactamase in *Pseudomonas aeruginosa*. *Nat.* **226**, 1054–6.

GAFFNEY, D. F., FOSTER, T. J. *and* SHAW, W. V. (1978). Chloramphenicol acetyltransferases determined by R plasmids from Gram-negative bacteria. *JGM* **109**, 351–8.

GARDNER, P., SMITH, D. H., BEER, H. *and* MOELLERING, JR., R. C. (1969). Recovery of resistance (R) factors from a drug-free community. *Lancet.* **II**, 774–6.

GARROD, L. P., LAMBERT, H. P. *and* O'GRADY, F. (1973). *Antibiotic and Chemotherapy*. 4th edition, Churchill Livingstone.

GASSON, M. *and* WILLETTS, N. (1975). Five control systems preventing transfer of *Escherichia coli* K-12 sex factor F. *JB* **122**, 518–25.

—— —— (1976). Transfer gene expression during fertility inhibition of the *Escherichia coli* K-12 sex factor by the I-like plasmid R62. *MGG* **149**, 329–33.

—— —— (1977). Further characterization of the F fertility inhibition system of 'unusual' Fin$^+$ plasmids. *JB* **131**, 413–20.

GEFTER, M. L., HIROTA, Y., KORNBERG, T., WECHSLER, J. A. *and* BARNOUX, C. (1971). Analysis of DNA polymerases II and III in mutants of *Escherichia coli* thermosensitive for DNA synthesis. *PNAS* **68**, 3150–3.

GELLERT, M., MIZUUCHI, K., O'DEA, M. H., ITOH, T. *and* TOMIZAWA, J.-I. (1977). Nalidixic acid resistance: a second character involved in DNA-gyrase activity. *PNAS* **74**, 4772–6.

GENETELLO, C., VAN LAREBEKE, N., HOLSTERS, M., DE PICKER, A., VAN MONTAGU, M. *and* SCHELL, J. (1977). The Ti plasmids of *Agrobacterium* as conjugating plasmids. *Nat.* **265**, 561–3.

GHOSAL, D. *and* SAEDLER, H. (1977). Isolation of the mini-insertions IS6 and IS7 of *E. coli*. *MGG* **158**, 123–8.

GILARDI, G. L. (1972). Infrequently encountered *Pseudomonas* species causing infections in humans. *Annals of Internal Medicine* **77**, 211–15.

GILBERT, W. *and* DRESSLER, D. (1968). DNA replication: the rolling circle model. *CSH* **33**, 473–84.

GILL, R., HEFFRON, F., DOUGAN, G. *and* FALKOW, S. (1978). Analysis of sequences transposed by complementation of two classes of transposition-deficient mutants of Tn3. *JB* **136**, 742–56.

GOEBEL, W. (1970a). Degradation of DNA in a temperature-sensitive mutant of *Escherichia coli* defective in DNA synthesis, harboring the colicinogenic factor E1. *BBA* **224**, 353–60.

—— (1970b). Studies on extrachromosomal DNA elements. Replication of the colicinogenic factor ColE1 in two temperature-sensitive mutants of *Escherichia coli* defective in DNA replication. *European Journal of Biochemistry* **15**, 311–20.

—— (1971). Formation of complex ColE1 DNA by replication. *BBA* **232**, 32–42.

—— (1972). Replication of the DNA of the colicinogenic factor E1 (ColE1) at the restrictive temperature in a replication mutant thermosensitive for DNA polymerase III. *NNB* **237**, 67–70.

—— (1973). The influence of *dnaA* and *dnaC* mutations on the initiation of plasmid DNA replication. *BBRC* **51**, 1000–7.

—— (1974). Integrative suppression of temperature-sensitive mutants with a lesion in the initiation of DNA replication. Replication of autonomous plasmids in the suppressed state. *European Journal of Biochemistry* **43**, 125–30.

—— *and* BONEWALD, R. (1975). Class of small multicopy plasmids originating from the mutant antibiotic resistance factor R1*drd19B2*. *JB* **123**, 658–65.

—— and KREFT, J. (1974). Complex ColE1 DNA in *Escherichia coli* and *Proteus mirabilis*. *MGG* **129**, 149–66.

—— and SCHREMPF, H. (1972a). Replication of the minicircular DNA of *E. coli* 15 is dependent on DNA polymerase I but independent of DNA polymerase III. *BBRC* **49**, 591–600.

—— —— (1972b). Isolation of minicircular deoxyribonucleic acids from wild strains of *Escherichia coli* and their relationship to other bacterial plasmids. *JB* **111**, 696–704.

—— —— (1972c). Replication of plasmid DNA in temperature-sensitive DNA replication mutants of *Escherichia coli*. *BBA* **262**, 32–41.

GOTTESMAN, M. M. and ROSNER, J. L. (1975). Acquisition of a determinant for chloramphenicol resistance by bacteriophage lambda. *PNAS* **72**, 5041–5.

GRATIA, A. (1925). Sur un remarquable exemple d'antagonisme entre deux souches de Colibacille. *Comptes Rendus de la Société de Biologie*. **93**, 1040–1.

—— and FRÉDÉRICQ, P. (1946). Diversité des souches antibiotiques de *B. coli* et étendue variable de leur champ d'action. *Comptes Rendus de la Société de Biologie*. **140**, 1032–3.

GRINDLEY, N. D. F. (1978). IS1 insertion generates duplication of a nine base pair sequence at its target site. *Cell* **13**, 419–26.

—— HUMPHREYS, G. O. and ANDERSON, E. S. (1973). Molecular studies of R factor compatibility groups. *JB* **115**, 387–98.

—— and KELLEY, W. S. (1976). Effects of different alleles of the *E. coli* K12 *polA* gene on the replication of non-transferring plasmids. *MGG* **143**, 311–18.

GRINSTED, J., SAUNDERS, J. R., INGRAM, L. C., SYKES, R. B. and RICHMOND, M. H. (1972). Properties of an R factor that originated in *Pseudomonas aeruginosa* 1822. *JB* **110**, 529–37.

GRINTER, N. J. and BARTH, P. T. (1976). Characterization of SmSu plasmids by restriction endonuclease cleavage and compatibility testing. *JB* **128**, 394–400.

GROSS, J. and GROSS, M. (1969). Genetic analysis of an *E. coli* strain with a mutation affecting DNA polymerase. *Nat.* **224**, 1166–8.

GRYCZAN, T. J. and DUBNAU, D. (1978). Construction and properties of chimeric plasmids in *Bacillus subtilis*. *PNAS* **75**, 1428–32.

GUEROLA, N., INGRAHAM, J. L. and CERDÁ-OLMEDO, E. (1971). Induction of closely linked multiple mutations by nitrosoguanidine. *NNB* **230**, 122–5.

GUERRY, P., LeBLANC, D. J. and FALKOW, S. (1973). General method for the isolation of plasmid deoxyribonucleic acid. *JB* **116**, 1064–6.

—— and FALKOW, S. (1971). Polynucleotide sequence relationships among some bacterial plasmids. *JB* **107**, 372–4.

GUINÉE, P., UGUETO, N. and VAN LEEUWEN. (1970). *Escherichia coli* with resistance factors in vegetarians, babies and non-vegetarians. *Applied Microbiology* **20**, 531–5.

GUINEY, D. G. and DAVIS, C. E. (1978). Identification of a conjugative R plasmid in *Bacteroides ochraceus* capable of transfer to *Escherichia coli*. *Nat.* **274**, 181–2.

—— and HELINSKI, D. R. (1975). Relaxation complexes of plasmid DNA and protein. III. Association of protein with the 5' terminus of the broken DNA strand in the relaxed complex of plasmid ColE1. *JBC* **250**, 8796–803.

GUISO, N. and ULLMANN, A. (1976). Expression and regulation of lactose genes carried by plasmids. *JB* **127**, 691–7.

GUNSALUS, I. C., HERMANN, M., TOSCANO, JR., W. A., KATZ, D. and GARG, G. K. (1975). Plasmids and metabolic diversity. In: *Microbiology 1974*.

GUSTAFSSON, P. and NORDSTRÖM, K. (1975). Random replication of the stringent plasmid R1 in *Escherichia coli* K-12. *JB* **123**, 443–8.

—— —— (1978). Temperature-dependent and amber copy mutants of plasmid R1 *drd-19* in *Escherichia coli*. *Plasmid* **1**, 134–44.

—— —— and PERRAM, J. W. (1978). Selection and timing of replication of plasmids R1*drd-19* and F′*lac* in *Escherichia coli*. *Plasmid* **1**, 187–203.

GUYER, M. S. (1978). The $\gamma\delta$ sequence of F is an insertion sequence. *JMB* **126**, 347–65.

—— and CLARK, A. J. (1977). Early and late transfer of F genes by Hfr donors of *E. coli* K-12. *MGG* **157**, 215–22.

—— FIGURSKI, D. and DAVIDSON, N. (1976). Electron microscope study of a plasmid chimaera containing the replication region of the F plasmid of *Escherichia coli*. *JB* **127**, 988–97.

GYLES, C. L., PALCHAUDHURI, S. and MAAS, W. K. (1977). Naturally occurring plasmid carrying genes for enterotoxin production and drug resistance. *Science* **198**, 198–200.

HAAS, D. and HOLLOWAY, B. W. (1978). Chromosome mobilisation of the R plasmid R68.45: a tool in *Pseudomonas* genetics. *MGG* **158**, 229–37.

HANSEN, J. B. and OLSEN, R. H. (1978a). Isolation of large bacterial plasmids and characterization of the P2 incompatibility group plasmids pMG1 and pMG5. *JB* **135**, 227–38.

—— —— (1978b). Inc P2 group of *Pseudomonas*, a class of uniquely large plasmids. *Nat.* **274**, 715–17.

HARDY, K. G. (1975). Colicinogeny and related phenomena. *Bact. Rev.* **39**, 464–515.

—— and MEYNELL, G. G. (1972). A model relating the replication and expression of colicin factor E2-P9. *Gen. Res.* **20**, 331–4.

—— DOWMAN, J. E. and SPRATT, B. G. (1973). Two major groups of colicin factors: their evolutionary significance. *MGG* **125**, 217–30.

HARTLEY, C. L., CLEMENTS, H. M. and LINTON, K. B. (1977). *Escherichia coli* in the faecal flora of man. *J. App. Bact.* **43**, 261–9.

—— HOWE, K., LINTON, A. H., LINTON, K. B. and RICHMOND, M. H. (1975). Distribution of R-plasmids among the O-antigen types of *E. coli* isolated from human and animal sources. *AAC* **8**, 112–31.

—— and RICHMOND, M. H. (1975). Antibiotic resistance and survival of *E. coli* in the alimentary tract. *British Medical Journal* **4**, 71–4.

HASHIMOTO, H. and ROWND, R. H. (1975). Transition of the R factor NR1 in *Proteus mirabilis*.: level of drug resistance in non-transitioned and transitioned cells. *JB* **123**, 56–68.

HASHIMOTO, T. and SEKIGUCHI, M. (1976). Isolation of temperature-sensitive mutants of R plasmid by *in vitro* mutagenesis with hydroxylamine. *JB* **127**, 1561–3.

HASHIMOTO-GOTOH, T. and SEKIGUCHI, M. (1977). Mutations to temperature-sensitivity in R plasmid pSC101. *JB* **131**, 405–12.

HATHAWAY, B. G. and BERGQUIST, P. L. (1973). Temperature-sensitive mutations affecting the replication of F-prime factors in *Escherichia coli* K 12. *MGG* **127**, 297–306.

HAYAKAWA, Y. and MATSUBARA, K. (1979). Construction and some properties of packageable plasmid F. *MGG* **169**, 107–12.

HAYES, W. (1952). Genetic recombination in *Bact. coli* K12: analysis of the stimulating effect of ultraviolet light. *Nat.* **169**, 1017.

—— (1953). Observations on a transmissible agent determining sexual differentiation in *Bact. coli*. *JGM* **8**, 72–88.

—— (1968). *The Genetics of Bacteria and their Viruses*. Second edition. Blackwell.

HEDGES, R. W., CRESSWELL, J. M. *and* JACOB, A. E. (1976). A non-transmissible variant of RP4 suitable as cloning vehicle for genetic engineering. *FEBS Letters* **61**, 186–8.

—— DATTA, N., KONTOMICHALOU, P. *and* SMITH, J. T. (1974). Molecular specificities of R factor-determined beta-lactamases: correlation with plasmid compatibility. *JB* **117**, 56–62.

—— *and* JACOB, A. (1974). Transposition of ampicillin resistance from RP4 to other replicons. *MGG* **132**, 31–40.

—— —— (1975). A 90 megadalton R factor of compatibility group C in a *Vibrio cholerae* El Tor isolate from southern USSR. *JGM* **89**, 383–6.

HEFFRON, F., BEDINGER, P., CHAMPOUX, J. J. *and* FALKOW, S. (1977a). Deletions affecting the transposition of an antibiotic resistance gene. *PNAS* **74**, 702–6.

—— RUBENS, C. *and* FALKOW, S. (1975a). Translocation of a plasmid DNA sequence which mediates ampicillin resistance: molecular nature and specificity of insertion. *PNAS* **72**, 3623–7.

—— —— —— (1977b). Transposition of a plasmid deoxyribonucleic acid sequence that mediates ampicillin resistance: identity of laboratory-constructed plasmids and clinical isolates. *JB* **129**, 530–3.

—— SUBLETT, R., HEDGES, R. W., JACOB, A. *and* FALKOW, S. (1975b). Origin of the TEM beta-lactamase gene found on plasmids. *JB* **122**, 250–6.

HEINARU, A. L., DUGGLEBY, C. J. *and* BRODA, P. (1978). Molecular relationships of degradative plasmids determined by *in situ* hybridisation of their endonuclease-generated fragments. *MGG* **160**, 347–51.

HELINSKI, D. R., LOVETT, M. A., WILLIAMS, P. H., KATZ, L., KUPERSZTOCH-PORTNOY, Y. M., GUINEY, D. G. *and* BLAIR, D. G. (1975). Plasmid deoxyribonucleic acid replication. In: *Microbiology, 1974*.

HELMSTETTER, C. E., COOPER, S., PIERUCCI, O. *and* REVELAS, E. (1968). On the bacterial life cycle. *CSH* **33**, 809–22.

HELMUTH, R. *and* ACHTMAN, M. (1975). Operon structure of DNA transfer cistrons on the F sex factor. *Nat.* **257**, 652–6.

—— —— (1978). Cell–cell interactions in conjugating *Escherichia coli*: purification of F pili with biological activity. *PNAS* **75**, 1237–41.

HEPBURN, A. G. *and* HINDLEY, J. (1979). Regions of DNA sequence homology between an octopine and a nopaline Ti plasmid of *Agrobacterium tumefaciens*. *MGG* **169**, 163–72.

HERNALSTEENS, J. P., DE GREVE, H., VAN MONTAGU, M. *and* SCHELL, J. (1978). Mutagenesis by insertion of the drug resistance transposon Tn7 applied to the Ti plasmid of *Agrobacterium tumefaciens*. *Plasmid* **1**, 218–25.

HERSCHMAN, H. R. *and* HELINSKI, D. R. (1967). Purification and characterization of colicin E2 and colicin E3. *JBC* **242**, 5360–8.

HERSHFIELD, V. (1979). Plasmids mediating multiple drug resistance in group B *Streptococcus*: transferability and molecular properties. *Plasmid* **2**, 137–49.

—— BOYER, H. W., YANOFSKY, C., LOVETT, M. A. *and* HELINSKI, D. R. (1974). Plasmid ColE1 as a molecular vehicle for cloning and amplification of DNA. *PNAS* **71**, 3455–9.

—— LEBLANC, D. J. *and* FALKOW, S. (1973). Membrane attachment of R-factor deoxyribonucleic acid in compatible and incompatible cell pairs following conjugation. *JB* **115**, 1208–11.

HICKSON, F. T., ROTH, T. F. *and* HELINSKI, D. R. (1968). Circular forms of a bacterial sex factor. *PNAS* **58**, 1731–8.

HIGGINS, N. P., PEEBLES, C. L., SUGINO, A. *and* COZZARELLI, N. R. (1978). Purification of subunits of *Escherichia coli* gyrase and reconstitution of enzymatic activity. *PNAS* **75**, 1773–7.

HILL, M. J., DRASAR, B. S., ARIES, V., CROWTHER, V. S., HAWKSWORTH, G. *and* WILLIAMS, R. E. O.(1971). Bacteria and aetiology of cancer of large bowel. *Lancet* **I**, 95–100.

HIRAGA, S. (1976). Novel F prime factors able to replicate in *Escherichia coli* Hfr strains. *PNAS* **73**, 198–202.

HIROTA, Y., GEFTER, M. *and* MINDICH, L. (1972). A mutant of *Escherichia coli* defective in DNA polymerase II activity. *PNAS* **69**, 3238–42.

HIRSCH, H. J., STARLINGER, P. *and* BRACHET, P. (1972). Two kinds of insertions in bacterial genes. *MGG* **119**, 191–206.

HOHN, B. *and* KORN, D. (1969). Cosegregation of a sex factor with the *Escherichia coli* chromosome during curing by acridine orange. *JMB* **45**, 385–9.

HOLLOWAY, B. W. (1978). Isolation and characterization of an R' plasmid in *Pseudomonas aeruginosa*. *JB* **133**, 1078–82.

—— (1979). Plasmids that mobilize bacterial chromosome. *Plasmid* **2**, 1–19.

—— *and* KRISHNAPILLAI, V. (1975). Bacteriophages and bacteriocins. In: *Genetics and Biochemistry of* Pseudomonas, 99–132. P. H. Clarke and M. H. Richmond, eds. Wiley.

HOLSTERS, M., DE WAELE, D., DEPICKER, A., MESSENS, E., VAN MONTAGU, M. *and* SCHELL, J. (1978a). Transfection and transformation of *Agrobacterium tumefaciens*. *MGG* **163**, 181–7.

—— SILVA, B., VAN VLIET, F., HERNALSTEENS, J. P., GENETELLO, C., VAN MONTAGU, M. *and* SCHELL, J. (1978b). *in vivo* transfer of the Ti plasmid of *Agrobacterium tumefaciens* to *Escherichia coli*. *MGG* **163**, 335–8.

HOOYKAAS, P. J. J., KLAPWIJK, P. M., NUTI, M. P., SCHILPEROORT, R. A. *and* RORSCH, A. (1977). Transfer of the *Agrobacterium tumefaciens* Ti plasmid to avirulent agrobacteria and to *Rhizobium ex planta*. *JGM* **98**, 477–84.

HOPKINS, A. S., MURRAY, N. E. *and* BRAMMAR, W. J. (1976). Characterization of λtrp-transducing bacteriophages made *in vitro*. *JMB* **107**, 549–69.

HOPWOOD, D. A. (1978). Extrachromosomally determined antibiotic production. *Ann. Rev. Micro.* 373–92.

—— CHATER, K. F., DOWDING, J. E. *and* VIVIAN, A. (1973). Advances in *Streptomyces coelicolor* genetics. *Bact. Rev.* **37**, 371–405.

—— *and* MERRICK, M. J. (1977). Genetics of antibiotic production. *Bact. Rev.* **41**, 595–635.

—— *and* WRIGHT, H. M. (1976). Genetic studies on SCP1 strains of *Streptomyces coelicolor* A3(2). *JGM* **95**, 107–20.

—— —— (1978). Bacterial protoplast fusion: recombination in fused protoplasts of *Streptomyces coelicolor*. *MGG* **162**, 307–17.

HOWARTH, S. (1965). Resistance to the bacteriocidal effect of ultraviolet irradiation conferred on enterobacteria by the colicine factor *coll*. *JGM* **40**, 43–55.

HOWE, K. *and* LINTON, A. H. (1976). The distribution of O-antigen types of *Escherichia coli* in normal calves, compared with man, and their R plasmid carriage. *J. App. Bact.* **40**, 317–30.

—— —— *and* OSBORNE, A. D. (1976a). A longitudinal study of *Escherichia coli* in cows and calves with special reference to the distribution of O-antigen types and antibiotic resistance. *J. App. Bact.* **40**, 331–40.

—— —— —— (1976b). An investigation of calf carcass contamination by *Escherichia coli* from the gut contents at slaughter. *J. App. Bact.* **41**, 37–45.

—— —— —— (1976c). The effect of tetracycline on the coliform gut flora of broiler chickens with special reference to antibiotic resistance and O-serotypes of *Escherichia coli*. *J. App. Bact.* **41**, 453–64.

HRADECNA, Z. *and* SZYBALSKI, W. (1967). Fractionation of the complementary stands of coliphage λ based on the asymmetric distribution of the poly I, G-binding sites. *Virol.* **32**, 633–43.

Hu, S., Ohtsubo, E. *and* Davidson, N. (1975a). Electron microscope hetero-duplex studies of sequence relations among plasmids of *Escherichia coli*: structure of F13 and related F-primes. *JB* **122**, 749–63.

—— —— —— *and* Saedler, H. (1975b). Electron microscope heteroduplex studies of sequence relations among bacterial plasmids: identification and mapping of the insertion sequences IS1 and IS2 in F and R. *JB* **122**, 764–75.

—— Ptashne, K., Cohen, S. N. *and* Davidson, N. (1975c). αβ sequence of F is IS3. *JB* **123**, 687–92.

Hughes, C. *and* Meynell, G. G. (1977). Rapid screening for plasmid DNA. *MGG* **151**, 175–9.

Hughes, V., Le Grice, S., Hughes, C. *and* Meynell, G. G. (1978).Two major groups of colicin factors: their molecular weights. *MGG* **159**, 219–21.

Humphreys, G. O., Grindley, N. D. F. *and* Anderson, E. S. (1972). DNA-protein complexes of Δ-mediated transfer systems. *BBA* **287**, 355–60.

—— Willshaw, G. A. *and* Anderson, E. S. (1975). A simple method for the preparation of large quantities of pure plasmid DNA. *BBA* **383**, 457–63.

—— —— Smith, H. R. *and* Anderson, E. S. (1976). Mutagenesis of plasmid DNA with hydroxylamine. Isolation of mutants of multicopy plasmids. *MGG* **145**, 101–8.

Iida, S. (1977). Directed integration of an F′ plasmid by integrative suppression. *MGG* **155**, 153–62.

—— Meyer, J. *and* Arber, W. (1978). The insertion element IS1 is a natural constituent of coliphage P1 DNA. *Plasmid* **1**, 357–65.

Ikeda, H. *and* Tomizawa, J-I. (1968). Prophage P1, an extrachromosomal replication unit. *CSH* **33**, 791–8.

Ingram, L. C., Anderson, J. D., Arrand, J. E. *and* Richmond, M. H. (1974). A probable example of R factor recombination in the human gastro-intestinal tract. *J. Med. Microb.* **7**, 251–7.

Inselburg, J. (1973). Colicin factor DNA: a single non-homologous region in ColE2-E3 heteroduplex molecules. *NNB* **241**, 234–7.

—— (1974). Replication of colicin E1 plasmid DNA in minicells from a unique replication initiation site. *PNAS* **71**, 2256–9.

—— (1977a). Isolation, mapping and examination of effects of TnA insertions in ColE1 plasmids. *JB* **129**, 482–91.

—— (1977b). Studies of colicin E1 plasmid functions by analysis of deletions and TnA insertions of the plasmid. *JB* **132**, 332–40.

—— *and* Applebaum, B. (1978). Proteins synthesized in minicells containing plasmid ColE1 and its mutants. *JB* **133**, 1444–51.

—— *and* Fuke, M. (1970). Replicating DNA: structure of colicin factor E1. *Science* **169**, 590–2.

—— —— (1971). Isolation of catenated and replicating DNA molecules of colicin factor E1 from minicells. *PNAS* **68**, 2839–42.

—— *and* Oka, A. (1975). Discontinuous replication of colicin E1 plasmid deoxyribonucleic acid. *JB* **123**, 739–42.

Iordanescu, S. (1977). Relationships between cotransducible plasmids in *Staphylococcus aureus. JB* **129**, 71–5.

Inuzuka, M. *and* Helinski, D. R. (1978). Requirement of a plasmid-encoded protein for replication *in vitro* of plasmid R6K. *PNAS* **75**, 5381–5.

Ippen-Ihler, K., Achtman, M. *and* Willetts, N. (1972). A deletion map of the *E. coli* K12 sex factor F: the order of eleven transfer cistrons. *JB* **110**, 857–63.

ISHII, K., HASHIMOTO-GOTOH, T. *and* MATSUBARA, K. (1978). Random replication and random assortment model for plasmid incompatibility. *Plasmid* 1, 435–46.

ITAKURA, K., HIROSE, T., CREA, R., RIGGS, A. D., HEYNECKER, H. L., BOLIVAR, F. *and* BOYER, H. W. (1977). Expression in *Escherichia coli* of a chemically synthesized gene for the hormone somatostatin. *Science* 198, 1056–63.

JACOB, A. E., CRESSWELL, J. M., HEDGES, R. W., COETZEE, J. N. *and* BERINGER, J. E. (1976). Properties of plasmids constructed by the *in vitro* insertion of DNA from *Rhizobium leguminosarum* or *Proteus mirabilis* into RP4. *MGG* 315–23.

—— DOUGLAS, G. J. *and* HOBBS, S. J. (1975). Self-transferable plasmids determining the hemolysin and bacteriocin of *Streptococcus faecalis* var. *zymogenes*. *JB* 121, 863–72.

—— *and* HOBBS, S. J. (1974). Conjugal transfer of plasmid-borne multiple antibiotic resistance in *Streptococcus faecalis* var. *zymogenes*. *JB* 117, 360–72.

JACOB, F., BRENNER, S. *and* CUZIN, F. (1963). On the regulation of DNA replication in bacteria. *CSH* 28, 329–48.

—— *and* MONOD, J. (1961). Genetic regulatory mechanisms in the synthesis of proteins. *JMB* 3, 318–56.

—— *and* WOLLMAN, E. (1956). Recombinaison génétique et mutants de fertilité chez *Escherichia coli* K12. *C. R. Acad. Sci.* 242, 303–6.

—— —— (1958). Genetic and physical determinations of chromosomal segments in *E. coli*. *Symposia of the Society for Experimental Biology* 12, 75–92.

JACOBSON, A. (1972). The role of F pili in the penetration of bacteriophage f1. *Journal of Virology* 10, 835–43.

JACOBY, G. A. (1974a). Properties of R plasmids determining gentamicin resistance by acetylation in *Pseudomonas aeruginosa*. *AAC* 6, 239–52.

—— (1974b). Properties of an R plasmid in *Pseudomonas aeruginosa* producing amikacin (BB-K8), butirosin, kanamycin, tobramycin, and sisomicin resistance. *AAC* 6, 807–10.

—— (1977). Classification of plasmids in *Pseudomonas aeruginosa*. in: *Microbiology, 1977*.

—— *and* MATTHEW, M. (1979). The distribution of β-lactamase genes on plasmids found in *Pseudomonas*. *Plasmid* 2, 41–7.

—— ROGERS, J. E., JACOB, A. E. *and* HEDGES, R. W. (1978). Transposition of *Pseudomonas* toluene-degrading genes and expression in *Escherichia coli*. *Nat.* 274, 179–80.

—— *and* SUTTON, L. (1977). Restriction and modification determined by a *Pseudomonas* R plasmid. *Plasmid* 1, 115–16.

JAMIESON, A. F. *and* BERGQUIST, P. L. (1976). Genetic mapping of chromosomal mutations affecting the replication of the F factor of *Escherichia coli*. *MGG* 148, 221–3.

—— —— (1977). Role of *dnaB43* in plasmid incompatibility. *MGG* 150, 161–70.

JOHNSRUD, L., CALOS, M. P. *and* MILLER, J. H. (1978). The transposon Tn9 generates a 9 bp repeated sequence during integration. *Cell* 15, 1209–20.

JOHNSTON, A. W. B., BEYNON, J. L., BUCHANAN-WOLLASTON, A. V., SETCHELL, S. M., HIRSCH, P. R. *and* BERINGER, J. E. (1978). High frequency transfer of nodulating ability between strains and species of *Rhizobium*. *Nature* 276, 634–6.

JONES, R. T. *and* CURTISS, R. III. (1970). Genetic exchange between *Escherichia coli* strains in the mouse intestine. *JB* 103, 71–80.

JORDAN, E., SAEDLER, H. *and* STARLINGER, P. (1968). O^c and strong polar mutations in the *gal* operon are insertions. *MGG* 102, 353–63.

KAHN, M. *and* HELINSKI, D. R. (1978). Construction of a novel plasmid-phage hybrid: use of the hybrid to demonstrate ColE1 replication *in vivo* in the absence of a ColE1-specified protein. *PNAS* **75**, 2200–4.

KANEY, A. R. *and* ATWOOD, K. C. (1972). Incompatibility of integrated sex factors in double male strains of *Escherichia coli*. *Gen*. **70**, 31–9.

KASAMATSU, H. *and* ROWND, R. (1970). Replication of R factors in *Proteus mirabilis*: replication under relaxed control. *JMB* **51**, 473–89.

KAULFERS, P-M., LAUFS, R. *and* JAHN, G. (1978). Molecular properties of transmissible R factors of *Haemophilus influenzae* determining tetracycline resistance. *JGM* **105**, 243–52.

KEDES, L. H., CHANG, A. C. Y., HOUSEMAN, D. *and* COHEN, S. N. (1975a). Isolation of histone genes from unfractionated sea urchin DNA by subculture cloning in *E. coli*. *Nat*. **255**, 533–8.

—— COHN, R. H., LOWRY, J. C., CHANG, A. C. Y. *and* COHEN, S. N. (1975b). The organization of sea urchin histone genes. *Cell* **6**, 359–69.

KEGGINS, K. M., LOVETT, P. S. *and* DUVALL, E. J. (1978). Molecular cloning of genetically active fragments of *Bacillus* DNA in *Bacillus subtilis* and properties of vector plasmid pUB113. *PNAS* **75**, 1423–7.

KENNEDY, N., BEUTIN, L., ACHTMAN, M., SKURRAY, R., RAHMSDORF, U. *and* HERRLICH, P. (1977). Conjugation proteins encoded by the F sex factor. *Nat*. **270**, 580–5.

KERR, A., MANIGAULT, P. *and* TEMPÉ, J. (1977). Transfer of virulence *in vivo* and *in vitro* in *Agrobacterium*. *Nat*. **265**, 560–1.

KINGSBURY, D. T. *and* HELINSKI, D. R. (1973a). Temperature-sensitive mutants for the replication of plasmids in *Escherichia coli*: requirement for deoxyribonucleic acid polymerase I in the replication of the plasmid ColE1. *JB* **114**, 1116–24.

—— —— (1973b). Temperature-sensitive mutants for the replication of plasmids in *Escherichia coli*. I. Isolation and specificity of host and plasmid mutations. *Gen*. **74**, 17–31.

—— SIECKMANN, D. G. *and* HELINSKI, D. R. (1973). Temperature-sensitive mutants for the replication of plasmids in *Escherichia coli*. II. Properties of host and plasmid mutations. *Gen*. **74**, 1–16.

KINGSMAN, A. *and* WILLETTS, N. (1978). The requirements for conjugal DNA synthesis in the donor strain during F*lac* transfer. *JMB* **122**, 287–300.

KIRBY, R. *and* HOPWOOD, D. A. (1977). Genetic determination of methylenomycin synthesis by the SCP1 plasmid of *Streptomyces coelicolor* A3(2). *JGM* **98**, 239–52.

—— WRIGHT, L. F. *and* HOPWOOD, D. A. (1975). Plasmid-determined antibiotic synthesis and resistance in *Streptomyces coelicolor*. *Nat*. **254**, 265–7.

KLAPWIJK, P. M., SCHEULDERMAN, T. *and* SCHILPEROORT, R. A. (1978). Coordinated regulation of octopine degradation and conjugative transfer of Ti plasmids in *Agrobacterium tumefaciens*: evidence for a common regulatory gene and separate operons. *JB* **136**, 775–85.

KLECKNER, N. (1977). Translocatable elements in prokaryotes. *Cell* **11**, 11–23.

—— CHAN, R. K., TYE, B. K. *and* BOTSTEIN, D. (1975). Mutagenesis by insertion of a drug-resistance element carrying an inverted repetition. *JMB* **97**, 561–75.

—— ROTH, J. *and* BOTSTEIN, D. (1977). Genetic engineering *in vivo* using translocatable drug-resistance elements. New methods in bacterial genetics. *JMB* **116**, 125–59.

KLINE, B. C. (1973). Role of DNA transcription in the initiation of *Escherichia coli* sex factor (F) DNA replication. *BBRC* **50**, 280–8.

—— *and* MILLER, J. R. (1975). Detection of non-integrated plasmid deoxyribonucleic acid in the folded chromosome of *Escherichia coli*: physicochemical approach to studying the unit of segregation. *JB* **121**, 165–72.

—— —— CRESS, D. E., WLODARCZYK, M., MANIS, J. J. *and* OTTEN, M. R. (1976). Non-integrated plasmid–chromosome complexes in *Escherichia coli*. *JB* **127**, 881–9.

KOLLEK, R., OERTEL, W. *and* GOEBEL, W. (1978). Isolation and characterization of the minimal fragment required for autonomous replication ('basic replicon') of a copy mutant (pKN102) of the antibiotic resistance factor R1. *MGG* **162**, 51–7.

KONINGS, R. N. H., ANDREOLI, P. M., VELTKAMP, E. *and* NIJKAMP, H. J. J. (1976). Clo DF13 plasmid deoxyribonucleic acid-directed *in vitro* synthesis of biologically active cloacin DF13 and Clo DF13 immunity protein. *JB* **126**, 861–8.

KONRAD, E. B. *and* LEHMAN, I. R. (1974). A conditional lethal mutant of *Escherichia coli* K-12 defective in the 5'→3' exonuclease associated with DNA polymerase I. *PNAS* **71**, 2048–51.

KONTOMICHALOU, P., MITANI, M. *and* CLOWES, R. C. (1970). Circular R-factor molecules controlling penicillinase synthesis, replicating in *Escherichia coli* under either relaxed or stringent control. *JB* **104**, 34–44.

—— PAPACHRISTOU, E. *and* ANGELATOU, F. (1976). Multiresistant plasmids from *Pseudomonas aeruginosa* highly resistant to either or both gentamicin and carbenicillin. *AAC* **9**, 866–73.

KOOL, A. J., BORSTLAP, A. J. *and* NIJKAMP, H. J. J. (1975a). Bacteriocinogenic Clo DF13 minicells of *Escherichia coli* synthesize a protein that accounts for immunity to bacteriocin Clo DF13: action of the immunity protein *in vivo* and *in vitro*. *AAC* **8**, 76–85.

—— POLS, C. *and* NIJKAMP, H. J. J. (1975b). Bacteriocinogenic Clo DF13 minicells of *Escherichia coli* synthesize a protein that accounts for immunity to bacteriocin Clo DF13: purification and characterization of immunity protein. *AAC* **8**, 67–75.

—— VAN ZEBEN, M. S. *and* NIJKAMP, H. J. J. (1974). Identification of messenger ribonucleic acids and proteins synthesized by the bacteriocinogenic factor Clo DF13 in purified minicells of *Escherichia coli*. *JB* **118**, 213–24.

KOPECKO, D. J., BREVET, J. *and* COHEN, S. N. (1976). Involvement of multiple translocating DNA segments and recombinational hotspots in the structural evolution of bacterial plasmids. *JMB* **108**, 333–60.

—— *and* COHEN, S. N. (1975). Site-specific *recA*-independent recombination between bacterial plasmids: involvement of palindromes at the recombinational loci. *PNAS* **72**, 1373–7.

KORFHAGEN, T. R., FERREL, J. A., MENEFEE, C. L. *and* LOPER, J. C. (1976). Resistance plasmids of *Pseudomonas aeruginosa*. Change from conjugative to non-conjugative in a hospital population. *AAC* **9**, 810–16.

—— SUTTON, L. *and* JACOBY, G. A. (1978). Classification and physical properties of *Pseudomonas* plasmids. In: *Microbiology, 1978*.

KORNBERG, A. (1974). *DNA Synthesis*. W. H. Freeman and Co., San Francisco.

KOYAMA, A. H., WADA, C., NAGATA, T. *and* YURA, T. (1975). Indirect selection for plasmid mutants: isolation of ColVB*trp* mutants defective in self-maintenance in *Escherichia coli*. *JB* **122**, 73–9.

—— *and* YURA, T. (1975). Plasmid mutations affecting self-maintenance and host growth in *Escherichia coli*. *JB* **122**, 80–8.

KRETSCHMER, P. J., CHANG, A. C. Y. *and* COHEN, S. N. (1975). Indirect selection of bacterial plasmids lacking identifiable phenotypic properties. *JB* **124**, 225–31.

—— *and* COHEN, S. N. (1977). Selected transposition of plasmid genes: frequency and regional specificity of translocation of the Tn3 element. *JB* **130**, 888–99.

KRISHNAPILLAI, V. (1975). Resistance to ultraviolet light and enhanced mutagenesis conferred by *Pseudomonas aeruginosa* plasmids. *Mutation Research* **29**, 363–72.

KÜHN, S., FRITZ, H-J. *and* STARLINGER, P. (1979). Close vicinity of IS1 integration sites in the leader sequence of the *gal* operon of *E.coli*. *MGG* **167**, 235–41.

KUPERSZTOCH, Y. M. *and* HELINSKI, D. R. (1973). A catenated DNA molecule as an intermediate in the replication of the resistance transfer factor R6K in *Escherichia coli*. *BBRC* **54**, 1451–9.

KUPERSZTOCH-PORTNOY, Y. M., LOVETT, M. A. *and* HELINSKI, D. R. (1974). Strand and site specificity of the relaxation event for the relaxation complex of the antibiotic resistance plasmid R6K. *Biochem*. **13**, 5484–90.

LACEY, R. W. (1975). Antibiotic resistance plasmids of *Staphylococcus aureus* and their clinical importance. *Bact. Rev*. **39**, 1–32.

LANE, D. *and* CHANDLER, M. (1977). Mapping of the drug resistance genes carried by the R-determinant of the R100.1 plasmid. *MGG* **157**, 17–23.

—— —— SILVER, L., BRUSCHI, A. *and* CARO, L. (1979). The construction and replication properties of hybrid plasmids composed of the r-determinant of R100.1 and the plasmids pCR1 or pSC201. *MGG* **168**, 337–40.

LANG, D. *and* MITANI, M. (1970). Simplified quantitative electron microscopy of biopolymers. *Biopolymers* **9**, 373–9.

LAUFS, R. *and* KAULFERS, P-M. (1977). Molecular characterization of a plasmid specifying ampicillin resistance and its relationship to other R factors from *Haemophilus influenzae*. *JGM* **103**, 277–86.

LAVALLÉ, R. *and* JACOB, F. (1961). Sur la sensibilité des épisomes sexuels et colicinogènes d'*E. coli* K-12 à la désintégration du radiophosphore. *C. R. Acad. Sci.*, **252**, 1678–80.

LAWN, A. M., MEYNELL, E. *and* COOKE, M. (1971). Mixed infections with bacterial sex factors: sex pili of pure and mixed phenotype. *Annales de l'Institut Pasteur* **120**, 3–8.

—— —— MEYNELL, G. G. *and* DATTA, N. (1967). Sex pili and the classification of sex factors in the enterobacteriaceae. *Nat*. **216**, 343–6.

LEBLANC, D. J. *and* FALKOW, S. (1973). Studies on superinfection immunity among transmissible plasmids in *Escherichia coli*. *JMB* **74**, 689–701.

—— HAWLEY, R. J., LEE, L. N. *and* ST MARTIN, E. J. (1978). 'Conjugal' transfer of plasmid DNA among oral streptococci. *PNAS*. **75**, 3484–7.

LEDERBERG, E. M. *and* COHEN, S. N. (1974). Transformation of *Salmonella typhimurium* by plasmid deoxyribonucleic acid. *JB* **119**, 1072–4.

LEDERBERG, J. (1952). Cell genetics and hereditary symbiosis. *Physiological Reviews* **32**, 403–30.

—— (1956). Conjugal pairing in *E. coli*. *JB* **71**, 497–8.

—— CAVALLI, L. L. *and* LEDERBERG, E. M. (1952). Sex compatibility in *E. coli*. *Gen*. **37**, 720–30.

—— *and* TATUM, E. L. (1946). Novel genotypes in mixed cultures of biochemical mutants of bacteria. *CSH* **11**, 113–14.

LEHRBACH, P., KUNG, A. H. C., LEE, B. T. O. *and* JACOBY, G. A. (1977). Plasmid modification of radiation and chemical mutagen sensitivity in *Pseudomonas aeruginosa*. *JGM* **98**, 167–76.

LEIBOWITZ, M. J. *and* WICKNER, R. B. (1976). A chromosomal gene required for killer plasmid expression, mating and spore maturation in *Saccharomyces cerevisiae*. *PNAS* **73**, 2061–5.

LEVINTHAL, M. (1974). Bacterial genetics excluding *E. coli*. *Ann. Rev. Micro*. **28**, 219–30.

LEVY, S. B., FITZGERALD, G. B. *and* MACONE, A. B. (1976a). Spread of antibiotic-resistant plasmids from chicken to chicken and from chicken to man. *Nat.* **260**, 40–2.

—— —— (1976b). Changes in intestinal flora of farm personnel after introduction of a tetracycline-supplemented feed on a farm. *New England Journal of Medicine* **295**, 583–8.

LIEBOWITZ, P. J. *and* FOX, M. S. (1978). The F plasmid may co-segregate with either DNA strand of the *Escherichia coli* chromosome. *JB* **136**, 455–59.

LINDAHL, G., HIROTA, Y. *and* JACOB, F. (1971). On the process of cellular division in *Escherichia coli*: replication of the bacterial chromosome under control of prophage P2. *PNAS* **68**, 2407–11.

LINNANE, A. W. *and* NAGLEY, P. (1978). Mitochondrial genetics in perspective: the derivation of a genetic and physical map of the yeast mitochondrial genome. *Plasmid* **1**, 324–45.

LINTON, A. H. (1977). Antibiotic resistance: the present situation reviewed. *The Veterinary Record* **100**, 354–60.

—— HANDLEY, B., OSBORNE, A. D., SHAW, B. G., ROBERTS, T. A. *and* HUDSON, W. R. (1976). Contamination of pig carcasses at two abattoirs by *Escherichia coli* with special reference to O-serotypes and antibiotic resistance. *J. App. Bact.* **42**, 89–110.

—— HOWE, K., BENNETT, P. M., RICHMOND, M. H. *and* WHITESIDE, E. J. (1977a). The colonisation of the human gut by antibiotic resistant *Escherichia coli* from chickens. *J. App. Bact.* **43**, 465–9.

—— —— HARTLEY, C. L., CLEMENTS, H. M., RICHMOND, M. H. *and* OSBORNE, A. D. (1977b). Antibiotic resistance among *Escherichia coli* O-serotypes from the gut and carcasses of commercially slaughtered broiler chickens: a potential public health hazard. *J. App. Bact.* **42**, 365–78.

LIVINGSTON, D. M. *and* KLEIN, H. L. (1977). Deoxyribonucleic acid sequence organization of a yeast plasmid. *JB* **131**, 472–81.

LOVETT, M. A., GUINEY, D. G. *and* HELINSKI, D. R. (1974a). Relaxation complexes of plasmids ColE1 and ColE2: unique site of the nick in the open circular DNA of the relaxed complexes. *PNAS* **71**, 3854–7.

—— *and* HELINSKI, D. R. (1975). Relaxation complexes of plasmid DNA and protein. II. Characterization of the proteins associated with the unrelaxed and relaxed complexes of plasmid ColE1. *JBC* **250**, 8790–5.

—— —— (1976). Method for the isolation of the replication region of a bacterial replicon: construction of a mini-F′*km* plasmid. *JB* **127**, 982–7.

—— KATZ, L. *and* HELINSKI, D. R. (1974b). Unidirectional replication of plasmid ColE1 DNA. *Nat.* **251**, 337–40.

—— SPARKS, R. B. *and* HELINSKI, D. R. (1975). Bidirectional replication of plasmid R6K DNA in *Escherichia coli*: correspondence between origin of replication and position of single-strand break in relaxed complex. *PNAS* **72**, 2905–9.

LOWBURY, E. J. L. (1975). Ecological importance of *Pseudomonas aeruginosa*: medical aspects. In: *Genetics and Biochemistry of* Pseudomonas. P. H. Clarke and M. H. Richmond, eds. Wiley.

—— KIDSON, A., LILLY, H. A., AYLIFFE, G. A. J. *and* JONES, R. J. (1969). Sensitivity of *Pseudomonas aeruginosa* to antibiotics: emergence of strains highly resistant to carbenicillin. *Lancet* **II**, 448–452.

LUIBRAND, G., BLOHM, D., MAYER, H. *and* GOEBEL, W. (1977). Characterization of small ampicillin resistance plasmids (Rsc) originating from the mutant antibiotic resistance factor R1*drd19B2*. *MGG* **152**, 43–51.

MAAS, R. (1963). Exclusion of an F*lac* episome by an Hfr gene. *PNAS* **50**, 1051–5.

—— *and* MAAS, W. K. (1962). Introduction of a gene from *Escherichia coli* B into Hfr and F⁻ strains of *Escherichia coli* K-12. *PNAS* **48**, 1887–93.

MAAS, W. K. *and* GOLDSCHMIDT, A. D. (1969). A mutant of *Escherichia coli* permitting replication of two F factors. *PNAS* **62**, 873–80.

MACHATTIE, L. *and* JACKOWSKI, J. B. (1977). Physical structure and deletion effects of the chloramphenicol resistance element Tn9 in phage lambda. In: *Insertion elements, Plasmids and Episomes*, A. Bukhari, J. A. Shapiro and S. Adhya, eds. Cold Spring Harbor.

MCINTIRE, S. *and* WILLETTS, N. (1978). Plasmid cointegrates of Flac and lambda prophage. *JB* **134**, 184–92.

MACRINA, F. L., KOPECKO, D. J., JONES, K. R., AYERS, D. J. *and* MCCOWEN, S. M. (1978). A multiple plasmid-containing *Escherichia coli* strain: convenient source of size reference plasmid molecules. *Plasmid* **1**, 417–20.

MANIS, J. J. *and* KLINE, B. C. (1978). F plasmid incompatibility and copy number genes: their map locations and interactions. *Plasmid* **1**, 492–507.

MANNING, P. A. *and* REEVES. (1975). Recipient ability of bacteriophage-resistant mutants of *Escherichia coli* K12. *JB* **124**, 576–7.

MARÉ, I. J. (1968). Incidence of R factors among Gram-negative bacteria in drug-free human and animal communities. *Nat.* **220**, 1046–7.

MARINUS, M. G. *and* ADELBERG, E. A. (1970). Vegetative replication and transfer replication of deoxyribonucleic acid in temperature-sensitive mutants of *Escherichia coli* K-12. *JB* **104**, 1266–72.

MARMUR, J., ROWND, R., FALKOW, S., BARON, L. S., SCHILDKRAUT, C. *and* DOTY, P. (1961). The nature of intergeneric episomal infection. *PNAS* **47**, 972–9.

MARVIN, D. *and* HOHN, B. (1969). Filamentous bacterial viruses. *Bact. Rev.* **33**, 172–209.

MASTERS, M. (1975). Strains of *Escherichia coli* diploid for chromosomal origin of DNA replication. *MGG* **143**, 105–11.

—— *and* BRODA, P. (1971). Evidence for the bidirectional replication of the *Escherichia coli* chromosome. *NNB* **232**, 137–40.

MATSUBARA, K. (1968). Properties of sex factor and related episomes isolated from purified *E. coli* zygote cells. *JMB* **38**, 89–108.

—— (1976). Genetic structure and replication of a replicon of plasmid λdv. *JMB* **102**, 427–39.

—— *and* KAISER, A. D. (1968). λdv: an autonomously replicating DNA fragment. *CSH* **33**, 769–775.

—— *and* OTSUJI, Y. (1978). Preparation of plasmids from lambdoid phages and studies on their incompatibilities. *Plasmid* **1**, 284–96.

MATTES, R., BURKARDT, H. J. *and* SCHMITT, R. (1979). Repetition of tetracycline resistance determinant genes on R plasmid pRSD1 in *Escherichia coli*. *MGG* **168**, 173–84.

MATURIN, L. *and* CURTISS, R. 1977. Degradation of DNA by nucleases in intestinal tract of rats. *Science* **198**, 216–18.

MESELSON, M. *and* STAHL, F. W. (1958). The replication of DNA in *Escherichia coli*. *PNAS* **44**, 671–82.

MESSER, W., BERGMANS, H. E. N., MEIJER, M., WOMACK, J. E., HAUSEN, F. G. *and* VON MEYENBURG, K. (1978). Mini-chromosomes: plasmids which carry the *E. coli* origin. *MGG* **162**, 269–75.

MEYER, R., FIGURSKI, D. *and* HELINSKI, D. R. (1975). Molecular vehicle properties of the broad host range plasmid RK2. *Science* **190**, 1226–8.

MEYERS, J. A., SANCHEZ, D., ELWELL, L. P. *and* FALKOW, S. (1976). Simple agarose gel electrophoretic method for the identification and characterization of plasmid deoxyribonucleic acid. *JB* **127**, 1529–37.

174 References

Meynell, E. and Datta, N. (1966). The relation of resistance transfer factors to the F-factor (sex-factor) of *Escherichia coli* K12. *Gen. Res.* **7**, 134–40.

—— Meynell, G. G. and Datta, N. (1968). Phylogenetic relationships of drug-resistance factors and other transmissible plasmids. *Bact. Rev.* **32**, 55–83.

Mickel, S. and Bauer, W. (1976). Isolation, by tetracycline selection, of small plasmids derived from R-factor R12 in *Escherichia coli* K-12. *JB* **127**, 644–55.

—— Ohtsubo, E. and Bauer, W. (1977). Heteroduplex mapping of small plasmids derived from R-factor R12: *in vivo* recombination occurs at IS1 insertion sequences. *Gene* **2**, 193–210.

Miki, T., Easton, A. M. and Rownd, R. H. (1978a). Mapping of the resistance genes of the R plasmid NR1. *MGG* **158**, 217–24.

—— Horiuchi, T. and Willetts, N. S. (1978b). Identification and characterization of four new *tra* cistrons on the *E. coli* K12 sex factor F. *Plasmid* **1**, 316–23.

Miller, C. A. and Cohen, S. N. (1978). Phenotypically cryptic *Eco*RI endonuclease activity specified by the ColE1 plasmid. *PNAS* **75**, 1265–9.

Milliken, C. E. and Clowes, R. C. (1973). Molecular structure of an R factor, its component drug-resistance determinants and transfer factor. *JB* **113**, 1026–33.

Minkley, E. G. and Ippen-Ihler, K. (1977). Identification of a membrane protein associated with the expression of the surface exclusion region of the F transfer operon. *JB* **129**, 1613–22.

—— Polen, S., Brinton, C. C. and Ippen-Ihler, K. (1976). Identification of the structural gene for F pilin. *JMB* **108**, 111–21.

Mitsuhashi, S. Harada, K. and Hashimoto, H. (1960). Multiple resistance of bacteria and transmission of drug-resistance to other strains by mixed cultivation. *Japanese Journal of Experimental Medicine* **30**, 179–84.

Moody, E. E. M. and Runge, R. (1972). The integration of autonomous transmissible plasmids into the chromosome of *Escherichia coli* K12. *Gen. Res.* **19**, 181–6.

Monner, D. A., Jonsson, S. and Boman, H. G. (1971). Ampicillin-resistant mutants of *Escherichia coli* K-12 with lipopolysaccharide alterations affecting mating ability and susceptibility to sex specific bacteriophages. *JB* **107**, 420–32.

Montoya, A. L., Chilton, M-D., Gordon, M. F., Sciaky, D. and Nester, E. W. (1977). Octopine and nopaline metabolism in *Agrobacterium tumefaciens* and crown gall tumor cells: role of plasmid genes. *JB* **129**, 101–7.

—— Moore, L. W., Gordon, M. F. and Nester, E. W. (1978). Multiple genes coding for octopine-degrading enzymes in *Agrobacterium*. *JB* **136**, 909–15.

Morris, C. F., Hashimoto, H., Mickel, S. and Rownd, R. (1974). Round of replication mutant of a drug resistance factor. *JB* **118**, 855–66.

Morrow, J. F., Cohen, S. N., Chang, A. C. Y., Boyer, H. W., Goodman, H. M. and Helling, R. B. (1974). Replication and transcription of eukaryotic DNA in *Escherichia coli*. *PNAS* **71**, 1743–7.

Mukai, T., Matsubara, K. and Takagi, Y. (1976). Cloning bacterial genes with plasmid λ*dv*. *MGG* **146**, 269–74.

Murray, N. E., Brammar, W. J. and Murray, K. (1977). Lambdoid phages that simplify the recovery of *in vitro* recombinants. *MGG* **150**, 53–61.

Mylroie, J. R., Friello, D. A., Siemens, T. V. and Chakrabarty, A. M. (1977). Mapping of *Pseudomonas putida* chromosomal genes with a recombinant sex-factor plasmid. *MGG* **157**, 231–7.

Nakahara, H., Ishikawa, T., Sarai, S., Kondo, I. and Mitsuhashi, S. (1977). Frequency of heavy metal resistance in bacteria from inpatients in Japan. *Nat.* **266**, 165–7.

NAKAMURA, H. (1974). Plasmid-instability in *acrA* mutants of *Escherichia coli* K12. *JGM* **84**, 85–93.

NAKAZAWA, T., HAYASHI, E., YOKOTA, T., EBINA, Y. *and* NAKAZAWA, A. (1978). Isolation of TOL and RP4 recombinants by integrative suppression. *JB* **134**, 270–7.

NALIN, D. R., MCLAUGHLIN, J., RAHAMAN, M., YUNUS, M. *and* CURLIN, G. (1975). Enterotoxigenic *E. coli* and idiopathic diarrhoea in Bangladesh. *Lancet* **II**, 1113–16.

NATIONAL INSTITUTES OF HEALTH. (1978). Recombinant DNA research. Proposed revised guidelines. *Federal Register* **43**, 33042–178.

NEVERS, P. *and* SAEDLER, H. (1978). Mapping and characterization of an *E. coli* mutant defective in IS1-mediated deletion formation. *MGG* **160**, 209–214.

NISEN, P. D., KOPECKO, D. J., CHOI, J. *and* COHEN, S. N. (1977). Site specific DNA deletions ocurring adjacent to the termini of a transposable ampicillin resistance element (Tn3). *JMB* **117**, 975–98.

NISIOKA, T., MITANI, M. *and* CLOWES, R. C. (1969). Composite circular forms of R-factor deoxyribonucleic acid molecules. *JB* **97**, 376–85.

NISHIMURA, A., NISHIMURA, Y. *and* CARO, L. (1973). Isolation of Hfr strains from R$^+$ and ColV2$^+$ strains of *Escherichia coli* and derivation of an R'*lac* factor by transduction. *JB* **116**, 1107–12.

NISHIMURA, Y., CARO, L., BERG, C. M. *and* HIROTA, Y. (1971). Chromosomal replication in *Escherichia coli*. IV. Control of chromosome replication and cell division by an integrated episome. *JMB* **55**, 441–56.

NOMURA, M. (1963). Mode of action of colicines. *CSH* **28**, 315–24.

NORDSTRÖM, K., INGRAM, L. C. *and* LUNDBÄCK, A. (1972). Mutations in R factors of *Escherichia coli* causing an increased number of R-factor copies per chromosome. *JB* **110**, 562–9.

NOVICK, R. (1974). Studies on plasmid replication. III. Isolation and characterization of replication-defective mutants. *MGG* **135**, 131–47.

—— (1976). Plasmid–protein relaxation complexes in *Staphylococcus aureus*. *JB* **127**, 1177–87.

—— CLOWES, R. C., COHEN, S. N., CURTISS, R. III., DATTA, N. *and* FALKOW, S. (1976). Uniform nomenclature for bacterial plasmids: a proposal. *Bact. Rev.* **40**, 168–9.

—— *and* HOPPENSTEADT, F. C. (1978). On plasmid incompatibility. *Plasmid* **1**, 421–5.

—— *and* ROTH, C. (1968). Plasmid-linked resistance to inorganic salts in *Staphylococcus aureus*. *JB* **95**, 1335–42.

—— SMITH, K., SHEEHY, R. J. *and* MURPHY, E. (1973). A catenated intermediate in plasmid replication. *BBRC* **54**, 1460–9.

—— *and* SCHWESINGER, M. (1976). Independence of plasmid incompatibility and replication control functions in *Staphylococcus aureus*. *Nat.* **262**, 623–6.

—— WYMAN, L., BOUANCHAUD, D. *and* MURPHY, E. (1975). Plasmid life cycles in *Staphylococcus aureus*. In: *Microbiology, 1974*.

NOVOTNY, C. P. *and* FIVES-TAYLOR, P. (1974). Retraction of F-pili. *JB* **117**, 1306–11.

—— —— (1978). Effects of high temperature on *Escherichia coli* F pili. *JB* **133**, 459–64.

OCHIAI, K., YAMANAKA, T., KIMURA, K., *and* SAWADA, O. (1959). Studies on inheritance of drug resistance between *Shigella* strains and *Escherichia coli* strains. *Nippon Iji Shimpo* **1861**, 34–46 (in Japanese).

OHKI, M. *and* TOMIZAWA, J-I. (1968). Asymmetric transfer of DNA strands in bacterial conjugation. *CSH* **33**, 651–7.

OHTSUBO, E. (1970). Transfer-defective mutants of sex factors in *Escherichia coli*. II. Deletion mutants of an F-prime and deletion mapping of cistrons involved in genetic transfer. *Gen.* **64**, 189–97.

—— DEONIER, R. C., LEE, H. J. *and* DAVIDSON, N. (1974). Electron microscope heteroduplex studies of sequence relations among plasmids of *Escherichia coli*: IV. The F sequences in F14. *JMB* **89**, 565–84.

—— FEINGOLD, J., OHTSUBO, H., MICKEL, S. *and* BAUER, W. (1977). Bidirectional replication in *Escherichia coli* of three small plasmids derived from R factor R12. *Plasmid* **1**, 8–18.

—— NISHIMURA, Y. *and* HIROTA, Y. (1970). Transfer-defective mutants of sex factors in *E. coli*. I. Defective mutants and complementation analysis. *Gen.* **64**, 173–88.

—— ROSENBLOOM, M., SCHREMPF, H., GOEBEL, W. *and* ROSEN, J. (1978). Site specific recombination involved in the generation of small plasmids. *MGG* **159**, 131–41.

OHTSUBO, H. *and* OHTSUBO, E. (1978). Nucleotide sequence of an insertion element, IS1. *PNAS* **75**, 615–19.

OKA, A. (1978). Fine cleavage map of a small colicin E1 plasmid carrying genes responsible for replication and colicin E1 immunity. *JB* **133**, 916–24.

—— *and* INSELBURG, J. (1975). Replicative intermediates of colicin E1 plasmid DNA in minicells. *PNAS* **72**, 829–33.

OLIVER, D. R., BROWN, B. L. *and* CLEWELL, D. B. (1977). Characterization of plasmids determining hemolysin and bacteriocin production in *Streptococcus faecalis*. *JB* **130**, 948–50.

OLSEN, R. H. (1978). Evolution of *Pseudomonas* R-plasmids: consequences of Tn1 insertion and resultant partial diploidy to chromosome and Tra⁻ R-plasmid mobilization. *JB* **133**, 210–16.

—— SIAK, J-S. *and* SHIPLEY, P. L. (1977). *Pseudomonas* plasmid RP1-encoded surface components: a somatic receptor for phage PRD1. In: *Microbiology, 1977*.

ØRSKOV, I., ØRSKOV, F., JANN, B. *and* JANN, K. (1977). Serology, chemistry and genetics of O and K antigens of *Escherichia coli*. *Bact. Rev.* **41**, 667–710.

OTTOW, J. C. G. (1975). Ecology, physiology and genetics of fimbriae and pili. *Ann. Rev. Micro.* **29**, 79–108.

OU, J. T. *and* ANDERSON, T. F. (1970). Role of pili in bacterial conjugation. *JB* **102**, 648–54.

OZEKI, H., STOCKER, B. A. D. *and* DE MARGERIE, H. (1959). Production of colicine by single bacteria. *Nat.* **184**, 337–9.

—— —— *and* SMITH, S. M. (1962). Transmission of colicinogeny between strains of *Salmonella typhimurium* grown together. *JGM* **28**, 671–87.

PALCHAUDHURI, S. *and* CHAKRABARTY, A. (1976). Isolation of plasmid deoxyribonucleic acid from *Pseudomonas putida*. *JB* **126**, 410–16.

—— *and* MAAS, W. K. (1977a). Physical mapping of a DNA sequence common to plasmids of incompatibility group FI. *PNAS* **74**, 1190–4.

—— —— (1977b). Physical mapping of genes on the F plasmid of *Escherichia coli* responsible for inhibition of growth of female-specific bacteriophages. *JB* **132**, 740–3.

—— —— *and* OHTSUBO, E. (1976). Fusion of two F-prime factors in *Escherichia coli* studied by electron microscope heteroduplex analysis. *MGG* **146**, 215–31.

—— MAZAITIS, A. J., MAAS, W. K. *and* KLEINSCHMIDT, A. K. (1972). Characterization by electron microscopy of fused F-prime factors in *Escherichia coli*. *PNAS* **62**, 1873–6.

PARKER, R. C., WATSON, R. M. *and* VINOGRAD, J. (1977). Mapping of closed circular DNAs by cleavage with restriction endonucleases and calibration by agarose gel electrophoresis. *PNAS* **74**, 851–5.

PERLMAN, D. (1978). Frequency of replication from alternative origins in the composite R plasmid NR1. *JB* **133**, 729–36.

—— *and* ROWND, R. H. (1975). Transition of the R factor NR1 in *Proteus mirabilis*: molecular structure and replication of NR1 deoxyribonucleic acid. *JB* **123**, 1013–34.

—— —— (1976). Two origins of replication in composite R plasmid DNA. *Nat.* **259**, 281–4.

—— *and* STICKGOLD, R. (1977). Selective amplification of genes on the R plasmid, NR1, in *Proteus mirabilis*: an example of the induction of selective gene amplification. *PNAS* 2518–22.

—— TWOSE, T. M., HOLLAND, M. J. *and* ROWND, R. H. (1975). Denaturation mapping of R factor deoxyribonucleic acid. *JB* **123**, 1035–42.

PETIT, A. *and* TEMPÉ, J. (1978). Isolation of *Agrobacterium* Ti-plasmid regulatory mutants. *MGG* **167**, 147–55.

—— —— KERR, A., HOLSTERS, M., VAN MONTAGU, M. *and* SCHELL, J. (1978). Substrate induction of conjugative activity of *Agrobacterium tumefaciens* Ti plasmids. *Nat.* **271**, 570–1.

PETROCHEILOU, V., GRINSTED, J. *and* RICHMOND, M. H. (1976). R plasmid transfer *in vivo* in the absence of antibiotic selection pressure. *AAC* **10**, 753–61.

—— *and* RICHMOND, M. H. (1976). Distribution of R plasmids among the O-antigen types of *Escherichia coli* isolated from various clinical sources. *AAC* **9**, 1–5.

—— —— (1977). Absence of plasmid or *Escherichia coli* K12 infection among laboratory personnel engaged in R-plasmid research. *Gene* **2**, 323–7.

PFISTER, A., DEVRIES, J. K. *and* MAAS, W. K. (1976). Expression of a mutation affecting F incompatibility in the integrated but not the autonomous state of F. *JB* **127**, 348–53.

PINNEY, R. J. *and* SMITH, J. T. (1974). Fertility inhibition of an N group R factor by a group X R factor, R6K. *JGM* **82**, 415–18.

PORTHOUSE, A., BROWN, D. F. J., SMITH, R. G. *and* ROGERS, T. (1976). Gentamicin-resistance in *Staphylococcus aureus*. *Lancet* **I**, 20–1.

PRENTKI, P., CHANDLER, M. *and* CARO, L. (1977). Replication of the prophage P1 during the cell cycle of *Escherichia coli*. *MGG* **152**, 71–6.

PRICE, D. J. E. *and* SLEIGH, J. D. (1970). Control of infection due to *Klebsiella aerogenes* in a neurosurgical unit by withdrawal of all antibiotics. *Lancet* **II**, 1213–15.

PRITCHARD, R. H. (1978). Recombinant DNA is safe. *Nat.* **273**, 696.

—— BARTH, P. T. *and* COLLINS, J. (1969). Control of DNA synthesis in bacteria. *Symposia of the Society for General Microbiology* **19**, 263–97.

—— CHANDLER, M. G. *and* COLLINS, J. (1975). Independence of F replication and chromosome replication in *Escherichia coli*. *MGG* **138**, 143–55.

PTASHNE, K. *and* COHEN, S. N. (1975). Occurrence of insertion sequence (IS) regions on plasmid deoxyribonucleic acid as direct and inverted nucleotide sequence duplications. *JB* **122**, 776–81.

RABBITTS, T. H. (1976). Bacterial cloning of plasmids carrying genes of rabbit globin messenger RNA. *Nat.* **260**, 221–5.

RADLOFF, R., BAUER, W. *and* VINOGRAD, J. (1967). A dye-buoyant-density method for the detection and isolation of closed circular duplex DNA: the closed circular DNA in HeLa cells. *PNAS* **57**, 1514–20.

RAEBURN, J. A. (1976). Antibiotic management of cystic fibrosis. *J. Antimicrobial Chemotherapy* **2**, 107–9.

RATZKIN, B. *and* CARBON, J. (1977). Functional expression of cloned yeast DNA in *Escherichia coli. PNAS* **74**, 487–91.

REANNEY, D. (1976). Extrachromosal elements as possible agents of adaptation and development. *Bact. Rev.* **40**, 552–90.

REED, N. D., SIECKMANN, D. G. *and* GEORGI, C. E. (1969). Transfer of infectious drug resistance in microbially defined mice. *JB* **100**, 22–6.

REEVES, P. (1972). *The Bacteriocins*. Chapman and Hall, London.

—— *and* WILLETTS, N. S. (1974). Plasmid-specificity of the origin of transfer of the sex factor F. *JB* **120**, 125–30.

REIF, H. J. *and* SAEDLER, H. (1975). IS1 is involved in deletion formation in the *gal* region of *E. coli* K12. *MGG* **137**, 17–28.

REINER, A. M. (1974). *E. coli* females defective in conjugation and in absorption of a single-stranded DNA phage. *JB* **119**, 183–91.

RHEINWALD, J. G., CHAKRABARTY, A. M. *and* GUNSALUS, I. C. (1973). A transmissible plasmid controlling camphor oxidation in *Pseudomonas putida. PNAS* **70**, 885–9.

RICHMOND, A., SIMBERKOFF, M. S., RAHAL, J. J. *and* SCHAEFLER, S. (1975). R factors in gentamicin-resistant organisms causing hospital infection. *Lancet* **II**, 1176–8.

RICHMOND, M. H. (1972). A comparison of the exo-penicillinases mediated by a chromosomal gene in a strain of *Staphylococcus aureus* PS80 and by a plasmid gene in *Staphylococcus aureus* 8325. *Gen. Res.* **19**, 187–9.

——*and* SYKES, R. B. (1972). The chromosomal integration of a β-lactamase gene derived from the P-type R factor RP1 in *Escherichia coli. Gen. Res.* **20**, 231–7.

ROBERTS, M., ELWELL, L. P. *and* FALKOW, S. (1977). Molecular characterization of two beta-lactamase-specifying plasmids isolated from *Neisseria gonorrhoae. JB* **131**, 557–63.

—— *and* FALKOW, S. (1977). Conjugal transfer of R plasmids in *Neisseria gonorrhoae*. Nat. **266**, 630–1.

—— —— (1978). Plasmid-mediated chromosomal gene transfer in *Neisseria gonorrhoeae. JB* **134**, 66–70.

ROBERTS, R. J. (1978). Restriction and modification enzymes and their recognition sequences. *Gene* **4**, 183–93.

ROBINSON, M. K., BENNETT, P. M. *and* RICHMOND, M. H. (1977). Inhibition of TnA translocation by TnA. *JB* **129**, 407–14,

—— —— GRINSTED, J. *and* RICHMOND, M. H. (1978). The stable carriage of two TnA units on a single replicon. *MGG* **160**, 339–46.

ROE, E., JONES, R. J. *and* LOWBURY, E. J. L. (1971). Transfer of antibiotic resistance between *Pseudomonas aeruginosa, Escherichia coli* and other Gram-negative bacilli in burns. *Lancet* **I**, 149–52.

ROMERO, E. *and* MEYNELL, E. (1969). Covert *fi⁻* R factors in *fi⁺R⁺* strains of bacteria. *JB* **97**, 780–6.

ROTH, T. F. *and* HELINSKI, D. R. (1967). Evidence for circular forms of a bacterial plasmid. *PNAS* **58**, 650–7.

ROUSSEL, A. F. *and* CHABBERT, Y. A. (1978). Taxonomy and epidemiology of Gram-negative bacterial plasmids studied by DNA-DNA filter hybridization in formamide. *JGM* **104**, 269–76.

ROWE, B., GROSS, R. J. *and* SCOTLAND, S. M. (1975). Serotyping of enteropathogenic *Escherichia coli*. Lancet **II**, 925–6.

ROWND, R. (1969). Replication of a bacterial plasmid under relaxed control. *JMB* **44**, 387–402.

—— *and* MICKEL, S. (1971). Dissociation and reassociation of RTF and R-determinants of the R-factor NR1 in *Proteus mirabilis*. *NNB* **234**, 40–3.

—— NAKAYA, R. *and* NAKAMURA, A. (1966). Molecular nature of the drug-resistance factors of the Enterobacteriaceae. *JMB* **17**, 376–93.

—— PERLMAN, D. *and* GOTO, N. (1975). Structure and replication of R-factor deoxyribonucleic acid in *Proteus mirabilis*. In: *Microbiology, 1974*.

—— MIKI, T., APPELBAUM, E. R., MILLER, J. R., FINKELSTEIN, M. *and* BARTON, C. R. (1978). Dissociation, amplification, and reassociation of composite R-plasmid DNA. In: *Microbiology, 1978*.

ROYER-POKORA, B. *and* GOEBEL, W. (1976). Plasmids controlling synthesis of hemolysin in *Escherichia coli*. II. Polynucleotide sequence relationship among hemolytic plasmids. *MGG* **144**, 177–83.

RUBENS, C., HEFFRON, F. *and* FALKOW, S. (1976). Transposition of a plasmid sequence that mediates ampicillin resistance: independence of host *rec* functions and orientation of insertion *JB* **128**, 425–34.

RUPP. W. D. *and* IHLER, G. (1968). Strand selection during bacterial mating. *CSH* **33**, 647–50.

RUSH, M., NOVICK, R. *and* DELAP, R. (1975). Detection and quantitation of *Staphylococcus aureus* penicillinase plasmid deoxyribonucleic acid by reassociation kinetics. *JB* **124**, 1417–23.

RYDER, R. W., SACK, D. A., KAPIKIAN, A. Z., McLAUGHLIN, J. C., CHAKRABARTY, J., RAHMAN, A. S. M. M., MERSON, M. H. *and* WELLS, J. G. (1976). Enterotoxigenic *Escherichia coli* and reovirus-like agent in rural Bangladesh. *Lancet* **I**, 659–63.

SACK, R. B. (1975). Human diarrhoeal disease caused by enterotoxigenic *Escherichia coli*. *Ann. Rev. Micro*. **29**, 333–53.

SADIKARO, J. *and* NOMURA, M. (1975). *In vitro* synthesis of the E3 immunity protein directed by ColE3 plasmid deoxyribonucleic acid. *JBC* **250**, 1123–1131.

SAEDLER, H., *and* HEISS, B. (1973). Multiple copies of the insertion-DNA sequences IS1 and IS2 in the chromosome of *E. coli* K-12. *MGG* **122**, 267–77.

—— REIF, H. J., HU, S. *and* DAVIDSON, N. (1974). IS2, a genetic element for turn-off and turn-on of gene activity in *E. coli*. *MGG* **132**, 265–89.

SAGAI, H., HASUDA, K., IYOBE, S., BRYAN, L. E., HOLLOWAY, B. W. *and* MITSUHASHI, S. (1976). Classification of R plasmids by incompatibility in *Pseudomonas aeruginosa*. *AAC* **10**, 573–8.

—— IYOBE, S. *and* MITSUHASHI, S. (1977). Inhibition and facilitation of transfer among *Pseudomonas aeruginosa* R plasmids. *JB* **131**, 765–9.

SAITOH, T. *and* HIRAGA, S. (1975). F deoxyribonucleic acid superinfected into phenocopies of donor strains. *JB* **121**, 1007–13.

SAKAKIBARA, Y., SUZUKI, K. *and* TOMIZAWA, J. (1976). Formation of catenated molecules by replication of colicin E1 plasmid DNA in cell extracts. *JMB* **108**, 569–82.

—— *and* TOMIZAWA, J-I. (1974). Replication of colicin E1 DNA in cell extracts. *PNAS* **71**, 802–6.

SAN BLAS, F., THOMPSON, R. *and* BRODA, P. (1974). An *Escherichia coli* K12 mutant apparently carrying two autonomous F-prime factors. *MGG* **130**, 153–63.

SANDERS, J. P. M., HEYTING, C., VERBEET, M., MEIJLINK, F. C. P. W. *and* BORST, P. (1977). The organisation of genes in yeast mitochondrial DNA: III. Comparison of the physical maps of the mitochondrial DNAs from three wild-type *Saccharomyces* strains. *MGG* **157**, 239–61.

SANTOS, D. S., PALCHAUDHURI, S. *and* MAAS, W. K. (1976). Genetic and physical characteristics of an enterotoxin plasmid. *JB* **124**, 1240–7.

SARATHY, P. V. *and* SIDDIQI, O. (1973). DNA synthesis during bacterial conjugation. II. Is DNA replication in the Hfr obligatory for chromosome transfer? *JMB* **78**, 443–51.

SAUNDERS, J. R. (1978). Anaerobes and transferable drug resistance. *Nat.* **274**, 113–14.

SAVAGE, D. C. (1977). Microbial ecology of the gastrointestinal tract. *Ann. Rev. Micro.* **31**, 107–33.

SCAIFE, J. *and* GROSS, J. D. (1962). Inhibition of multiplication of an F*lac* factor in Hfr cells of *Escherichia coli* K-12. *BBRC* **7**, 403–7.

SCHALLER, K. *and* NOMURA, M. (1976). Colicin E2 is a DNA endonuclease. *PNAS* **73**, 3989–93.

SCHNÖS, M., *and* INMAN, R. B. (1970). Position of branch points in replicating lambda DNA. *JMB* **51**, 61–73.

SCHOTTEL, J., MANDEL, A., CLARK, D., SILVER, S. *and* HEDGES, R. W. (1974). Volatilization of mercury and organomercurials determined by inducible R-factor systems in enteric bacteria. *Nat.* **251**, 335–7.

SCHREMPF, H. *and* GOEBEL, W. (1977). Characterization of a plasmid from *Streptomyces coelicolor* A3(2). *JB* **131**, 251–8.

SCHWEIZER, M. *and* HENNING, U. (1977). Action of a major cell envelope membrane protein in conjugation of *Escherichia coli* K–12. *JB* **129**, 1651–2.

SCIAKY, D., MONTOYA, A. L. *and* CHILTON, M-D. (1978). Fingerprints of *Agrobacterium* Ti plasmids. *Plasmid* **1**, 238–53.

SENIOR, B. W. *and* HOLLAND, I. B. (1971). Effect of colicin E3 upon the 30S ribosomal subunit of *Escherichia coli*. *PNAS* **68**, 959–63.

SHAHAM, M., CHAKRABARTY, A. M. *and* GUNSALUS, I. C. (1973). Camphor plasmid-mediated chromosomal transfer in *Pseudomonas putida*. *JB* **116**, 944–9.

SHAPIRO, J. A. (1969). Mutations caused by the insertion of genetic material into the galactose operon of *Escherichia coli*. *JMB* **40**, 93–105.

—— ADHYA, S. *and* BUKHARI, A. I. (1977). New pathways in the evolution of chromosome structure. In: *DNA Insertion Elements, Episomes and Plasmids*. A. I. Bukhari, J. A. Shapiro and S. Adhya, eds. Cold Spring Harbor.

—— *and* SPORN, P. (1977). Tn402: a new transposable element determining trimethoprim resistance that inserts in bacteriophage lambda. *JB* **129**, 1632–5.

SHARP, P. A., COHEN, S. N. *and* DAVIDSON, N. (1973). Electron microscope heteroduplex studies of sequence relations among plasmids of *Escherichia coli*. II. Structure of drug resistance (R) factors and F factors. *JMB* **75**, 235–55.

—— HSU, M-T., OHTSUBO, E. *and* DAVIDSON, N. (1972). Electron microscope heteroduplex studies of sequence relations among plasmids of *Escherichia coli*. I. Structure of F-prime factors. *JMB* **71**, 471–97.

SHAW, W. V. *and* HOPWOOD, D. A. (1976). Chloramphenicol acetylation in *Streptomyces*. *JGM* **94**, 159–66.

SHEEHY, R. J., ORR, C. *and* CURTISS, R. (1972). Molecular studies on entry exclusion in *Escherichia coli* minicells. *JB* **112**, 861–9.

—— *and* NOVICK, R. P. (1975). Studies on plasmid replication. V. Replicative intermediates. *JMB* **93**, 237–53.

SHIMADA, K., WEISBERG, R. A. *and* GOTTESMAN, M. E. (1972). Prophage lambda at unusual chromosome locations. I. Location of the secondary attachment sites and the properties of the lysogens. *JMB* **63**, 483–503.

SHINE, J., SEEBURG, P. H., MARTIAL, J. A., BAXTER, J. D. *and* GOODMAN, H. M. (1977). Construction and analysis of recombinant DNA for human chorionic somatomammotropin. *Nat.* **270**, 494–9.

SHIVAKUMAR, A. G. *and* DUBNAU, D. (1978). Differential effect of hydroxyurea on the replication of plasmid and chromosomal DNA in *Bacillus subtilis*. *JB* **136**, 1205–7.

SIDDIQI, O. *and* FOX, M. S. (1973). Integration of donor DNA in bacterial conjugation. *JMB* **77**, 101–23.

SILVA, M. L. M., MAAS, W. K. *and* GYLES, C. L. (1978). Isolation and characterization of enterotoxin-deficient mutants of *Escherichia coli*. *PNAS* **75**, 1384–1388.

SILVER, L., CHANDLER, M., BOY DE LA TOUR, E. *and* CARO, L. (1977). Origin and direction of replication of the drug resistance plasmid R100.1 and of a resistance transfer factor derivative in synchronized cultures. *JB* **131**, 929–42.

SILVER, R. P. *and* FALKOW, S. (1970a). Specific labeling and physical characterization of R-factor deoxyribonucleic acid in *Escherichia coli*. *JB* **104**, 331–9.

—— —— (1970b). Studies on resistance transfer deoxyribonucleic acid in *Escherichia coli*. *JB* **104**, 340–4.

SISTROM, W. R. (1977). Transfer of chromosomal genes mediated by plasmid R68.45 in *Rhodospeudomonas sphaeroides*. *JB* **131**, 526–32.

SKURRAY, R. A., GUYER, M. S., TIMMIS, K., CABELLO, F., COHEN, S. N., DAVIDSON, N. *and* CLARK, A. J. (1976a). Replication region fragments cloned from *Flac*⁺ are identical to *Eco*RI fragment f5 of F. *JB* **127**, 1571–5.

—— HANCOCK, R. E. W. *and* REEVES, P. (1974). Con⁻ mutants: class of mutants in *Escherichia coli* K-12 lacking a major cell wall protein and defective in conjugation and adsorption of bacteriophage. *JB* **119**, 726–35.

—— NAGAISHI, H. *and* CLARK, A. J. (1976b). Molecular cloning of DNA F sex factor of *Escherichia coli* K-12. *PNAS* **73**, 64–8.

—— —— —— (1978). Construction and *Bam*HI analysis of chimaeric plasmids containing *Eco*RI DNA fragments of the F sex factor. *Plasmid* **1**, 174–86.

—— WILLETTS, N. *and* REEVES, P. (1976c). Effect of *tra* mutations on F factor specified immunity to lethal zygosis. *MGG* **146**, 161–5.

SMITH, D. H. (1967). R factor infection of *Escherichia coli* lyophilized in 1946. *JB* **94**, 2071–2.

SMITH, H. R., GRINDLEY, N. D. F., HUMPHREYS, G. O. *and* ANDERSON, E. S. (1973a). Interactions of group H resistance factors with the F factor. *JB* **115**, 623–8.

—— HUMPHREYS, G. O. *and* ANDERSON, E. S. (1974). Genetic and molecular characterization of some non-transferring plasmids. *MGG* **129**, 229–42.

—— —— GRINDLEY, N. D. F., GRINDLEY, J. N. *and* ANDERSON, E. S. (1973b). Molecular studies of an *fi*⁺ plasmid from strains of *Salmonella typhimurium*. *MGG* **126**, 143–51.

—— —— WILLSHAW, G. A. *and* ANDERSON, E. S. (1976). Characterization of plasmids coding for the restriction endonuclease *Eco*RI. *MGG* **143**, 319–25.

SMITH, H. W. (1975a). Survival of orally administered *E. coli* K12 in alimentary tract of man. *Nat.* **225**, 500–4.

—— (1975b). Persistence of tetracycline resistance in pig *E. coli*. *Nat.* **258**, 628–30.

—— *and* GYLES, C. L. (1970). The relationship between different transmissible plasmids introduced by F into the same strain of *Escherichia coli* K12. *JGM* **62**, 277–85.

182 References

—— and HALLS, S. (1967). The transmissible nature of the genetic factor in *Escherichia coli* that controls haemolysin production. *JGM* **47**, 153–61.

—— and LINGGOOD, M. (1971). Observations of the pathogenic properties of the K88, Hly and Ent plasmids of *Escherichia coli* with particular reference to porcine diarrhoea. *J. Med. Micro.* **4**, 467–485.

—— PARSELL, Z. and GREEN, P. (1978). Thermosensitive H1 plasmids determining citrate utilization. *JGM* **109**, 305–11.

—— and TUCKER, J. F. (1978). The effect of antimicrobial feed additives on the colonization of the alimentary tract of chickens *Salmonella typhimurium*. *J. Hyg.* **80**, 217–31.

SMITH, M. G. (1977). *In vivo* transfer of an R factor within the lower gastro-intestinal tract of sheep. *J. Hyg.* **79**, 259–68.

So, M., BOYER, H. W., BETLACH, M. and FALKOW, S. (1976). Molecular cloning of an *Escherichia coli* plasmid that encodes for the production of heat-stable enterotoxin. *JB* **128**, 463–72.

—— CRANDALL, J. F., CROSA, J. H. and FALKOW, S. (1975a). Extrachromosomal determinants that contribute to bacterial pathogenicity. In: *Microbiology, 1974*.

—— CROSA, J. H. and FALKOW, S. (1975b). Polynucleotide sequence relationships among Ent plasmids and the relationship between Ent and other plasmids. *JB* **121**, 234–8.

—— DALLAS, W. S. and FALKOW, S. (1978a). Characterization of an *Escherichia coli* plasmid encoding for synthesis of heat-labile toxin: molecular cloning of the toxin determinant. *Infection and Immunity* **21**, 405–11.

—— GILL, R. and FALKOW, S. (1975c). Generation of a ColE1–Ap^R cloning vehicle which allows the detection of inserted DNA. *MGG* **142**, 239–49.

—— HEFFRON, F. and FALKOW, S. (1978b). Method for the genetic labeling of cryptic plasmids. *JB* **133**, 1520–23.

—— HEFFRON, F. and MCCARTHY, B. J. (1979). The *E. coli* gene encoding heat stable toxin is a bacterial transposon flanked by inverted repeats of IS1. *Nat.* **277**, 453–6.

SOX, T. E., MOHAMMED, W., BLACKMAN, E., BISWAS, G. and SPARLING, P. F. (1978). Conjugative plasmids in *Neisseria gonorrhoeae*. *JB* **134**, 278–86.

STADLER, J. and ADELBERG, E. A. (1972). Temperature dependence of sex-factor maintenance in *Escherichia coli* K-12. *JB* **109**, 447–9.

STALLIONS, D. R. and CURTISS, R. (1971). Chromosome transfer and recombinant formation with deoxyribonucleic acid temperature-sensitive strains of *Escherichia coli JB* **105**, 886–95.

—— —— (1972). Bacterial conjugation under anaerobic conditions. *JB* **111**, 294–5.

STANIER, R. Y., PALLERONI, N. J. and DOUDOROFF, M. (1966). The aerobic pseudomonads: a taxonomic study. *JGM* **43**, 159–273.

STANISICH, V. A., BENNETT, P. M. and RICHMOND, M. H. (1977). Characterization of a translocation unit encoding resistance to mercuric ions that occurs on a non-conjugative plasmid in *Pseudomonas aeruginosa*. *JB* **129**, 1227–33.

STARLINGER, P. and SAEDLER, H. (1976). IS-elements in microorganisms. *Current Topics in Microbiology and Immunology*. **75**, 111–52.

STAUDENBAUER, W. L. (1976). Replication of small plasmids in extracts of *Escherichia coli*: requirement for both DNA polymerase I and III. *MGG* **149**, 151–8.

—— (1977). Replication of the ampicillin resistance plasmid RSF1030 in extracts of *Escherichia coli*: separation of the replication cycle into early and late stages. *MGG* **156**, 27–34.

—— LANKA, E. and SCHUSTER, H. (1978). Replication of small plasmids in extracts of *Escherichia coli*. Involvement of the *dnaB* and *dnaC* proteins in the replication of early replicative intermediates. *MGG* **162**, 243–9.

STEWART, F. M. *and* LEVIN, B. R. (1977). The population biology of bacterial plasmids: *a priori* conditions for the existence of conjugationally transmitted factors. *Gen*. **87**, 209–28.

STOCKER, B. A. D., SMITH, S. M. *and* OZEKI, H. (1963). High infectivity of *Salmonella typhimurium* newly infected by the ColI factor. JGM **30**, 201–21.

SUEOKA, N. *and* YOSHIKAWA, H. (1963). Regulation of chromosome replication in *Bacillus subtilis*. *CSH* **28**, 47–54.

STRUHL. K., CAMERON, J. R. *and* DAVIS, R. W. (1976). Functional genetic expression of eukaryotic DNA in *Escherichia coli*. *PNAS* **73**, 1471–5.

—— *and* DAVIS, R. W. (1977). Production of a functional eukaryotic enzyme in *Escherichia coli*: cloning and expression of the yeast structural gene for imidazole–glycerol phosphate dehydratase (*his3*). *PNAS* **74**, 5255–9.

SUMMERS, A. O. *and* JACOBY, G. A. (1977). Plasmid-determined resistance to tellurium compounds. *JB* **129**, 276–81.

SWANN REPORT. (1969). Joint committee on the use of antibiotics in animal husbandry and veterinary medicine. *Cmnd* 4190. London HMSO.

SYKES, R. B. *and* MATTHEW, M. (1976). The β-lactamases of gram-negative bacteria and their role in resistance to β-lactam antibiotics. *J. Antimicrobial Chemotherapy* **2**, 115–57.

—— *and* RICHMOND, M. H. (1970). Intergeneric transfer of a β-lactamase gene between *Pseudomonas aeruginosa* and *Escherichia coli*. *Nat*. **226**, 952–4.

TACON, W. *and* SHERRATT, D. (1976). ColE replication in DNA polymerase I-deficient strains of *Escherichia coli*. *MGG* **147**, 331–5.

TANAKA, N., CRAMER, J. H. *and* ROWND, R. H. (1976). NR1 *Eco*RI restriction endonuclease map of the composite R plasmid NR1. *JB* **127**, 619–39.

—— WEISBLUM, B., SCHNÖS, M. *and* INMAN, R. B. (1975). Construction and characterization of a chimeric plasmid composed of DNA from *Escherichia coli* and *Drosophila melanogaster*. *Biochem*. **14**, 2064–72.

TAYLOR, D. E. *and* GRANT, R. B. (1977). Incompatibility and surface exclusion properties of H1 and H2 plasmids. *JB* **131**, 174–8.

TAYLOR, D. P., GREENBERG, J. *and* ROWND, R. H. (1977). Generation of miniplasmids from copy number mutants of the R plasmid NR1. *JB* **132**, 986–995.

TELFORD, J., BOSELEY, P., SCHAFFNER, W. *and* BIRNSTIEL, M. (1977). Novel screening procedure for recombinant plasmids. *Science* **195**, 391–3.

THOMAS, M., CAMERON, J. R. *and* DAVIS, R. W. (1974). Viable molecular hybrids of bacteriophage lambda and eukaryotic DNA. *PNAS* **71**, 4579–83.

THOMPSON, R., *and* BRODA, P. (1973). DNA polymerase III and the replication of F and ColVB*trp* in *Escherichia coli* K-12. *MGG* **127**, 255–8.

—— HUGHES, S. G. *and* BRODA, P. (1974). Plasmid identification using specific endonucleases. *MGG* **133**, 141–9.

TIMMIS, K. N., ANDRÉS, I. *and* ACHTMAN, N. (1978a). Fertility repression of F-like conjugative plasmids: physical mapping of the R6-5 *finO* and *finP* cistrons and identification of the *finO* protein. *PNAS* **75**, 5836–40.

—— —— *and* SLOCOMBE, P. M. (1978b). Plasmid incompatibility: cloning and analysis of an *inc* FII determinant of R6-5. *Nat*. **273**, 27–32.

—— CABELLO, F., ANDRÉS, I., NORDHEIM, A., BURKHARDT, H. J. *and* COHEN, S. N. (1978c). Instability of plasmid DNA sequences: macro and micro evolution of the antibiotic resistance plasmid R6-5. *MGG* **167**, 11–9.

—— —— *and* COHEN, S. N. (1974). Utilization of two distinct modes of replication of a hybrid plasmid constructed *in vitro* from separate replicons. *PNAS* **71**, 4556–60.

—— —— —— (1975). Cloning, isolation and characterization of replication regions of complex plasmid genomes. *PNAS* **72**, 2242–6.

—— —— —— (1976). Covalently closed circular DNA molecules of low superhelix density as intermediate forms in plasmid replication. *Nat.* **261**, 513–16.

—— —— —— (1978d). Cloning and characterization of *Eco*RI and *Hin*dIII restriction endonuclease-generated fragments of antibiotic resistance plasmids R6-5 and R6. *MGG* **162**, 121–37.

—— COHEN, S. N. *and* CABELLO, F. (1978e). DNA cloning and the analysis of plasmid structure and function. *Progress in Molecular and Subcellular Biology* **6**, 1–58. F. Hahn, ed. Springer.

TOMIZAWA, J. I., OHMORI, H. *and* BIRD, R. E. (1977). The origin of replication of colicin E1 plasmid DNA. *PNAS* **74**, 1865–9.

—— SAKAKIBARA, Y. *and* KAKEFUDA, T. (1974). Replication of colicin E1 plasmid DNA in cell extracts. Origin and direction of replication. *PNAS* **71**, 2260–64.

—— —— —— (1975). Replication of colicin E1 plasmid DNA added to cell extracts. *PNAS* **72**, 1050–54.

TOMOEDA, M., INUZUKA, M. *and* DATE, T. (1975). Bacterial sex pili. *Progress in Biophysics and Molecular Biology* **30**, 25–36.

TOOZE, J. (ed.) (1973). *The Molecular Biology of Tumor Viruses*. Cold Spring Harbor.

TRESGUERRES, E. F., NANDADASA H. G. *and* PRITCHARD, R. H. (1975). Suppression of initiation-negative strains of *Escherichia coli* by integration of the sex factor F. *JB* **121**, 554–61.

TWEATS, D. J., THOMPSON, M. J., PINNEY, R. J. *and* SMITH, J. T. (1976). R factor mediated resistance to ultraviolet light in strains of *Escherichia coli* deficient in known repair functions. *JGM* **93**, 103–10.

UBELAKER, M. H. *and* ROSENBLUM, E. D. (1978). Transduction of plasmid determinants in *Staphylococcus aureus* and *Escherichia coli*. *JB* **133**, 699–707.

UHLIN, B. E. *and* NORDSTRÖM, K. (1975). Plasmid incompatibility and control of replication: copy mutants of the R-factor R1 in *Escherichia coli* K-12. *JB* **124**, 641–9.

—— —— (1977). R plasmid gene dosage effects in *Escherichia coli* K-12: copy mutants of the R plasmid R1*drd-19*. *Plasmid* **1**, 1–7.

—— —— (1978). A runaway-replication mutant of plasmid R1*drd-19*: temperature-dependent loss of copy number control. *MGG* **165**, 167–79.

VAN BRUNT, J., WAGGONER, B. T. *and* PATO, M. L. (1977). Re-examination of F plasmid replication in a *dnaC* mutant of *Escherichia coli*. *MGG* **150**, 285–92.

VAN DE POL, H., VELTKAMP, E. *and* NIJKAMP, H. J. J. (1978). Genetic analysis of the mobilization of the non-conjugative plasmid Clo DF13. *MGG* **160**, 139–49.

VAN EMBDEN, J. D. A., ENGEL, H. W. B. *and* VAN KLINGEREN, B. (1977). Drug resistance in group D streptococci of clinical and non-clinical origin: prevalence, transferability and plasmid properties. *ACC* **11**, 925–32.

—— VAN LEEUWEN, W. J. *and* GUINÉE, P. A. M. (1976). Interference with propagation of typing bacteriophage by extrachromosal elements in *Salmonella typhimurium*: bacteriophage type 505. *JB* **127**, 1414–26.

—— VELTKAMP, E., STUITJE, T., ANDREOLI, P. M. *and* NIJKAMP, H. J. J. (1978). Integration of a transposable DNA sequence which mediates ampicillin resistance into CloDF13 plasmid DNA: determination and orientation of TnA insertions. *Plasmid* **1**, 204–17.

VAN HEYNINGEN, S. (1977). Cholera toxin. *Biological Reviews* **52**, 509–49.

VAN KLINGEREN, B., VAN EMBDEN, J. D. A. *and* DESSENS-KROON, M. (1977). Plasmid-mediated chloramphenicol resistance in *Haemophilus influenzae*. *AAC* **11**, 383–7.

VAN LAREBEKE, N., ENGLER, G., HOLSTERS, M., VAN DEN ELSACKER, S., ZAENEN, I., SCHILPEROORT, R. A. *and* SCHELL, J. (1974). Large plasmid in *Agrobacterium tumefaciens* essential for crown gall-inducing ability. *Nat.* **252**, 169–170.

—— GENETELLO, C., HERNALSTEENS, J. P., DE PICKER, A., ZAENEN, I., MESSENS, E., VAN MONTAGU, M. *and* SCHELL, J. (1977). Transfer of Ti plasmids between *Agrobacterium* strains by mobilisation with the conjugative plasmid RP4. *MGG* **152**, 119–24.

VAPNEK, D., LIPMAN, M. B. *and* RUPP, W. D. (1971). Physical properties and mechanism of transfer of R factors in *Escherichia coli*. *JB* **108**, 508–14.

—— *and* RUPP, W. D. (1971). Identification of individual sex factor DNA strands and their replication during conjugation in thermosensitive DNA mutants of *E. coli*. *JMB* **60**, 413–24.

VELTKAMP, E., POLS, K., VAN EE, J. H. *and* NIJKAMP, H. J. J. (1976). Replication of the bacteriocinogenic plasmid Clo DF13: action of the plasmid protein cloacin DF13 on CloDF13 DNA. *JMB* **106**, 75–95.

—— *and* NIJKAMP, H. J. J. (1974). Replication of the bacteriocinogenic plasmid CloDF13 in thermosensitive *Escherichia coli* mutants defective in initiation or elongation of deoxyribonucleic acid replication. *JB* **120**, 1227–37.

—— —— (1976). Characterization of a replication mutant of the bacteriocinogenic plasmid CloDF13. *BBA* **425**, 356–67.

VILLEMS, R., DUGGLEBY, C. J. *and* BRODA, P. (1978). Restriction endonuclease mapping of DNA using *in situ* digestion in two-dimensional gels. *FEBS Letters* **89**, 267–70.

VISCONTI, N. *and* DELBRÜCK, M. (1953). The mechanism of genetic recombination in phage. *Gen.* **38**, 5–33.

VON GRAEVENITZ, A. (1977). The role of opportunistic bacteria in human disease. *Ann. Rev. Micro.* **31**, 447–71.

VON MEYENBURG, K., HANSEN, F. G., NEILSEN, L. D. *and* RIISE, E. (1978). Origin of replication, *oriC*, of the *Escherichia coli* chromosome on specialized transducing phage, *λasn*. *MGG* **160**, 287–95.

WACHSMUTH, I. K., FALKOW, S. *and* RYDER, R. W. (1976). Plasmid-mediated properties of a heat-stable enterotoxin-producing *Escherichia coli* associated with infantile diarrhoea. *Infection and Immunity* **14**, 403–7.

WADE, N. (1976). Recombinant DNA: a critic questions the right to free enquiry. *Science* **194**, 303–6.

WAID, J. S. (1973). The possible importance of transfer factors in the bacterial degradation of herbicides in natural ecosystems. *Residue Reviews* **44**, 65–71.

WALKER, M. S. *and* WALKER, J. B. (1970). Streptomycin biosynthesis and metabolism. *JBC* **245**, 6683–9.

WALZ, A., RATZKIN, B. *and* CARBON, J. (1978). Control of expression of a cloned yeast (*Saccharomyces cerevisiae*) gene (*trp5*) by a bacterial insertion element (IS2). *PNAS* **75**, 6172–6.

WANG, P. Y. *and* IYER, V. N. (1978). Analogs of the *dnaB* gene of *Escherichia coli* K-12 associated with conjugative R plasmids. *JB* **124**, 765–70.

—— RELF, J., PALCHAUDHURI, S. *and* IYER, V. N. (1978). Plasmid conferring increased sensitivity to mercuric chloride and cobalt chloride found in some laboratory strains of *Escherichia coli* K-12. *JB* **133**, 1042–3.

WARREN, G. *and* SHERRATT, D. (1978). Incompatibility and transforming efficiency of ColE1 and related plasmids. *MGG* **161**, 39–47.

—— TWIGG, A. J. *and* SHERRATT, D. J. (1978). ColE1 plasmid mobility and relaxation complex. *Nat.* **274**, 259–61.

WATANABE, T. (1963). Infectious heredity of multiple drug resistance in bacteria. *Bact. Rev.* **27**, 87–115.

—— *and* OGATA, Y. (1970). Genetic stability of various resistance factors in *Escherichia coli* and *Salmonella typhimurium*. *JB* **102**, 363–8.

WATSON, B., CURRIER, T. C., GORDON, M. P., CHILTON, M-D. *and* NESTER, E. W. (1975). Plasmid required for virulence of *Agrobacterium tumefaciens*. *JB* **123**, 255–64.

WATSON, J. D. (1976). *The Recombinant DNA Scare*. Report of the Director of the Cold Spring Harbor Laboratory.

WEISS, A. A., MURPHY, S. D. *and* SILVER, S. (1977). Mercury and organomercurial resistances determined by plasmids in *Staphylococcus aureus*. *JB* **132**, 197–208.

WEISS, R. (1975). Virological hazards in routine procedures. *Nat.* **255**, 445–7.

WENSINK, P. C., FINNEGAN, D. J., DONELSON, J. E. *and* HOGNESS, D. S. (1974). A system for mapping DNA sequences in the chromosomes of *Drosophila melanogaster*. *Cell* **3**, 315–25.

WHEELIS, M. L. (1975). The genetics of dissimilatory pathways in *Pseudomonas*. *Ann. Rev. Micro.* **29**, 505–24.

WICKNER, R. B. (1976). Killer of *Saccharomyces cerevisiae*: a double-stranded ribonucleic acid plasmid. *Bact. Rev.* **40**, 757–73.

WILKINS, B. M. *and* HOLLOM, S. E. (1974). Conjugational synthesis of F*lac*⁺ and ColI DNA in the presence of rifampicin and in *Escherichia coli* K12 mutants defective in DNA synthesis. *MGG* **134**, 143–56.

WILLETTS, N. S. (1970). The interaction of an I-like R factor and transfer-deficient mutants of F*lac* in *E. coli* K12. *MGG* **108**, 365–73.

—— (1971). The plasmid-specificity of two proteins required for conjugation in *E. coli*. *NNB* **230**, 183–5.

—— (1972a). Location of the origin of transfer of the sex factor F. *JB* **112**, 773–8.

—— (1972b). The genetics of transmissible plasmids *Ann. Rev. of Gen.* **6**, 257–68.

—— (1974a). Mapping loci for surface exclusion and incompatibility on the F factor of *Escherichia coli* K-12 *JB* **118**, 778–82.

—— (1974b). Kinetics of inhibition of F*lac* transfer by R100 in *E. coli*. *MGG* **129**, 123–30.

—— (1977a). The genetics of conjugation. In: *R Factors*. S. Mitsuhashi, Ed. University of Tokyo Press.

—— (1977b). The transcriptional control of fertility in F-like plasmids. *JMB* **112**, 141–8.

—— *and* ACHTMAN, M. (1972). Genetic analysis of transfer by the *Escherichia coli* sex factor F, using P1 transductional complementation. *JB* **110**, 843–51.

—— *and* BASTARRACHEA, F. (1972). The generation and physico-chemical characterization of *E. coli* strains carrying fused F-primes derived from KLF1 and F57. *PNAS* **69**, 1481–5.

—— *and* McINTIRE, S. (1978). Isolation and characterization of λ*tra* transducing phages from EDFL223 (F*lac traB*::EDλ4). *JMB* **126**, 525–549.

—— *and* MAULE, J. (1974). Interactions between the surface exclusion systems of some F-like plasmids. *Gen. Res.* **24**, 81–9.

—— —— (1979). Investigations of the conjugation gene *tra*I: *tra*I mutants and λ*tra*I transducing phages. *MGG* **169**, 325–336.

—— —— *and* McINTIRE, S. (1975). The genetic location of *traO*, *finP* and *tra-4* on the *E. coli* K12 sex factor F. *Gen. Res.* **26**, 255–63.

WILLIAMS, P. A. *and* MURRAY, K. (1974). Metabolism of benzoate and the methylbenzoates by *Pseudomonas putida (arvilla) mt-2*: evidence for the existence of a TOL plasmid. *JB* **120**, 416–23.

—— *and* WORSEY, M. J. (1976). Ubiquity of plasmids coding for toluene and xylene metabolism in soil bacteria: evidence for the existence of new TOL plasmids. *JB* **125**, 818–28.

WILLIAMS, P. H., BOYER, H. W. *and* HELINSKI, D. R. (1973). Size and base composition of RNA in supercoiled plasmid DNA. *PNAS* **70**, 3744–8.

WILLSHAW, G. A., SMITH, H. R. *and* ANDERSON, E. S. (1978). Molecular studies of F*ı̨me* resistance plasmids, particularly in epidemic *Salmonella typhimurium*. *MGG* **159**, 111–16.

WILSON, C. R. *and* BALDWIN, J. N. (1978). Characterization and construction of molecular cloning vehicles within *Staphylococcus aureus*, *JB* **136**, 402–13.

WISE, E. M. *and* ABOU-DONIA, M. M. (1975). Sulfonamide resistance mechanism in *Escherichia coli*: R plasmids can determine sulfonamide-resistant dihydropteroate synthases. *PNAS* **72**, 2621–5.

WOMBLE, D. D. *and* ROWND, R. H. (1977). Properties of the relaxation complex of supercoiled deoxyribonucleic acid and protein of R plasmid NR1 in *Escherichia coli*. *JB* **131**, 145–52.

—— WARREN, R. L. *and* ROWND, R. H. (1976). Partially supercoiled replication intermediates of R plasmid DNA are resistant to relaxation. *Nat.* **264**, 676–8.

WOOD, T. H. (1967). Genetic recombination in *Escherichia coli*: clone heterogeneity and the kinetics of segregation. *Science* **157**, 319–21.

WONG, C. L. *and* DUNN, N. W. (1974). Transmissible plasmid coding for the degradation of benzoate and *m*-toluate in *Pseudomonas arvilla mt-2*. *Gen. Res.* **23**, 227–32.

WORSEY, M. J. *and* WILLIAMS, P. A. (1975). Metabolism of toluene and xylenes by *Pseudomonas putida (arvilla) mt-2*: Evidence for a new function of the TOL plasmid. *JB* **124**, 7–13.

WRIGHT, H. M. *and* HOPWOOD, D. A. (1977). A chromosomal gene for chloramphenicol acetyltransferase in *Streptomyces acrimycini*. *JGM* **102**, 417–21.

WRIGHT, L. F. *and* HOPWOOD, D. A. (1976). Identification of the antibiotic determined by the SCP1 plasmid of *Streptomyces coelicolor* A3(2). *JGM* **95**, 96–106.

WYMAN, L. *and* NOVICK, R. P. (1974). Studies on plasmid replication. IV. complementation of replication-defective mutants by an incompatibility-deficient plasmid. *MGG* **135**, 149–61.

YAGI, Y. *and* CLEWELL, D. B. (1976). Plasmid-determined tetracycline resistance in *Streptococcus faecalis*: tandemly repeated resistance determinants in amplified forms of pAMa1. *JMB* **102**, 583–600.

—— —— (1977). Identification and characterization of a small sequence located at two sites on the amplifiable tetracycline resistance plasmid pAMa1 in *Streptococcus faecalis*. *JB* **129**, 400–6.

—— FRANKE, A. E. *and* CLEWELL, D. B. (1975). Plasmid-determined resistance to erythromycin: comparison of strains of *Streptococcus faecalis* and *Streptococcus pyogenes* with regard to plasmid homology and resistance inducibility. *ACC* **7**, 871–3.

YAMAGATA, H. *and* UCHIDA, H. (1972). Spectinomycin resistance mutations affecting the stability of sex-factors in *Escherichia coli*. *JMB* **67**, 533–5.

YASUDA, S. *and* HIROTA, Y. (1977). Cloning and mapping of the replication origin of *Escherichia coli*. *PNAS* **74**, 5458–62.

ZAENEN, I., VAN LAREBEKE, N., TENCHY, H., VAN MONTAGU, M. *and* SCHELL, J. (1974).

Supercoiled circular DNA in crown-gall inducing *Agrobacterium* strains. *JMB* **86**, 109–27.

ZEUTHEN, J., MOROZOW, E. *and* PATO, M. L. (1972). Pattern of replication of a colicin factor during the cell cycle of *Escherichia coli*. *JB* **112**, 1425–7.

—— *and* PATO, M. L. (1971). Replication of the F'*lac* factor in the cell cycle of *Escherichia coli*. *MGG* **111**, 242–4.

Author Index

Abe, M., 78
Abou-Donia, M. M., 117
Achtman, M., 36, 50, 83, 86–7, 89–90, 92
Adelberg, E. A., 68, 70, 88
Adhya, S., 2, 38–9, 46, 137, 140
Akagawa, H., 135
Akiba, T., 1
Alberts, B., 53
Alföldi, L., 141
Allet, B., 42, 45
Allison, D. P., 84
Ambler, R. P., 140
Amyes, S. G. B., 117
Anandan, J., 119
Anderson, E. S., 8–10, 12, 15–16, 24, 26–7, 33, 95, 105–6, 108, 110, 119, 139, 147
Anderson, J. D., 111, 113
Anderson, R. A., 121
Anderson, T. F., 85
Andreoli, P. M., 46, 128
Andrés, I., 29, 50, 71
Andresdottir, V., 79
Angelaton, F., 114
Anon., 121
Anthony, W. M., 70
Appelbaum, E. R., 22
Applebaum, B., 46
Appleton, J., 133
Arber, W., 40
Aries, V., 103
Arrand, J. E., 113
Asche, L. V., 119
Aserkoff, B., 110, 124
Atwood, K. C., 76
Austin, S., 72
Ausubel, F. M., 144
Ayers, D. J., 13
Ayliffe, G. A. J., 114, 124

Bachmann, B. J., 95
Backman, K., 144
Baldwin, J. N., 144
Baltimore, D., 145–6

Bannister, D., 119
Barate de Bertalmio, M., 142
Barnard, T., 121
Barnes, W. M., 11
Barnonx, C., 67
Baron, L. S., 5–6
Barth, P. T., 26, 30, 45–6, 69, 77, 79–81, 98, 138
Barton, C. R., 22
Bastarrachea, F., 75
Bastia, D., 60
Bauer, W., 8, 10, 59, 62
Baxter, J. D., 144
Bayley, S. A., 14, 22, 130, 132
Bazaral, M., 54, 77
Bazzicalupo, P., 68
Beale, G., 140
Beard, J. P., 84–5
Beckwith, J. R., 35, 40
Bedinger, P., 44
Beer, H., 119
Bennett, J. V., 110, 124
Bennett, P. M., 43–5, 109–10
Benson, S., 130, 138
Benveniste, R., 120
Benzinger, R., 10
Berg, C. M., 68–70
Berg, D., 44–6, 71, 80
Berg, P., 145–6
Bergeron, B., 142
Bergmans, H. E. N., 139
Bergquist, P. L., 73, 75
Beringer, J. E., 98, 134, 143
Betlach, M. C., 59, 70, 74, 122, 143–4
Beutin, L., 89–90
Bex, F., 72
Beynon, J. L., 134
Bezanson, G. S., 74
Bibb, M. J., 10, 135
Bird, R. E., 59–60, 68–9, 74
Birnstiel, M., 11
Bishop, J. O., 61, 75
Bishop, S. F., 85
Biswas, G., 115, 139
Blackman, E., 115, 139

Blair, D. G., 12, 59–60, 68
Blattner, F. R., 59
Blohm, D., 61
Boesman–Finkelstein, M., 121
Bolívar, F., 59, 70, 74, 143–4
Boman, H. G., 87
Bomhoff, G., 134
Bonewald, R., 62
Bonhoeffer, F., 88
Bonnevalle, I., 72
Bopp, L. H., 45
Borst, P., 140
Borstlap, A. J., 128
Boseley, P., 11
Botstein, D., 45–6, 141
Bonanchand, D. H., 24, 65
Bouché, J-P., 68
Boucher, C., 142
Boulnois, G. J., 88
Bowman, C. M., 127
Boy de la Tour, E., 42, 59
Boyer, H. W., 59, 68, 70, 74, 122, 142–5
Brachet, P., 39
Bradley, D. E., 46, 98, 125
Brammar, W. J., 143–4
Brenner, D. J., 25–6
Brenner, S., 63, 72, 77, 80–1, 88, 146
Brevet, J., 46, 140
Brinton, C. C., 84–5, 90
Broda, P., 8, 14, 22, 26, 33, 35–6, 40, 42–3, 47, 50, 67, 69, 70, 75–6, 83–4, 87, 92–5, 111, 130, 132
Brodt, P., 97
Brown, B. L., 98, 122
Brown, D. F. J., 115
Brown, W. M., 144
Brüning, H. J., 144
Bryan, L. E., 15, 24, 114
Buchanan-Wollaston, A. V., 134
Bukhari, A. I., 2, 38–9, 44, 46, 137, 140
Burkhardt, H. J., 22, 29, 71
Burman, L., 84, 98, 113

Cabello, F., 4, 29, 50, 57, 70–1, 80, 140, 142, 144
Cairns, J., 35
Calos, M. P., 43, 45
Cameron, J. R., 142, 144
Campbell, A., 35
Cannon, F. C., 3, 141, 144
Canosi, U., 10
Carbon, J., 142, 144
Carnahan, J., 84
Caro, L., 42, 59, 62, 68–70, 79, 84
Cavalli, L. L., 1, 85
Cerdá-Olmedo, E., 73
Chabbert, Y. A., 24, 26
Chakrabarty, A. M., 45, 98, 129–30, 132, 147
Chakrabarty, J., 121
Champoux, J. J., 44, 70
Chan, R. K., 45–6
Chandler, M., 16, 42, 59, 62, 69, 79
Chandler, P. M., 97–8
Chang, A. C. Y., 10–11, 47, 80, 142–44
Chang, B. J., 73
Chang, S., 10, 47
Chargaff, E., 145, 147
Chase, D. G., 121
Chater, K. F., 98, 135
Chesney, R. H., 69
Chilton, M-D., 50, 133–4
Choi, C. L., 45
Choi, J., 44
Chou, G. I. N., 130, 132
Citarella, R. V., 6, 25
Clark, A. J., 41, 46, 50, 71, 75–6, 87–9
Clark, D., 118
Clarke, L., 142, 144
Clayton, D. A., 142, 144
Clements, H. M., 109–10
Clewell, D. B., 8, 20, 40, 59, 68, 98, 116, 122
Clowes, R. C., ix, 12, 15–18, 24, 77–8
Coetzee, J. N., 143
Cohen, S. N., ix, 4, 8, 10–11, 16–17, 24, 28–9, 31–2, 37–40, 42–4, 46–7, 50, 57, 70–1, 77, 80, 89, 96, 126, 137, 140, 142–5
Cohn, R. H., 142
Collins, J., 61, 67, 70, 77, 79, 80, 144
Collins, J. F., 83–4, 93–4, 111
Comer, S., 115
Connolly, J. C., 84
Contente, S., 10
Cooke, M., 97
Cooper, S., 61, 79
Cornelis, G., 45, 138
Cosloy, S. D., 10
Courvalin, P., 120
Couturier, M., 72
Cozzarelli, N. R., 14, 70
Cramer, J. H., 40, 50
Crandall, J. F., 121–2
Cranston, J. W., 68
Crea, R., 144
Cress, D. E., 62, 65
Cresswell, J. M., 143
Crosa, J. H., 26, 55, 57–8, 93, 121–2, 138, 143–4
Crowther, V. S., 103
Cruickshank, R., 102
Cullum, J., 42–3, 76, 87, 93–4
Curlin, G., 121

Currier, T. C., 8, 133
Curtiss, R. III, ix, 7–8, 16, 24, 65, 68, 76–7, 84–5, 87–8, 95, 97, 113, 144, 147
Cuzin, F., 63–4, 72, 74–5, 77, 80–1, 88

Dahlberg, J. E., 127
Dallas, W. S., 122
Danna, K. J., 50
Date, T., 84
Datta, N., ix, 1, 16, 23–4, 30, 43, 45, 69, 77, 80, 92, 137
Davidson, N., 8, 12, 14, 16, 26, 28–33, 36–43, 70–1, 89, 96, 126, 137
Davies, J. E., 45, 117, 120
Davies, J. K., 126, 128
Davis, B. D., 83, 102, 145
Davis, C. E., 119, 138
Davis, D. B., 79
Davis, R. W., 26, 28, 142, 144–5
Dean, H. F., 119
De Graaff, J., 114
De Greve, H., 46
DeLap, R., 61, 140
Delbrück, M., 76
Della Latta, P., 65
De Margerie, H., 128
Demiri, E., 141
Dénarié, J., 142
Denniston-Thompson, K., 59
Deonier, R. C., 14, 28, 33, 37, 40–3, 70, 89
Depicker, A., 10, 133–4
Desmyter, A., 72
Dessens-Kroon, M., 115
DeVries, J. K., 43, 73, 75
De Waele, D., 10
Dixon, R. A., 3, 141
Donachie, W. D., 61
Donelson, J. E., 144
Donoghue, D. J., 72, 143
Doty, P., 5–6
Dondoroff, M., 129
Dougan, G., 44, 46
Douglas, G. J., 98
Dove, W. F., 35
Dowding, J. E., 98, 120, 135
Drasar, B. S., 103
Dressler, D., 54
Drummond, M. H., 50, 133–4
Dubnan, D., 10, 144
Dubnan, E., 74
Duggleby, C. J., 14, 22, 26, 33, 47, 50, 130, 132
Dugnid, J. P., 102
Dulbecco, R., 102
Dunn, N. W., 132
Dunny, G. M., 98
Durkacz, B. W., 65
Duvall, E. J., 144

Easton, A. M., 16
Ebina, Y., 45, 130
Echols, H., 75
Eckhardt, T., 11
Ehrlich, S. D., 138, 140, 144
Eichenlaub, R., 59
Eisen, H. M., 102
Elsom, S. W., 114
Elwell, L. P., 8, 11, 13, 115
Engberg, B., 79
Engel, H. W. B., 116
Engler, G., 133
Evans, D. G., 121

Evans, D. J., 121
Evenchick, B., 68
Evenchik, Z., 95

Faelen, M., 142
Falkinham, J. O., III, 76, 87
Falkow, S., ix, 5–6, 8, 11, 13, 16, 24–6, 28, 30, 43–6, 55, 57–8, 74, 77, 85, 88, 93, 115, 119, 121–2, 138, 143–4
Fanning, G. R., 25
Farrand, S. K., 134
Feingold, J., 59
Fennewald, M., 14, 132
Fenwick, R. G., 68, 88, 97
Ferrel, J. A., 118
Fiandt, M., 39
Field, M., 122
Figurski, D., 59, 71, 143
Finkelstein, M., 22, 79
Finkelstein, R. A., 121
Finland, M., 101
Finnegan, D. J., 91–2, 144
Fitzgerald, G. B., 110–11
Fisher, P. R., 133
Fives-Taylor, P., 85
Fodor, K., 141
Foster, T. J., 45, 96, 120
Fox, M. S., 65, 88
Frame, R., 61, 75
Franke, A. E., 116
Franklin, N. C., 35
Frazer, A. C., 7, 8, 65, 144
Frédéricq, P., 125–6
Freeman, R. F., 135
Freifelder, D., 7, 36
Frey, J., 62
Friello, D. A., 45, 98, 132
Fritz, H-J., 43
Fuke, M., 54, 56, 60
Fullbrook, P. D., 114
Furth, M. E., 59

Gallay, E., 42
Gaffney, D. F., 120
Gardner, P., 119
Garg, G. K., 129
Garrod, L. P., 117
Gasson, M., 92, 97
Gefter, M., 66–7
Gellert, M., 74
Gemski, P., 84
Genetello, C., 133–4, 138
Georgi, C. E., 113
Gerband, G. R., 24
Ghosal, D., 39, 45, 138
Gibson, D. T., 132
Gilbert, W., 54
Gill, R., 44–5
Gillespie, W. A., 113
Ginsberg, M. S., 102
Glover, S. W., 119
Goebel, W., 62, 66–70, 74, 122, 128, 135
Goldschmidt, A. D., 75
Goodman, H. M., 142, 144
Gorbach, S. C., 121
Gordon, M. P., 50, 133–4
Goto, N., 17, 19, 21–2
Gottesman, M. E., 35, 36
Gottesman, M. M., 45
Graf, L. H., 122
Grant, R. B., 26
Gratia, A., 125
Green, P., 108
Greenberg, J., 62

Greene, P. J., 143–4
Grindley, J. N., 33
Grindley, N. D. F., 9, 24, 26–7, 33, 43, 59, 66
Grinsted, J., 44–5, 113–14
Grinter, N. J., 26, 30, 45, 46, 98, 138
Gross, J., 66, 74
Gross, M., 66
Gross, R. J., 121
Gryczan, T. J., 144
Guerola, N., 73
Guerry, P., 8, 25–6, 28, 30, 88
Guinée, P. A. M., 107, 111
Guiney, D. G., 12, 59–60, 138
Guiso, N., 138
Gunsalus, I. C., 129–30, 132
Gustafsson, P., 78–9
Guyer, M. S., 39, 41–2, 71, 87
Gylee, C. L., 122

Haas, D., 98
Hadley, R. G., 37
Haenni, C., 75
Hall, S., 89
Halls, S., 122
Hancock, R. E. W., 87
Handley, B., 109
Hansen, F. G., 139
Hansen, J. B., 11, 14
Harada, K., 1
Hardy, K. G., 125–8, 130
Hartley, C. L., 109–11
Hashimoto, H., 1, 17, 61
Hashimoto, T., 10
Hashimoto-Gotoh, T., 65, 73, 76
Hasuda, K., 24
Hathaway, B. G., 73
Hausen, F. G., 139
Hawksworth, G., 103
Hawley, R. J., 98
Hayakawa, Y., 72
Hayashi, E., 45, 130
Hayes, W., 1, 3, 95
Hedges, R. W., 30, 43, 45, 118–19, 130, 138, 143
Heffron, F., 43–6, 57–8, 93, 119, 138
Heinaru, A., 22, 26, 33, 47, 132
Heiss, B., 39, 42
Helinski, D. R., 7, 8, 12, 54, 57–60, 66–8, 70–4, 77, 128, 143
Helling, R. B., 142, 144
Helmstetter, C. E., 61, 79
Helmuth, R., 84, 87, 89, 90
Henning, U., 87
Hepburn, Λ. G., 133
Hermann, M., 129
Hernalsteens, J. P., 46, 133–4, 138
Herrlich, P., 89, 90
Herschman, H. R., 128
Hershfield, V., 74, 98, 143
Heynecker, H. L., 59, 70, 74, 143–4
Heyting, C., 140
Hickson, F. T., 7
Higgins, N. P., 70
Hill, M. J., 103
Hindley, J., 133
Hiraga, S., 74, 139
Hirose, T., 144
Hirota, Y., 66–70, 89, 96, 139
Hirsch, H. J., 39
Hirsch, P. R., 134
Hobbs, S. J., 98
Hoesselbarth, R., 88

Hoggan, S. A., 98
Hogness, D. S., 144–5
Hohn, B., 5, 65, 68, 85
Holland, I. B., 127
Holland, M. J., 19
Hollom, S. E., 88
Holloway, B. W., 24, 73, 95, 98, 119, 125
Holsters, M., 10, 133–4, 138
Hooykaas, P. J. J., 134
Hopkins, A. S., 144
Hopwood, D. A., 10, 98, 116, 120, 135, 141
Horiuchi, T., 89
Houseman, D., 144
Howarth, S., 119
Howe, K., 109–11
Howe, T. G. B., 45
Hradecna, Z., 87
Hsu, L., 10, 47
Hsu, M-T., 8, 28–30, 33, 36–7, 40–2, 89
Hu, M., 40
Hu, S., 28, 33, 40, 42, 70, 89
Hudson, W. R., 109
Hughes, C., 8, 11, 127
Hughes, S. G., 8, 47
Hughes, V., 127
Humphreys, G. O., 8–10, 24, 26–7, 33, 59, 110, 119

Ihler, G., 87
Iida, S., 40, 70
Ikeda, H., 3
Ikemura, T., 127
Inman, R. B., 19, 144
Ingraham, J. L., 73
Ingram, L. C., 61, 113–14
Inselburg, J., 46, 54–7, 60, 67, 76, 128
Inuzuka, M., 74, 84
Iordanescu, S., 12
Ippen-Ihler, K., 36, 89–90
Ishii, K., 76
Ishikawa, T., 118
Ishiki, Y., 1
Itakura, K., 144
Itoh, T., 74
Iyer, R., 97
Iyer, V. N., 68, 118
Iyobe, S., 24, 98

Jackowski, J. B., 45
Jacob, A., 43, 45, 98, 119, 130, 138, 143
Jacob, F., 5, 35, 60, 63–4, 69, 72, 75, 77, 80–1, 88, 95
Jacobson, A., 85
Jacoby, G. A., 24, 45, 114, 118–19, 130
Jahn, G., 115
Jamieson, A. F., 75
Jann, B., 104, 121
Jann, K., 104, 121
Janssens, J., 72
Johnson, K. E., 25
Johnsrud, L., 43, 45
Johnston, A. W. B., 98, 134
Jones, J. R., 121
Jones, K. R., 13
Jones, R. J., 114
Jones, R. T., 113
Jonsson, S., 87
Jordan, E., 39

Kahn, M., 72

Kaiser, A. D., 2
Kakefuda, T., 57, 74
Kaney, A. R., 76
Kapikian, A. Z., 121
Kasamatsu, H., 78
Katz, D., 129–30
Katz, L., 12, 57–9
Kaulfers, P-M., 115
Kedes, L-H., 142, 144
Keggins, K. M., 144
Kelley, W. S., 66
Kelly, R. B., 14
Kennedy, N., 89–90
Kerr, A., 133–5
Kester, H. C. M., 134
Khan, S., 140
Kidson, A., 114, 124
Kimura, K., 1
Kingsbury, D. T., 66, 72–3
Kingsman, A., 88
Kinnear, J. E., 15
Kirby, R., 135
Klapwijk, P. M., 134–5
Kleckner, N., 45–6, 141
Klein, H. L., 140
Kleinschmidt, A. K., 75
Kline, B. L., 62, 65, 68, 76
Knowles, J., 140
Kollek, R., 70
Kondo, I., 118
Konings, R. N. H., 128
Konisky, J., 127
Konrad, E. B., 66
Kontomichalou, P., 15, 43, 78, 114
Kool, A. J., 128
Kopecko, D. J., 13, 44–6, 140
Korfhagen, T. R., 24, 118, 130
Korn, D., 5, 65, 69
Kornberg, A., 14, 53, 68
Kornberg, T., 67
Koyama, A. H., 73
Koyame, K., 1
Kreft, J., 67
Kretschmer, P. J., 11, 44
Krishnapillai, V., 97–8, 119, 125
Kruger, K. E., 59
Kühn, S., 43
Kumira, S., 1
Kung, A. H. C., 119
Kupersztoch-Portnoy, Y. M., 12, 57, 59–60
Kusecek, B., 96

Lacey, R. W., 115
Laird, W. J., 122
Lambert, H. P., 117
Lane, D., 16
Lang, D., 12
Lanka, E., 74
Lansman, R. A., 142, 144
Laufs, R., 115
Lavallé, R., 5
Lawn, A. M., 97
LeBlanc, D. J., 8, 74, 85, 88, 98
Lederberg, E. M., 1, 10, 85
Lederberg, J., 1, 3, 83, 85
Lee, B. T. O., 119
Lee, H. J., 14, 40–3, 70
Lee, L. N., 98
Leggatt, F., 97
Le Grice, S., 127
Lehman, I. R., 66
Lehman, K., 88
Lehrbach, P., 119
Leibowitz, M. J., 140
Levin, B. R., 139

Levin, R., 134
Levinthal, M., 95
Levy, S. B., 110–11
Liebowitz, P. J., 65
Lilly, H. A., 114, 124
Lindahl, G., 69
Linggood, M., 121–2
Linnane, A. W., 141
Linton, A. H., 109–12
Linton, K. B., 109–10
Lipman, M. B., 88, 97
Livingston, D. M., 140
Loper, J. C., 118
Lovett, M. A., 12, 57–60, 71, 143
Lovett, P. S. 144
Low, K. B., 76, 95
Lowbury, E. J. L., 114, 124
Lowry, J. C., 142
Lundbäck, A., 61
Lurz, R., 71
Luttropp, L. K., 55, 57–8, 138

Maas, R., 74
Maas, W. K., 41, 43, 73–6, 122, 138
McCarthy, B. J., 45, 122
McCowen, S. M., 13
MacHattie, L., 45
McIntire, S., 41, 87–90
McLaughlin, J., 121
Macone, A. B., 110–11
Macrina, F. L., 13
Malamy, M. H., 39
Mandel, A., 118
Manigault, P., 133
Manis, J. J., 65, 76
Manning, P. A., 87
Maré, I. J., 119
Margulies, A. D., 88
Marinus, M. G., 68, 88
Marmion, B. P., 102
Marmur, J., 5, 6
Martial, J. A., 144
Marvin, D., 85
Masters, M., 69, 79, 139
Mata, L. T., 138
Matsubara, K., 2, 71–2, 76, 80, 88, 143
Mattes, R., 22
Matthew, M., 114, 118
Maturin, L., 147
Maule, J., 87, 90, 97
Mayer, H., 62
Mayer, L, W., 115
Mazaitis, A. J., 75
Meacock, P., 43
Meijer, M., 139
Meijlink, F. C. P. W., 140
Menefee, C, L., 118
Merlo, D. J., 50, 134
Merrick, M. J., 116, 135
Merson, M. H., 121
Meselson, M., 77
Messens, E., 10, 134
Messer, W., 139
Meyer, J., 40
Meyer, R., 14, 143
Meyers, J. A., 8, 11, 13
Meynell, E., 92, 97, 137
Meynell, G. G., 8, 11, 92, 127–8, 137
Mickel, S., 17–18, 59, 62
Miki, T., 16, 22, 89
Miller, C. A., 8, 16–17
Miller, J. H., 43, 45
Miller, J. R., 22, 65

Milliken, C. E., 15, 78
Mindich, L., 66
Minkley, E. G., 90
Mirels, L., 42–3
Mitani, M., 12, 15, 17–18, 78
Mitsuhashi, S., 1, 24, 98, 118
Miznuchi, K., 74
Moellering, R. C., Jr, 119
Mohammed, W., 115, 139
Monner, D. A., 87
Monod, J., 60
Montoya, A. L., 50, 133–4
Moody, E. E. M., 69
Moore, D. D., 59
Moore, L. W., 134
Morelli, G., 10, 83, 86–7
Morgan, A. F., 119
Morozow, E., 79
Morris, C. F., 61
Morris, D., 132
Morrow, J. F., 142, 144
Mukai, T., 143
Murphy, E., 57, 65
Murphy, S. D., 118
Murray, Keith, 130, 132
Murray, Kenneth, 143
Murray, N. E., 143–4
Mylroie, J. R., 98, 132

Nagaishi, H., 41, 46, 50, 89
Nagata, T., 73
Nagley, P., 141
Nakahara, H., 118
Nakamura, A., 17, 61
Nakamura, H., 73
Nakaya, R., 17, 61
Nakazawa, A., 45, 130
Nakazawa, T., 45, 130
Nalin, D. R., 121
Nandadasa, H. G., 69
Nathans, D., 50, 145
National Institutes of Health, 146–8
Neilsen, L. D., 139
Nester, E. W., 8, 50, 133–4
Nevers, P., 43
Nijkamp, H. J. J., 46, 61, 67–8, 95, 128–9
Nisen, P. D., 44
Nishimura, A., 69
Nishimura, Y., 68–70, 89, 96
Nisioka, T., 17–18
Nomura, M., 127–8
Nordheim, A., 29
Nordström, K., 61–2, 78–80
Novick, R., ix, 16, 24, 55, 57, 59, 61, 65, 73–7, 118
Novotny, C. P., 85
Nuti, M. P., 134
Nutter, R., 50

Ochiai, K., 1
O'Dea, M. H., 74
Oertel, W., 70
Ogata, Y., 16
O'Grady, F., 117
Oh, G. R., 40
Ohki, M., 87–8
Ohmori, H., 59, 60, 68, 74
Ohtsubo, E., 8, 14, 28–30, 33, 36–7, 40–3, 59, 62, 70, 75, 89, 96
Ohtsubo, H., 40, 59
Oishi, M., 10
Oka, A., 55, 67, 70
Okanishi, M., 135

Olarte, J., 138
Oliver, D. R., 122
Olsen, R. H., 11, 14, 95, 98
Orr, C., 85
Ørskov, F., 104, 121
Ørskov, I., 104, 121
Osborne, A. D., 109–11
Ostensson, R., 84
Otsuji, Y., 80
Otten, M. R., 65
Ottow, J. C. G., 84
Ou, J. T., 85
Overbeeke, N., 46
Ozeki, H., 92, 128

Palchaudhuri, S., 41, 43, 75–6, 118, 122, 130, 138
Palleroni, N. J., 129
Papachristou, E., 114
Parker, R. C., 50
Parsell, Z., 108
Pato, M. L., 70, 79
Peebles, C. L., 70
Pemberton, J. M., 133
Peñaranda, M. E., 138
Perlman, D., 17, 19–22, 59
Perram, J. W., 79
Petit, A., 135
Petrocheilou, V., 110, 113, 147
Pfister, A., 75
Pierucci, O., 61
Pinney, R. J., 97, 119
Polen, S., 90
Pols, C., 128
Pols, K., 129
Porthouse, A., 115
Postgate, J. R., 3, 141
Prentki, P., 79
Price, D. J. E., 110, 124
Pritchard, R. H., 61, 69, 77, 79–81, 145
Ptashne, K., 40, 42
Ptashne, M., 144

Rabbitts, T. H., 144
Radloff, R., 8, 10
Raeburn, J. A., 114
Rahal, J. J., 114
Rahaman, M., 121
Rahman, A. S. M. M., 121
Rahmsdorf, U., 89–90
Ratzkin, B., 142
Reanney, D., 139
Reed, N. D., 113
Reeves, P., 85, 87, 90, 125–6, 128
Reidel, G. E., 144
Reif, H. J., 39, 42
Reiner, A. M., 87
Relf, J., 118
Renshaw, J., 95
Revelas, E., 61
Rheinwald, J. G., 132
Richards, H., 80
Richmond, A., 114
Richmond, K. M. V., 45
Richmond, M. H., 43–5, 109–11, 113–15, 147
Riggs, A. D., 144
Riise, E., 139
Roberts, M., 115
Roberts, R. J., 48
Roberts, T. A., 109
Robinson, M. K., 44–5
Roblin, R. O., 145–6
Rochaix, J-D., 45

Rodriguez, R. L., 59, 70, 74, 143–4
Roe, E., 114
Rogers, J. E., 45, 130, 132
Rogers, T., 115
Rorsch, A., 134
Rosen, J., 62
Rosenbloom, M., 62
Rosenblum, E. D., 12
Rosner, J. L., 45
Roth, C., 118
Roth, J., 141
Roth, T. F., 7
Roth, Y., 69
Roussel, A. F., 26
Rowe, B., 121
Rownd, R. 5, 6, 16–22, 40, 50, 54, 59–61, 77–8
Royer-Pokora, B., 122
Rubens, C., 44–6, 138
Runge, R., 69
Rupp, W. D., 68, 87–8, 97
Rush, M., 61, 140
Ryder, R. W., 121

Sack, D. A., 121
Sack, G. H., 50
Sack, R. B., 121
Sadikaro, J., 128
Saedler, H., 38–40, 42–3, 45, 138
Sagai, H., 24, 98
St Martin, E. J., 98
Saitoh, T., 74
Sakakibara, Y., 57, 68, 74
San Blas, F., 75
Sanchez, D., 8, 11, 13
Sanders, J. P. M., 140
Santos, D. S., 122, 138
Sarai, S., 118
Sarathy, P. V., 88
Saul, M., 46
Saunders, J. R., 114–15, 139
Savage, D. C., 103
Sawada, O., 1
Scaife, J., 35, 40, 74
Scavizzi, M. R., 24
Schaefler, S., 114
Schaffner, W., 11
Schaller, K., 127
Schell, J., 10, 46, 133–5, 138
Schenlderman, T., 135
Schildkraut, C., 5–6
Schilperoort, R. A., 133–5
Schmitt, R., 22
Schnös, M., 19, 144
Schottel, J., 118
Schrempf, H., 62, 66–8, 128, 135
Schuster, H., 74
Schweizer, M., 87
Schwesinger, M., 76
Schwuchow, S., 83, 86–7
Sciacy, D., 133–4
Scotland, S. M., 121
Scott, J. R., 69
Seeburg, P. H., 144
Seibert, D., 115
Sekiguchi, M., 10, 65, 73
Semaka, S. D., 15
Senior, B. W., 127
Setchell, S. M., 134
Shaham, M., 132
Shahrabadi, M. S., 114
Shapiro, J. A., 1, 14, 38–9, 45–6, 130, 132, 137–8, 140
Sharp, P. A., 8, 16, 28–33, 36–42, 72, 89, 96, 126, 137, 143
Shaw, B. G., 109

Shaw, E. J., 43
Shaw, W. V., 120
Sheehy, R. J., 55, 57, 85
Sherratt, D., 46, 60, 65–6, 68, 80, 93
Shimada, K., 35–6
Shine, J., 59, 70, 74, 144
Shipley, P. L., 98
Shivakumar, A. G., 144
Siak, J-S., 98
Siddiqi, O., 88
Sieckmann, D. G., 73, 113
Siemens, T. V., 98
Silva, B., 133, 138
Silva, M. L. M., 122
Silver, L., 59, 62, 69
Silver, R. P., 16, 88, 121
Silver, S., 118
Simberkoff, M. S., 114
Simon, M., 26, 28
Singer, M. F., 146
Sistrom, W. R., 98
Skurray, R., 41, 46, 50, 71, 85, 87, 89–90
Sleigh, J. D., 110, 124
Slocombe, B., 114
Slocombe, P. M., 50, 71
Smith, D. H., 119
Smith, D. I., 117
Smith, H. R., 10, 24, 26, 33, 119
Smith, H. W., 108, 110, 121–2, 124, 147
Smith, J. T., 43, 97, 117, 119
Smith, K., 57
Smith, M. G., 113
Smith, P. L., 122
Smith, R. G., 115
Smith, S. M., 92
So, M., 45–6, 121–2, 144
Sox, T. E., 115, 139
Sparks, R. B., 58, 60
Sparling, P. F., 115, 139
Sporn, P., 45
Spratt, B. G., 127
Stacey, K. A., 95
Stadler, J., 70
Stahl, F. W., 77
Stallions, D. R., 84, 88, 95, 113
Stanier, R. Y., 129
Stanisich, V. A., 45
Starlinger, P., 38–9, 42–3
Staudenbauer, W. L., 74
Sternberg, N., 72
Sternglanz, R., 53
Stewart, F. M., 139
Stickgold, R., 19
Stocker, B. A. D., 92, 128
Struhl, K., 142, 144
Stuitje, T., 46
Sublett, 43, 45, 119
Sueoka, N., 61
Sugino, A., 70
Summers, A. O., 118
Sutton, L., 24, 119, 130
Suzuki, K., 68
Swain, R. H. A., 102
Swann Report, 123
Sykes, R. B., 43, 114, 118
Szybalski, W., 12, 39, 87

Tacon, W., 66
Tait, K. M., 144
Takagi, Y., 143
Tanaka, N., 40, 50, 144
Tatum, E. L., 83
Taylor, A. L., 95

Taylor, D. E., 26
Taylor, D. P., 62
Telford, J., 11
Tempé, J., 133–5
Tenchy, H., 133
Thomas, M., 144
Thompson, M. J., 119
Thompson, R., 8, 47, 67, 75, 89, 95
Threlfall, E. J., 105
Timmis, J. K., 71
Timmis, K. N., 4, 29, 50, 57, 70–1, 80, 96, 140, 142, 144
Tocchini-Valentini, G. P., 68
Tomizawa, J-I., 3, 57, 59, 60, 68, 74, 87–8
Tomoeda, M., 84
Tompkins, L. S., 88
Tooze, J., 133
Toscano, W. A., Jr, 129
Toussaint, A., 142
Trantner, T. A., 10
Tresguerres, E. F., 69
Tucker, J. F., 124
Tweats, D. J., 119
Twigg, A. J., 60, 93
Twose, T. M., 19
Tye, B. K., 45–6

Ubelaker, M. H., 12
Uchida, H., 73
Ugueto, N., 111
Uhlin, B. E., 61–2, 80
Ullmann, A., 138
Umezawa, H., 135

van Brunt, J., 70
van den Elsacker, S., 133
van der Elzen, H. M., 15, 114
van de Pol, H., 95
van Ee, J. H., 129
van Embden, J. D. A., 46, 107, 115–16
van Heyningen, S., 121
van Klingeren, B., 115–16
van Larebeke, N., 133–4
van Leeuwen, W. J., 107, 111
van Montagu, M., 10, 46, 133–5, 138
van Vliet, F., 133, 138
van Zeben, M. S., 128
Vapnek, D., 68, 88, 97
Vasil, M. L., 121
Veltkamp, E., 46, 61, 67–8, 95, 128–9
Verbeet, M., 140
Villems, R., 50
Vinograd, J., 8, 10, 50, 144
Visconti, N., 76
Vivian, A., 98, 135
von Graevenitz, A., 114
von Meyenburg, K., 139

Wachsmuth, I. K., 122
Wada, C., 73
Wade, N., 145
Waggoner, B. T., 70
Waid, J. S., 133
Walker, J. B., 120
Walker, M. S., 120
Walz, A., 142
Wang, P. Y., 68, 118
Ward, J. M., 10
Warren, G., 46, 60, 80, 93
Warren, R. L., 60

Watanabe, T., 1, 16
Watson, B., 133
Watson, J. D., 145
Watson, R. M., 50, 144
Wechsler, J. A., 67
Weisberg, R. A., 35–6
Weisblum, 120, 144
Weiss, A. A., 118
Weiss, R., 146
Weissman, S., 145
Wells, J. G., 121
Wensink, P. C., 144
Wheelis, M. L., 129
Whitehouse, R. L. S., 15
Whiteside, E. J., 110
Wickner, R. B., 140
Wiedemann, B., 113
Wilkins, B. M., 88
Willetts, N., 36, 41, 75–6, 85, 87, 88–93, 96–7

Wilhams, P. A., 14, 22, 129–30, 132
Williams, P. H., 12, 59, 67, 68, 70
Williams, R. E. O., 103
Willshaw, G. A., 8, 10, 24, 26, 110, 119
Wilson, C. R., 144
Wise, E. M., 117
Witchitz, J. L., 24
Wlodarczyk, M., 65
Wohlhieter, J. A., 6
Wollman, E., 35, 95
Womack, J. E., 139
Womble, D. D., 59–60
Wong, C. L., 132
Wood, T. H., 89
Wood, W. B., 102
Worsey, M. J., 14, 22, 129
Wright, H. M., 120, 135, 141
Wright, L. F., 135

Wyman, L., 65, 74–5

Yagi, Y., 20, 40, 116
Yamagata, H., 73
Yamanaka, T., 1
Yanofsky, C., 35, 143
Yarmolinsky, M., 72
Yasuda, S., 139
Yokota, T., 45, 130
Yoshikawa, H., 61
Yunus, M., 121
Yura, T., 73

Zaenen, I., 133–4
Zechel, K., 68
Zenthen, J., 70, 79
Zinder, N., 145
Zipser, D., 44
Zonzias, D., 140

Subject Index

acridine orange, 5, 65, 69
actinomycetes, 116
agarose gels, 8, 9, 11–14, 46
aggragates
  mating cell, 83
  plasmid, 16
Agrobacterium tumefaciens, 2, 133–5, 138
amikacin, 116–17
  resistance, 118
amoxycillin, 113, 117, 124
ampicillin, 107, 113, 117, 124
  resistance, 15–16, 27, 33, 43–6, 60, 70, 81–2, 101, 106, 109–10, 114–15, 117, 119, 143
antibiotic synthesis, 2, 116–18, 120, 135, 139
Ap (ampicillin resistance determinant), 15–16, 95
Azotobacter, 3

Bacillus, 103, 117
  circulans, 120
  megaterium, 125, 141
  subtilis, 125, 138, 144, 147
  bacteriocins, 2, 5, 105, 125–9
bacteriophages
  f1, 85–6
  If1, 105
  λ, ix, 2, 12, 34–5, 46, 59, 71–2, 87, 126, 128, 142 4;
    see also λdv
  M13, 3
  Mu, 44, 46, 142
  μ2, 105
  MS2, 85–6
  P1, 2, 33, 40, 66, 69, 89, 126, 128, 142; *see also* P1 as plasmid
  P2, 69
  P4, 72
  P7, 69
  φX174, 29
  Qβ, 85
Bacteroides, 103, 111
  fragilis, 102
  ochraceus, 138
Benzoate, 130
Butirosin, 117, 120

calves, 105, 109–10, 112, 121
CAM, 129–30

Campbell model, 20, 34–6, 42, 44
carbenicillin resistance, 103, 114, 117, 130
catechol, 130–1
cattle, 105, 109–10, 112
cefoxitin, 117
cell envelope, 87
cell fusion, 141
cell membrane, 63–5, 73–4, 88, 127
chemotaxis, 63, 98
chloramphenicol, 17, 19–20, 54, 61, 68, 77, 107, 115, 117, 124, 143
  resistance, 16, 27, 33, 45, 61, 101, 108, 110, 117, 119–20
chloroplasts, 141
cholera, 102, 121
clearing spin, 7, 8, 11, 130
cleavage maps, 41, 47–8
cloacin, 128–9
CloDF13, 61, 67–8, 95, 128–9
cloxacillin, 115, 117
  resistance, 101, 117
cointegrates, plasmid, 16
Col factors, 126–8, 138; *see also* bacteriocins
Col B(–K77), 127
Col B(–K98), 24
Col B2, 97
Col B4, 97
Col BM *trp lac*, 79
Col E1(–K30), 2, 12–13, 53–61, 63, 65–70, 72–4, 76–8, 80–1, 95, 126–8, 142–4
Col E2(–P9), 66, 127–8
Col E3(–CA38), 127–8
Col Ia, 73
Col Ib(–P9), 2, 24, 59, 67, 73, 88, 92, 126–8
Col K(–235), 127
Col V, 73
Col V(–K30), 67–8
Col V(–K94), 28, 30–1, 36, 38–9, 89, 126–7, 137
Col V2, 24, 90, 92, 97
Col VB*trp*, 73, 90, 97
conjugation systems, 12, 14–15, 83–99, 111–15, 122, 130, 134, 135, 137, 139, 147
  contact formation, 83–5, 111
  control of transfer, 90–3, 97–8, 125, 135
  DNA transfer, 87–9, 93, 95
  'epidemic spread', 92–3

conjugation systems – contd.
  origin of transfer, 41, 60, 87, 93, 97
  replication in, 88
  strand transferred, 87
  surface exclusion, 41, 85, 90, 97–8
  transfer genes, 89–93, 97
containment, 146–8
copy-number, 53, 60–3, 70, 76, 80–2
  mutants, 61–3, 81–2
cotrimoxazole, 107
cou, see DNA gyrase
crown gall, 133
cystic fibrosis, 114

degradative plasmids, 2, 22, 129–33, 139
deletion mutants, 39, 44, 46
Δ, 15–16, 24, 27, 59, 78, 95
denaturation mapping, 19, 59
density gradient centrifugation, 5, 7–8, 10, 16–22, 54, 57, 77
deoxyribonuclease I, 44
diarrhoea, 120–2
dnaA, 62, 66, 68–70, 78
DNAase *see* deoxyribonuclease
dnaB, 66, 68, 74, 78, 88
dnaD(= *dnaC*), 68, 70, 74, 78
dnaE see DNA polymerase III
dnaG, 68
DNA gyrase, 70, 74
DNA polymerase I, 65, 73–4, 81
DNA polymerase II, 66
DNA polymerase III, 66–7, 74, 78, 88
DNA precipitation, 8, 11
drug resistance *see* under individual drugs

EcoRI, 46, 48, 54, 57–60, 70
electron microscopy, 7, 9, 12, 19, 26–35, 53–7, 60; *see also* heteroduplexes
endonucleases *see* restriction endonucleases
Ent, 2, 121–2, 137–8
enteritis *see* diarrhoea
Enterobacter cloacae, 128–9
Enterobacteria, 24, 102–5, 111, 120
enterotoxins, 121–2
erythromycin, 115, 117
  resistance, 101, 116–17
Escherichia coli, 1–3, 10, 16, 22, 24, 27, 30, 53, 65–70, 73, 78, 87, 96, 101–3, 107–14, 119, 121, 125–30, 139, 142, 147
  K–12, 1, 35, 83–96, 147
ethidium bromide, 6, 10–11; *see also* density gradient centrifugation
exonuclease III, 44

F, 1–3, 28–31, 33–43, 46, 50, 53, 58–9, 61, 67–70, 74–6, 78, 83–97, 122, 126, 137
  F'14, 41–3
  F'*gal*, 28–30, 33, 36–8, 41, 89
  F'*lac*, 5, 24, 36–7, 42, 60, 63–5, 69, 71–3, 75, 79, 89–94, 142
fertility inhibition, 90–3, 97–8, 125
F prime factor formation, 34–7, 40–3
F⁻ strains, 85, 87, 94
fungi, 116–17, 140
furazolidone, 15
  resistance, 15, 106, 110

galactose epimerase, 64
β-galactosidase, 45, 60, 79, 138
genetic isolation, 98
gentamicin, 115–17
  resistance, 103, 114–15, 117
Gonococcus see Neisseria
growth promotion, 123

haemolysins, 122
Haemophilus influenzae, 102, 114, 123, 138

herbicides, 133
heteroduplexes, 25–33, 36–42, 46, 89, 128
Hfr strains, 34–7, 68–70, 74–6, 84–9, 95
Hind III, 47–8
Hly, 67–8, 122
hybridisation
  DNA·DNA, 25–7, 47, 61, 122, 132–4, 137–8
  DNA·RNA, 61
hydroxyapatite, 25
hydroxyurea, 144

immunity proteins, 80, 127, 129
incompatibility, 23, 74–6
  groups, 23–4, 26–7, 96–7, 105, 130, 137
insertion mutations, 29, 38, 44, 46, 98
insertion sequences, 20, 36–8
  IS1, 39–43, 46, 62, 122
  IS2, 39–42, 142
  IS3, 40–2
  IS4, 40–2
  γδ, 41–2
integrative suppression, 62, 68–70
inverted repeats, 31–2, 36–9, 43, 45
isolation of plasmid DNA, 5–11, 61, 130, 143

kanamycin, 116–17
  resistance, 16, 27, 33, 45, 106, 117–18
killer particles, 140
Klebsiella, 3, 104, 114

β-lactamases, 43, 114–17
lactose, 45, 138
λdv, 2, 59, 61, 71, 80, 126, 143–4
lethal zygosis, 41, 85
ligase, 47, 49, 66, 68
lincomycin, 115, 117
lysis, 7–8, 11
lysogeny, 2–3, 34–5, 80, 125, 128

metal resistance, 2, 45, 118
methylenomycin A, 135
mice, 113, 114
micromanipulation, 85
minicells, 7, 46, 65, 90, 122, 128, 144
mitochondria, 141
mitomycin C, 128–9
mutagenesis, 10, 73, 89, 119
mutants
  deletion, 39, 44, 46
  insertion, 29, 38, 44, 46, 98

NAH, 129–32
nalA see DNA gyrase
Neisseria gonorrhoeae, 102, 115, 123, 139
neomycin resistance, 106, 110, 117, 120
nitrocellulose, 8, 10, 47
nitrogenase, 141
nitrogen fixation, 3, 134, 141, 144–6
nopaline, 134
NR1 *see* R100
NR84, 22

OCT, 129–32
octopine, 134
Okazaki fragments, 67
opportunist pathogens, 101, 113
origin of transfer, 41, 60, 87, 93, 97

P1 as plasmid, 2, 78–9, 126
P307, 24, 122, 137
pBR322, 13, 143
pBR345, 59
penicillin, 108, 115–17, 138
  resistance, 101, 117; *see also* amoxycillin, ampicillin, carbenicillin and cloxacillin
phages *see* bacteriophages
phage typing, 104–5, 107–8

phasmids, 72
pI258, 2
pigs, 109–10, 112, 121
pilus, 84–5, 90, 93, 96–7
plasmid relationships, 22–33, 47, 97, 108, 114, 122, 127, 132, 134, 138
plasmids *see* under individual names
polA *see* DNA polymerase I
polB *see* DNA polymerase II
polyethylene glycol, 8, 10–11, 141
poultry, 109–12, 123–4
protein synthesis *in vitro*, 12, 46, 122, 128–9, 143–4
Proteus, 30, 101–2, 104
  mirabilis, 6, 17–22, 77–8, 114
protoplast fusion, 141
Providencia, 30
pSC101, 65, 80, 142–4
pSC134, 80–1
Pseudomonas, 14, 24, 30, 129–33, 139
  aeruginosa, 2, 73, 97, 101–2, 113–14, 118, 123, 125
  putida, 2, 131–2, 138, 147
pT169, 65

R1, R1–19, 13, 16, 24, 27–33, 40, 42, 47, 60–2, 73–4, 78–9, 81–2, 90, 92, 97–8, 126, 137
R6, R6–5, 16, 28, 31–3, 35–42, 47, 50, 70–1, 80, 96, 137, 142, 144
R6K, 15, 55–8, 74, 93, 97
R28K, 78
R64, R64–11, 24, 73, 88, 93, 97
R91, 98
R100, R100–1, 2, 16–22, 24, 28–9, 32–3, 36, 39–40, 42, 59, 61–2, 77–8, 81–2, 89–93, 96–7, 137
R538–1, 24, 90, 97
R931, 15
recA function, 42–5, 66, 75, 88
recombination
  in vitro, 3, 47, 70, 72, 89, 122, 141–7
  in vivo, 3, 12, 18, 34–47, 70, 87–9, 95–6, 118, 130, 134–5, 139–41, 146
relaxation, 56–60, 93
replication, 2, 5, 15, 17, 20, 23–4, 53–82, 88, 98, 129, 137–40
  control, 17, 53, 76–82
  intermediates, 53–7, 60, 74
  in vitro, 74
  origin and direction of, 53, 57–60, 69–70, 139
  semi-conservative, 54, 74
  termination, 53, 57–9
restriction, 2, 46, 98; *see also Eco*RI, *Hin*dIII, recombination *in vitro*
  endonucleases, 14, 26, 46–50, 143
  in mapping, 41, 49
Rhizobium, 134
ribosomes, 73, 127, 129
rifampicin, 68
RK2, 142
RNA priming, 66, 68
RP1, RP4, 2–3, 13, 24, 50, 97, 114, 130, 134, 141–3, 146
RSF1030, 74

S1 nuclease, 26, 44
S-a, 13, 24
Saccharomyces cerevisiae, 140–1
SAL, 129–32

Salmonella, 30, 102, 104, 123–4
  typhi, 102, 104–5, 107–8, 123, 138
  typhimurium, 2, 15, 22, 102, 106
  type 29, 16, 105–7
SCP1, 2, 135
SCP2, 135
segragation, 5–6, 53, 63–5, 70, 72, 74–6
serotypes, 104, 109–10, 121
Serratia, 101
  marcescens, 5–6, 22
shearing, 7, 11, 19, 25
sheep, 109–10, 112–13
Shigella, 1–2, 102–4, 121, 138
sodium dodecyl sulphate, 11
spheroplasts, 7, 141
staphylococci, 7, 83, 101–3, 116
Staphylococcus aureus, 2, 57, 59, 65, 70, 73–6, 101–2, 115–16, 142, 144
streptococci, 98, 103, 116
Streptococcus faecalis, 20, 98, 102, 116, 122
Streptococcus pyogenes, 102, 116, 138
Streptomyces, 117, 141
  acrimycini, 120
  coelicolor, 2, 98, 135
  venezuelae, 120
streptomycin, 17, 61, 84, 116–17
  resistance, 15–16, 27, 30, 33, 45, 61, 101, 106, 108–10, 117, 119, 138
sucrose gradient centrifugation, 6–7, 12–13, 61
sulphonamides, 15, 108, 117
  resistance, 15–16, 27, 30, 33, 45, 101, 106, 108–10, 117, 119, 138
surface exclusion, 41, 85, 90, 97–8
synchrony, 79

tetracycline, 17, 110–11, 113, 115, 117, 124
  resistance, 15–16, 20, 22, 27, 33, 37, 45, 81–2, 101, 106, 108–10, 117, 119, 143
Ti plasmids, 2, 133–5, 138, 141
TOL, 2, 129–32, 138
Toluates, 129–31
Toluene, 129–31
tra genes, 41, 89–93, 97
transduction, 12, 33, 66, 89, 116, 140
transformation, 10–11, 47, 130, 137, 140, 147
transition, 17–22, 40
transposition, 43–6, 118
transposons, 43–6, 95, 98, 117, 122, 130, 138
  TnA (Tn1, 2, 3), 43–6, 114–15, 123, 138
  Tn5, 44–6
  Tn7, 98
  TnTol, 45, 130
trimethoprim, 108, 117
  resistance, 45, 117
tumours, 133–5, 145

ultraviolet radiation, 95, 125, 128
  resistance to, 119

vegetarians, 111
Vibrio cholerae, 102, 121, 138

Xenopus laevis, 144
xylenes, 129–31

zygotic induction, 128